The Handyman's Guide to BUILDING MATERIALS

Handyman Club Library™

Handyman Club of America
Minneapolis, Minnesota

The Handyman's Guide to
BUILDING MATERIALS

Edited by Mark Johanson

CREDITS

Tom Carpenter
Director of Book Development

Mark Johanson
Book Products Development Manager, Editor

Dan Cary
Book Production Editor

**Roy Barnhart, Rex Cauldwell, Mark Johanson,
Chris Marshall, Michael Morris, Luke Rennie**
Contributing Writers

Mark Johanson
Book Design & Production

Bill Nelson, Chris Marshall
Book Production

**Kim Bailey, Scott Jacobson, Mark Johanson,
Ralph Karlen, Mark Macemon**
Photography

Luke Rennie
Photo Coordination

Craig Claeys, Mario Ferro, Bruce Kieffer
Illustrations

Carolyn Henry-Johanson
Editing & Proofreading

Sara Jensen
Indexing

PHOTOS & ILLUSTRATIONS

American Plywood Association
Pages 36, 37, 124, 126, 167

The Belden Brick Co.
Page 28

Premdor Inc.
Cover, page 98

The Quikrete Cos.
Pages 19, 26, 30

Wood Truss Council of America
Page 35

MetalWorks Steel Shingles
Page 106

*Additional photos and illustrations are credited on
pages of occurrence*

ISBN 1-58159-160-8

1 2 3 4 5 6 / 05 04 03 02

Handyman Club of America
12301 Whitewater Drive
Minnetonka, Minnesota 55343

www.handymanclub.com

The Handyman's Guide to
BUILDING MATERIALS

Table of Contents

The Handyman's Guide to
BUILDING MATERIALS

Successful home remodeling and home improvement depend on good, up-to-date information. The materials we use to update our kitchens or build our new additions change all the time. Keeping up with the changes isn't too difficult if you're a professional tradesman and work in the industry every day. But for the weekend do-it-your-selfer, reconciling your plans with what's really available can be a constant source of frustration.How many times have you hurried off to the home improvement center to pick up some weatherstripping or a plumbing fitting or even some dimensional lumber only to find that the product you need can't be found or a new and improved product has taken its place? So you buy the most similar item you can get your hands on, but then have to go back and redraw your plans to make it fit. The main purpose of this book, *The Handyman's Guide to Building Materials,* is to help you identify the best materials for your home improvement project while your still making your plans. It combines information from many sources into one handy volume, answering the questions that are most likely to come up as you begin your work. And at the same time, it provides useful, practical tips designed to help you make good decisions and save time and money in the process. Using this book will help you eliminate most of the guesswork from your next project, and we hope you find that to be a valuable service.

IMPORTANT NOTICE

For your safety, caution and good judgment should be used when following instructions described in this book. Take into consideration your level of skill and the safety precautions related to the tools and materials shown. Neither the publisher, *North American Membership Group, Inc.,* nor any of its affili-ates can assume responsibility for any damage to property or persons as a result of the misuse of the information provided. Consult your local building department for information on permits, codes, regulations and laws that may apply to your project.

PROJECT PLANNING

Even with small-scale remodeling projects, planning is as important to success as doing the work. This is particularly true of projects that require a building permit. Generally, any project that involves structural modifications to your home, or electrical or plumbing work, will require a permit. Projects that cost in excess of $1000 or so usually require a permit, although the amount varies widely from area to area.

Planning is also important when working with contractors and for arranging follow-up inspections. As helpful as building inspectors can be, they have their own schedules to keep, and you shouldn't count on instant approval the moment you telephone or stop by the building department.

But most of all, careful planning ensures that the job will be completed correctly, on time and at the lowest possible cost to you.

Building Guidelines

❏ **Watch out for buried lines.** Contact your local public utilities to identify the location of buried power lines and gas lines before you dig. Utilities will usually provide line location identification as a free service.

❏ **Research building codes.** Most municipalities enforce outdoor building restrictions. Footing and framing requirements on outdoor structures as well as minimum distance from city land and other property lines are common areas subject to regulation.

❏ **Discuss plans with your neighbors.** Your building project will likely be within the field of vision of your neighbors. As a courtesy, share plans with neighbors and give them the chance to raise objections or concerns before you start working.

Before you start digging, contact your local utility companies and have them flag buried power lines or gas and plumbing pipes. These companies usually will stake out rights-of-way for you at no charge to avoid the possibility of having you cut a cable or pipe. In most cases, the various utilities will coordinate and send out only one crew to mark electric, water, gas, phone and cable lines. And don't forget about your own utilities. Make sure you won't be interfering with your own well, septic tank or underground sprinkler system.

Coordinate deliveries carefully. There are many aspects of a home improvement project you can control, but time-sensitive deliveries are not one of them. If you're ordering ready-mix concrete for a masonry project, plan ahead and be fully prepared when the truck arrives. Have your forms set, know where you want the truck to park, and clear a path for wheelbarrows from the truck to the jobsite. Make sure to have plenty of help (and some extra wheelbarrows) lined up. It also pays to be ready for other deliveries, including lumber and roofing materials. Know where you want the materials dropped off and make sure you've got tarps on hand if you won't be using the materials right away.

Learn about rental equipment. Your local rental center may have just the equipment you need to shave hours of hard work from the project. Ask them to send a flyer or visit them early on in the planning process. Some of the products that are most likely to be of use in a building project include: gas-powered augers; pneumatic tools and paint sprayers; insulation blowers; sheetrock lifts; scaffolding; laser levels; and various power tools you may not own, including reciprocating saws, hammer drills, right angle drills and portable table saws.

Gather resources to generate ideas and help with planning and budgeting. Among the more helpful printed resources are: good home improvement and remodeling reference books; code books; catalogs from building centers (ask for them at the contractor's desk); building materials product literature; DIY, lifestyle and building trades magazines; and building center circulars from stores in your area (the best way to watch for sale prices). Also, walk around your neighborhood taking notes and making sketches of house features you find attractive.

Drafting tools for making quality project plan drawings include a smooth worksurface (a portable drafting table is shown here), a variety of pens and pencils including a mechanical pencil, an architect's scale, a compass, a triangle or two and one or more french curves.

PLAN DRAWINGS & PERMITS

It's really a personal choice how much time and care you wish to put into your plan drawings. For some do-it-yourselfers, creating the plan is the most enjoyable part of the process. Others would just as soon work on the fly, without any written plans at all. But if you are involved with a major home improvement or remodeling project, you'll almost certainly need to apply for building permits. And to make the application successful, you'll need written plans and drawings. They don't have to be professional quality, but they do need to be accurate, complete and clear.

Beyond the simple issue of permit application compliance, there is great value in taking the time to draw out some good project plans. Scaled drawings will help identify any issues of proportioning, and may help you catch mistakes in sizing. Careful perspective plans will also give you a good sense of what your project will look like

when it's done, and how it will fit in with its surroundings.

A scaled drawing is basically a shrunk-down, yet correctly proportioned drawing that shows your project's details and its dimensions. As a reference, it's good to have a scaled "working" drawing on hand as you build. The term "working" refers to the fact that you will follow these drawings closely when you build your project and use these drawings to determine the dimensions of the components you need to cut.

You can make good scaled drawings using a ruler and graph paper, but if professional-quality scaled working drawings are your goal you'll need an architect's scale (See page 11), drafting table, T-square, 45° triangle, 30 x 60° triangle, and a perhaps a compass for drawing circles and arcs.

Start by drawing two-dimensional floorplan (birdseye) and elevation view drawings to give you a sense of the overall proportions and help you to adjust those proportions that seem wrong. For most everything you build,

(Continued, page 10

CAD drawings, short for *computer aided design,* are a powerful tool you can use for making project plans. Many CAD software programs are available for use on personal computers. Unfortunately, good CAD software programs needed to create 3-D drawings with perspective views are still rather expensive. You can get inexpensive software that will do only 2-D drawings though, which may be the way to go. With these programs it's easy to draw in scale and change scale at any time. Most of the programs have dimensioning tools too, which makes it easy to add dimension lines and values to your drawings.

CAD drawings are fast to create and easy to revise. The more sophisticated and expensive programs that allow you to make 3-D perspective views also allow you to rotate the view and see your project from any viewpoint. The really sophisticated programs even enable you to create photo-realistic

Building Permits

Whether or not you need a building permit depends on the type and size of the project and your local codes.

How do you know if you need a permit? Ask! Even before finalizing your design, consult the municipal building and zoning department where you apply for permits. These folks will lead you through the application procedure. In most cases, you'll need to complete a form that describes your project, including overall dimensions, construction details and approximate cost. You might have to submit a sketch showing where the new construction will be located in relation to your house and property lines. The permit fee is usually based on a percentage of the project's cost.

Regulations for houses are far more complex than those that govern garden outbuildings. Your inspector's primary concerns probably will be setback requirements and sound construction practices. Setback requirements refer to the minimum distance a structure must be from your property lines. As far as sound construction practices are concerned, your building inspector can let you know of particular code requirements that apply in your area.

Key information for permit applications:

- **Plot location and complete address where the project will be built**

- **A site drawing that identifies the location of your project in relation to other permanent structures and property lines**

- **Detailed elevation and plan drawings that indicate overall size, materials and types of fasteners to be used**

- **Your estimated building cost**

- **Anticipated completion date**

Planning checklist

❑ *Study your house.* Identify the type and location of framing systems and members; identify load-bearing walls; investigate and map mechanical systems (wiring, plumbing, ductwork) in the project area.

❑ *Research ideas.* Look through magazines, books, catalogs and other sources to learn about your options. Do some rough sketching and dreaming. Drive around your area to see what others with similar homes have done to increase window and door curb appeal.

❑ *Make a rough plan.* When you have a rough idea in mind, consider consulting with a designer, architect or reputable builder for their opinion. Meet with your local building inspector to see if your ideas are realistic for your home before you invest more of your time or money.

❑ *Finalize your plan.* Plans should include drawings, specific lists of materials needed, costs, probable time frame, and they should note points where help is needed, both from contractors and from friends, family or neighbors. If working with a contractor, be sure to have a signed agreement well before the start of the project.

❑ *Get a permit.* Submit your plan drawings and cost estimates to your local building department, along with permit applications. Don't expect an immediate answer.

❑ *Arrange for deliveries.* Once your plan is approved, break larger projects into stages and set a schedule. Arrange for delivery, if needed, and be sure you have a clear area to store building materials. Don't forget to arrange for waste disposal in projects that involve demolition.

❑ *Arrange for inspections.* Most projects that require a permit also will require on-site inspection at one or more stages of the project. Find out from your inspector when he needs to inspect the process, and schedule him early. Be realistic in your scheduling, and be prepared to make adjustments or changes.

(Continued from page 8)

you'll draw a front view, top view and one or two side views. In addition, you should draw a site plan and detail drawings, such as a cross-section drawing of the footing plan showing depth, diameter and composition. You may want to detail some of the more complex joinery, especially at corners and at the points where rafters meet walls.

For a truer visual idea of what your project will look like, make *perspective drawings:* three-dimensional views foreshortened in such a way as to imitate the way your brain sees objects and give the illusion of depth. In other words, the drawing looks the way you would see it in reality.

Symbols used in plan drawings (right) are a shorthand way of explaining a lot of information in a limited space. The symbols shown to the right are about as universal as they get, but it's a good idea to bring along a key to your symbol usage for the inspector's benefit.

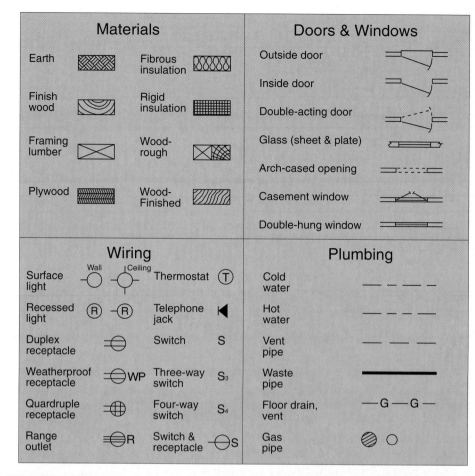

Materials		Doors & Windows	
Earth		Outside door	
Fibrous insulation		Inside door	
Finish wood		Double-acting door	
Rigid insulation		Glass (sheet & plate)	
Framing lumber		Arch-cased opening	
Wood-rough		Casement window	
Plywood		Double-hung window	
Wood-Finished			

Wiring				Plumbing	
Surface light	Wall / Ceiling	Thermostat	T	Cold water	
Recessed light	R / R	Telephone jack		Hot water	
Duplex receptacle		Switch	S	Vent pipe	
Weatherproof receptacle	WP	Three-way switch	S_3	Waste pipe	
Quadruple receptacle		Four-way switch	S_4	Floor drain, vent	—G—G—
Range outlet	R	Switch & receptacle	S	Gas pipe	

Plan Drawings

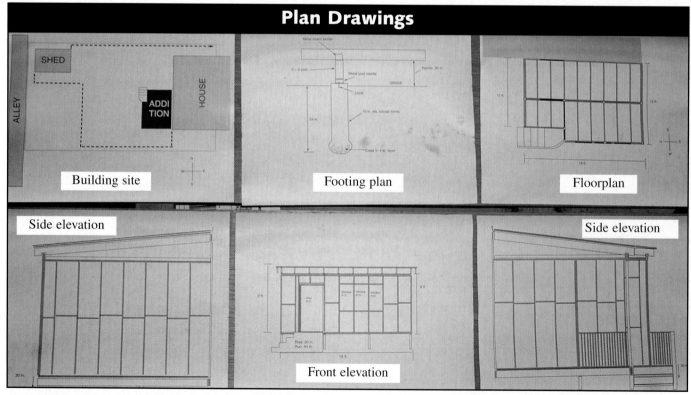

Building site

Footing plan

Floorplan

Side elevation

Front elevation

Side elevation

Plan drawings don't need to be fancy, just clear and complete. A full set should include a site drawing that shows where the project fits into the property, relative to the property lines and other permanent structures; a plan for footings or foundations (shown in cross section above); a birdseye floorplan; side elevations from each side of the new structure; and a front elevation. You'll also need to include estimates materials and costs. The plans above were made using a very basic computer drawing program. You'll also need to submit separate plans for plumbing and wiring, which require separate permits.

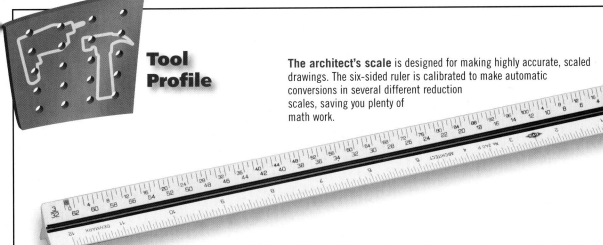

Tool Profile

The architect's scale is designed for making highly accurate, scaled drawings. The six-sided ruler is calibrated to make automatic conversions in several different reduction scales, saving you plenty of math work.

The Architect's Scale

An architect's scale is a ruler with six sides that architects use to draw in scaled increments. Each side is printed with gradations for different scales. The side with the number 16 marked at the left end is a full size ruler, meaning 1 inch equals 1 inch. The number 16 label means each inch is divided into sixteenths. The rest of the sides are marked with two different scales per side. One scale runs left to right, and the other runs right to left. To understand how to use an architect's scale, start by looking at the side marked on the left end with the fraction 3/32. Using that side and working from left to right means that every 3/32 inch equals 1 inch. In this scale, the real measurement of 12 inches would equal 128 inches and those divisions are marked off with the upper row of numbers on that side. On the right end of the same side of the scale, is a fraction label that says "3/16." Working from right to left and using the lower row of numbers marked on that side is the "3/16 inch equals 1 inch" scale. The other fraction-labeled scales work the same way. The sides with the ends labeled 1, 1½, and 3 are used for scaling at "1 inch equals 12 inches," "1½ inch equals 12 inches," and "3 inches equals 12 inches," respectively.

How to Read an Architect's Scale

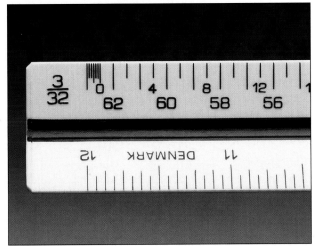

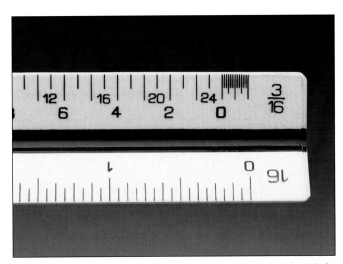

Reading an architect's scale. To understand how to use an architect's scale, start by looking at the side marked on the left end with the fraction "3/32." Using that side and working from left to right means that every 3/32 inch equals 1 inch. In this scale, the real measurement of 12 inches would equal 128 inches and those divisions are marked off with the upper row of numbers on that side. On the right end of the same side of the scale, is a fraction label that says "3/16." Working from right to left and using the lower row of numbers marked on that side offers the 3/16 inch equals 1 inch reduction scale.

*A first-time remodeler reveals some
real-life lessons learned while planning
and building a major project*

Before

No matter how much information you study or how much planning you do, every home improvement project you undertake will be a learning experience. Yes, good information and good planning are essential parts of the process, but each situation is different and even the best laid plans are still just educated guesswork. Until you actually cut the boards and drive the screws, you never really know for sure what you'll be facing. At least, that's how I feel now that I've completed my first major home remodeling project.

Over the years I've amassed a fair amount of actual experience in home repair and remodeling, especially while working construction jobs to help put myself through college. I even managed to make a career out of my inter-

est in DIY by writing, editing and helping create many books on do-it-yourself and wood-working subjects, most recently for the *Handyman Club of America.* But none of this experience fully prepared me for my first truly major DIY project: a 200-sq.-ft. addition to our house in Minnesota.

If you've spent much time around do-it-yourselfers and tradespeople, you've undoubtedly heard a lot of the conventional wisdom surrounding the home improvement pursuit: *"Measure twice, cut once." "There's no substitute for experience." "A building is only as strong as its foundation." "Make your best guess (estimating cost and time), then double it." "Buy the best tools you can afford." "The Devil is in the*

details." And on and on. The list is endless. But, it seems to me now, every last one of these bromides is true.

The following "case study" is an attempt to pass along some of the lessons I learned in the process of building my addition (and making plenty of mistakes along the way). Whether you're planning a simple window replacement or a major home renovation, I think you'll find at least a couple of these "lessons" to be of use. I can say with certainty that I wish I had known them before I started my own major project. But as that other old saw goes: *"Hindsight is always 20/20."*

Sequencing your project: Planning a major home improvement project involves answering many more questions than simply "What will it look like?" Completing your drawings, making your materials choices and receiving your permits is only phase one of the planning process. Perhaps equally important is the process of sequencing and budgeting your work. There is no set sequence that works for every project, however. It all really comes down to thinking ahead and applying some common sense. Seeing an example or two can help, too. The photos on the following pages illustrate a sequence of steps that was successful (somewhat, anyway) for my specific addition project. *M.J.*

Project description. The following case study in project sequencing involves a 200-square-foot, single-story room addition off the kitchen of a 110-year-old house. The house itself is built with balloon framing, but the addition was built using standard platform construction (the two types differ little in a single-story structure). Other than essential planning and permit acquisition, the primary preparatory work was the relocation of the electrical service entry point from the south to the north side of the west wall of the house.

1 Get footing hole inspection before pouring concrete

Foundation. New construction starts with the foundation, whether it's poured footings, a concrete slab or a basement with a floor and foundation walls. Generally, an addition is tied to the existing structure with a ledger that's attached to the rim joist on the house. Make sure the foundation extends below the frost line (48 in. as shown in inset above).

2

Support deck. You'll find several construction options for building the main platform that supports a new structure. The structure shown above is made with doubled 2 × 12 beams supported by 6 × 6 posts that are mounted to the concrete footings with metal post anchors. Then, 2 × 12 joists are laid across the beams to support the floor deck.

Inspectors are there to help. If you've never pulled a building permit before, walking into the office of the local building department that first time can be a bit frightening. After all, the job of a building inspector is to judge your plans and your work, right? But in just about every case, if you enter the office prepared and with a spirit of cooperation, you'll find that the officials who review your plans (as well as the inspectors who will visit the building site) are very knowledgeable and very willing to assist you in making improvements to your plan. Their main interest is not to serve as iron-fisted carpentry police, but to make sure that structures built in their jurisdiction are safe and well-made. Treat them with respect and a sense of teamwork, and the building inspector may well become your most reliable source of information and help.

3

Wall framing. Once the floor deck is up, the next logical step is to build the wall framing. Although 24 O.C. spacing is allowed in many cases, 16 O.C. is a good idea, even when using 2 × 6 lumber to build the stud walls. If the new walls have exterior exposure, it is unlikely that your local codes will allow you to use 2 × 4 studs and plates to frame them, especially if you live in an intemperate climate. The framed rough opening for the window seen above includes a header made out of doubled 2 × 6s with spacers between. Where possible, design rough openings to accommodate standard window sizes.

4

Wall sheathing. Attach the exterior wall sheathing as soon as possible once the wall framing is up. This will help prevent the framing from falling out of square, and will make for a sturdier base when attaching the rafters, which typically are supported by at least one stud wall. The shed style roof shown here is supported by a ledger as well.

Roof structure. You can't get the roof on too soon, especially if you're fighting the elements. The cold-set roll roofing on this project was installed over T&G sheathing hours before the first snowfall (a little colder than ideal, but the last chance for six months).

Windows and doors. Make cutouts for rough openings in the wall sheathing then install windows and doors.

5

Get framing inspection before proceeding

6

Building wrap. Most builders today install a layer of semi-permeable building wrap over the wall sheathing before installing the siding. The building wrap protects the wall cavity from water penetration, but still allows it to breathe. Some wrap material has a limited allowable exposure to sunlight, so it's a good idea to wait until you're just about ready to install the siding before you staple on the building wrap.

Hand-select your lumber. If you have the opportunity, it's worth taking the time to hand-select all of your building materials, particularly when it comes to framing lumber. Framing lumber, even within the same grade categories, varies tremendously from board to board. I've had the best luck finding good, straight boards in the inner area of freshly opened bundles: look for an accessible bundle that hasn't been pulled apart, and begin working toward the center. The pressure from the binding helps prevent the boards from warping and bowing. But whichever stock you choose, it's important that you wait to acquire it until you are ready to use it. Just a couple of days of laying around the worksite can allow the lumber to bend and bow in many ways.

If you don't have the opportunity to select and haul your own lumber, order from a supplier that allows you to return unused product. Order 20 or 30% more than you need, then hand-select from the supply that is delivered, returning the stock that does not meet your standards. Lumber is expensive: don't let yourself get stuck with wood that is sub-par.

Use the right product for the job. I only experienced one real "disaster" in this addition project, and it was my own fault. I tried to save a couple of dollars by using loose cellulose insulation instead of fiberglass to fill the space beneath the floor deck. To contain the insulation, I hung sheets of ¼ in. OSB from the bottoms of the floor beams. Then (too cheap to rent an insulation blower) I spent an entire day grating compressed bundles of cellulose through chicken wire until I'd filled the floor cavity to 14 in. in depth (to get the required R-44). Then I stapled a plastic vapor barrier over the floor joists before installing the floor decking/subfloor. This would have worked fine, if it wasn't for the major rainfall that occurred after I got the rafters up, but before the roof deck was in place. The tarp I'd attached over the rafters filled with water and gave way, flooding the framed addition and eventually working its way through the deck and vapor barrier to completely soak the cellulose, ruining it. The only solution was to remove the OSB from under the structure and pull out, by hand, all of the soaking wet cellulose. Then I replaced it with thick fiberglass batts, which is what I should have used in the first place. There is a reason, I discovered, that loose cellulose is billed as "attic insulation."

Landscape timbers aren't code-compliant for use as structural members. My addition is supported by nine 6 × 6 posts set on concrete footings. When I went to my local building center to purchase the posts, I found that the only 6 × 6 stock they carry are pressure-treated landscape timbers. But the timbers seemed beefy and sturdy, so I bought them, cut them to height, and built my structure on top of them. When it came time for my framing inspection, the inspector looked at the posts and shook his head in concern. "Those are landscape timbers. You can't use them as posts. Too many knots and defects." I panicked, expecting that I'd have to shore up the whole structure and replace the posts with construction-rated lumber. Then the

inspector asked me how many posts I'd used. When I told him there were nine he looked relieved. "You really only needed three or four," he informed me. "You're probably okay." So I got a little lucky. Because I overbuilt he was willing to overlook my poor materi-

als choice. But I learned a lesson: codes regulate many aspects of materials selection, not just dimension. Clearly and specifically include the lumber grade you're planning to use when filing your plans with the building department. And over-building is not a bad safety net.

Siding. Installing the siding signals that you're nearing the end of the exterior portion of your project. It's not a bad idea, when installing wood siding as above, to pre-prime the siding if you plan to paint it (weather allowing). If you're installing siding in cold weather, it's especially important to leave adequate expansion gaps where boards butt against one another or up to corner boards.

Trimwork and exterior finishing. Finishing up the decorative aspects of the exterior can be done on a catch-as-catch-can basis, but if the siding material is susceptible to water penetration, get the primer and paint on as soon as convenient.

16 or 24 O.C.? Many building codes now allow 24-in.-on-center (O.C.) framing in walls, floors and roofs. Obviously, spacing the framing members further apart can save time and materials costs. So I jumped at the opportunity, initially designing my addition 24-O.C. wherever I thought I could get away with it. I built the floor deck 24-O.C., using 2 × 12 lumber and ¾ in. tongue-in-groove "sturdi-floor" sheathing. But even then, I felt some deflection when I walked across the deck. This concerned me enough that I modified my plans and built the walls and roof structure 16-O.C.

It just felt sturdier. As I completed finishing the project, I was glad I'd made the switch for a couple of reasons. A few of the shorter walls would have included only three wall studs in 24-O.C. construction, but moving to 16-O.C. added a fourth member, making them stronger and better equipped to support wallcoverings and sheathing. Also, the 15-in.wide R-19 insulation batts I installed in the walls are much easier to handle than the 23-in.wide batts, which made the insulating job go more quickly. I ran the numbers, and I figure that switching to 16-O.C. added less than $100 to the total

cost of the project. It was well worth it, if only for peace of mind.

Tips for keeping costs down. The best way to way to improve your home inexpensively, of course, is to do as much of the work yourself as you can. This also has the added benefit of eliminating all the scheduling headaches that come with hiring contractors. In my addition, the only part of the job I shopped out was moving the electrical service drop. Coordinating with the electrician was a bit of a hassle and his bill for one day of work represented about 20% of the cost for the entire project, but I'm glad I chose not to tackle that particular job myself.

I also had some pretty good luck finding supplies on sale. If you have the storage space or the flexibility to alter your work schedule, buying materials on sale or close-out can bring surprisingly big savings. For example, I saved nearly $300 on the fir flooring; $200 on the cedar carsiding I used for the sauna walls; $150 on the sauna heater; and I

Interior finishing. The sequence for finishing the interior of a new construction project follows a fairly obvious sequence. If you'll be running wiring or plumbing in the walls, a good tip is to insulate half the wall thickness, install the wall components, then top off with the other half of the insulation.

Get rough wiring/plumbing inspections before installing wallcoverings

Wiring and wallcoverings. Install (or have installed) wiring and plumbing before installing vapor barriers and wallcoverings.

Floorcoverings. Wait until the walls and ceiling are completed (including taping and mudding sheetrock and painting) before installing the floorcoverings. Less construction activity lessens the chances of damaging the new floor.

got the turned railings for the porch and step rails at 70% off because they were being closed out at the end of the summer building season (I didn't get around to installing them for several months, but they were easy to store and still bundled so they held their shape).

Reclaiming used building materials can also yield some nice savings, but it is a bit risky, even if the materials are free. My basic rule of thumb was that if the material is decorative or will not undergo significant exposure, go ahead work in the used stuff if you can find it and it meets your project requirements. I had a couple of old frame-and-panels doors gathering dust in the basement, for example. They needed some fresh paint, but were otherwise in pretty good shape. So I designed the door opening in the closet to accommodate the old doors. I also found an old full-view, Douglas-fir framed exterior door with a polycarbonate lite panel next to a dumpster near my office. I took it home (with permission, of course), cleaned it up and installed it between the addition and the kitchen, where it looks beautiful. I turned down the chance to install some old double-hung windows, though. The low-cost, new windows that I bought are much more efficient and, I hope, I'll recoup the cost before too long in energy savings.

Cash in your IOUs. If you're like most handymen, you've done a lot of favors for family and friends and even acquaintances, and probably were more than happy to help. A major home improvement project is a great time to "cash in" some of those favors. A few tasks where help is especially useful are: pouring footings and foundations, installing rafters and ceiling joists, laying roof decking, and sheetrocking. In fact, the greatest frustration I experienced with the project shown here was attempting to sheetrock the ceiling by myself. After a couple of minor disasters, the panels I was willing to work with shrunk from full 4 × 8 sheets to thin, 16-in. wide strips. This eventually worked, but I paid the price when it came time to tape and mud the joints.

12

Finishing touches. Once the major construction work is completed, spend some time developing the little details that give your project some individuality. For this project, the finishing included applying a deep red oak finish to the fir flooring, with a topcoat of four thin coats of satin polyurethane. A small sauna (54 × 54 in.) was added in the corner of the room, as well as some built-in cabinets and a closet fitted with reclaimed doors. Finally, some decorative exterior trimwork was installed.

Get final wiring, plumbing and construction inspections

CONCRETE & MASONRY

Concrete and masonry products have many uses in home remodeling and construction. Perhaps the most important of these is for building footings and foundations. But bricks, blocks, pavers and concrete are all products that you're sure to run into constantly as a do-it-yourselfer. From backyard barbeques to in-ground swimming pools, concrete and masonry units are essential building materials.

If you're planning an addition to your home, you have two options for supporting it: you can either excavate deep enough to dig a basement with foundation walls made of poured concrete or concrete block, or you can dig holes and pour concrete footings that support the joists and beams that make up the undercarriage of the structure.

Masonry work is not for everyone: as do-it-yourself projects go, it falls into the "ambitious" category. Largely for this reason you'll find that most home centers have fairly limited options for masonry products, especially when it comes to brick and block. .Typically, at home centers, you'll find a couple common sizes of

concrete blocks and a few choices of bagged concrete, mortar mix, tube forms and tinting colors. You will probably find little or no brick selection, although they may stock a decent assortment of concrete pavers for landscaping and patios. If all you're interested in is a couple of bags of concrete to set some fence posts, you'll do well to pick them up at a building center.

Applications for concrete & masonry products

Backyard building projects

Foundations and walls

Slabs and sidewalks

Footings

But if you have anything more complex in mind, check with a concrete products supplier. In the *Yellow Pages,* you can find these listed under "Brick," "Concrete," "Mason Contractors" and "Mason Equipment." Landscape product suppliers can also be a good place to check. The Internet is also a good source for obtaining information on contractors and masonry topics.

Concrete: Concrete consists of gravel aggregate, sand and portland cement. Concrete is available in pre-mixed bags of dry ingredients, in ready-mixed form that's delivered to your worksite ready-to-pour in a truck, or in its raw components.

Pre-mixed concrete. Pre-mixed concrete comes in bags ranging from 40 to 80 pounds, but most of them are 60 pounds in weight and, when mixed with water, yield ½ cubic foot of concrete. The most common is standard concrete mix, which contains aggregate up to ⅜ in. in diameter. This type is suitable for just about any basic concrete project, including pouring footings for decks or additions, setting posts, or forming steps or sidewalks. Even at general home building centers you'll probably find a few other types of bagged concrete mix, each with its own purpose. Keep in mind that there are literally dozens of products available from concrete product suppliers, any of which might be the perfect solution for your situation. See page 21 for a sampling of these.

Ready-mix: Ready-mix concrete is obtained from a concrete supplier and delivered to your house. One of the advantages to using it is that you can let the suppliers help you decide how much material you need and which formulation is best for your project. Ready-mix concrete can also be picked up at the plant and hauled in special trailers you can rent from the plant or a rental center. Hauling it yourself enables you to control the delivery time precisely and avoid the delivery charge (although some of the savings will likely be offset by the trailer rental fee).

Site-mixed. Particularly for quantities of less than 1 cubic yard, it often makes the most sense to mix the concrete yourself. You can make it by

(Continued on page 21)

Soil Classification System

Soil Type	Description	Allowable Bearing lb./sq. ft.	Drainage	Frost Heave Potential	Expansion Potential
BR	Bedrock	30,000	Poor	Low	Low
GW	Well-graded gravel gravel-sand mixture	8,000	Good	Low	Low
GP	Poorly graded gravel Gravel-sand mixture	8,000	Good	Low	Low
SW	Well-graded sands gravelly sands	6,000	Good	Low	Low
SP	Poorly graded sands gravelly sands	5,000	Good	Low	Low
GM	Silty gravels gravel-sand-silt mixtures	4,000	Good	Med	Low
SM	Silty sand sand-silt mixtures	4,000	Good	Med	Low
GC	Clayey sands gravel-clay-sand mixtures	4,000	Med	Med	Low
SC	Clayey sands sand-clay mixture	4,000	Med	Med	Low
ML	Inorganic silts, fine sands, silty or clayey fine sands	2,000	Med	High	Low
CL	Inorganic clays, gravelly, sandy, silty, lean clays	2,000	Med	Med	Med
CH	Inorganic clays, fat clays	2,000	Poor	Med	High
MH	Inorganic silts, fine sandy or silty soils, elastic silts	2,000	Poor	High	High
OL	Organic silts, organic silty clays	400	Poor	Med	Med
OH	Organic clays of med-high plasticity	0	Unsatis-factory	Med	High
PT	Peat and highly organic soils	0	Unsatis-factory	Med	High

Before any construction begins, the you should determine what type of sub-base you'll be building on by testing the soil. Your local soil and water conservation district office of the USDA Soil Conservation Service can help you test and identify the soil in your yard. Information you'll need to determine the maximum bearing allowance of your soil are the depth to bedrock and seasonal high water, grain size and distribution, permeability and expansion potential, engineering and agriculture suitability and the soil pH and natural vegetation. These reduce down to rock, gravel, sand, silt, clay and organic soil. The type of soil will determine the weight and possibly size of your structure.

Continued from page 19

adding water to premixed bags of material, which is the easiest routine and yields consistent product. Or, you can blend your own Portland cement, sand, gravel and water to the ratio you need (See page 22). The mixing can be done by hand, using a shovel or masonry hoe and a mortar tub or wheelbarrow. Or, you can rent a power concrete mixer. Either way, mixing concrete is laborious and time consuming: it takes 54 60-pound bags of dry-mix just to make one cubic yard of material.

Concrete additives. Depending on the specific characteristics you need your concrete to possess, you may want to add any of a number of forti-fiers (usually called admixtures) to the material. This is especially true of concrete used for concrete repair work. Among the more common additives are: latex or acrylic liquid fortifier, to increase elasticity and bonding proper-ties; fiberglass reinforcement fibers to increase strength and crack resistance; and accelerator or retardants to increase or decrease the setting time or curing time. Tinting products also may be added to give the concrete greater decorative appeal if you're casting pavers or forming a garden walkway.

Site preparation. Whether you're laying blocks or pouring concrete, the success of the project depends greatly on the quality of the layout and site preparation work. If you're pouring a concrete slab or sidewalk, you'll need to excavate and grade the worksite, then prepare a stable, well-drained base for the concrete. Usually this is done by spreading and tamping a layer of compactible gravel (Class V). You'll also need to install forms and, in many cases, reinforcement in the form of re-bar or re-wire laid in the site.

Brick, block & mortar. See the section beginning on page 28 for informa-tion on choosing and buying these products.

Photo courtesy of Quikrete Cos.

Coloring concrete

While concrete is a versatile and durable building product, a wide expanse of dull gray is not very appealing visu-ally. One way to brighten the material up, especially when making walk-ways, pavers or other small proj-ects, is to add colorant to the mixture. Con-crete tinting products, like those to the left, are sold in many colors at concrete supply outlets.

Estimating Concrete

Concrete is calculated and sold in volume units of cubic feet and cubic yards. You'll need to determine the total vol-ume of concrete required for your footings or slab in order to purchase an accurate amount. If you buy ready-mix con-crete that comes delivered in a truck, your supplier will want your estimate in terms of cubic yards. Should you decide to buy premixed dry concrete instead from your local home center, it comes packaged in 60-pound bags that yield ½ cubic ft. Doing the math can be a bit befuddling, especially when it comes to calculating the volume of tubular footings. Fortu-nately, a handy chart is printed right on the pre-mix bags to help you estimate the number of bags you need for various-sized slabs and footings. Your ready-mix supplier can help you determine yardage if you explain the dimensions of your slab or the diameter, height and number of footings you need to pour. Or, use the chart below to help you figure what you need, based on some common concrete yields. If you calculate your own quantities, round up 10% to be safe.

Concrete quantity	Yields		
	4-IN.-THICK SLAB	**8-IN.-DIA. FOOTING**	**12-IN.-DIA. FOOTING**
¼ yard (14 bags*)	20 square ft.	14 @ 16 in. deep 5 @ 42 in. deep	6 @ 16 in. deep 2 @ 42 in. deep
½ yard (27 bags)	40 square ft.	28 @ 16 in. deep 10 @ 42 in. deep	12 @ 16 in. deep 4 @ 42 in. deep
1 yard (54 bags)	80 square ft.	57 @ 16 in. deep 21 @ 42 in. deep	25 @ 16 in. deep 9 @ 42 in. deep
*Bag quantities are 60-pound dry-mixed concrete			

Options for buying concrete

Ready-mix. When you purchase concrete and have it delivered, the concrete comes already mixed and ready to pour. Buying ready-mix is economical when you need several yards of concrete. You'll pay a delivery charge regardless of the size of the order, which makes batches of 1 yard or less more expensive. Have helpers with wheelbarrows on hand when the concrete arrives and create a path with boards to protect your lawn and make smooth wheelbarrow runs. You'll need to move quickly.

Rent a mixing trailer when you need more concrete than can feasibly be mixed in a wheelbarrow. You can haul this mixer behind your truck or car. They come powered by either a gas or electric motor. Some trailers can be filled with ready-mix at your concrete supplier so you are ready to pour when you get home.

Mixing concrete yourself

Mixing concrete is hard work, and the logistics can be daunting. You have two options: If your project requires only small amounts—setting posts, for example—consider buying pre-mixed concrete in a bag. It comes already packaged in the proper ratio of portland cement, sand and gravel. Just add water and blend the mixture in a wheelbarrow with a hoe.

A second alternative is to purchase the ingredients in bulk and mix them yourself—a cheaper but more labor-intensive process. Portland cement is sold in 1-cubic-ft. bags weighing 94 pounds. The gravel and sand are sold in bulk, by weight. If you have a pickup or a trailer, you can buy the ingredients, haul them home and shovel them into piles. Otherwise, you can have sand and gravel delivered by the truckload.

When mixing from scratch in a wheelbarrow, mix the cement and sand first. They must be blended to a uniform color, showing neither light nor dark streaks. Add water little by little, until the entire mixture is evenly moist. Mix in the gravel last. If you add gravel before the water it probably will be too difficult to mix by hand. If you get carried away with the water and the mix seems too soupy, add small amounts of cement, sand and gravel in the same proportions you used in the original mix.

If using a power mixer, blend the mixture in a different order. With the mixer stopped, load in the gravel and some water. Start the mixer and, while it is running, add the sand, cement and water as needed. Keep the mixer running for at least three minutes, or until the contents are a uniform color. Pour the concrete as soon as possible.

If you are mixing concrete yourself, here are some recommended proportions for slabs and footings.

Slabs (light traffic):
1 part cement, 2 parts sand, 4 parts gravel

Slabs (heavy traffic):
1 part cement, 1½ parts sand, 3 parts gravel

Footings:
1 part cement, 2 parts sand, 4 parts gravel

Ready-to-use: General purpose concrete for setting posts and building sidewalks, steps, patios, curbs, footings and floors.

Fiber-reinforced: For making walkways, patios, steps and footings; minimizes cracking, chipping and flaking.

High-early concrete mix: Commercial grade used for patios, driveway aprons, high-stress applications.

Fast-setting: For anchoring fence-, mailbox-, lamp posts, steps, sidewalks, swing sets.

Portland cement: The main ingredient in concrete; To make concrete, mix 3 parts gravel and 2 parts sand to 1 part Portland Cement (by volume).

Mortar mix: For laying brick, block or stone and repairing damaged joints in brick, block, and stone masonry.

Masonry cement: The main ingredient in Type N masonry mortar; mix: 3 parts masonry sand to 1 part masonry cement (by volume).

Mason's mix: Commercial-grade mortar mix for laying brick, block or stone for walls, columns.

Anchoring cement: For setting bolts, handrails or other metal parts to be anchored in concrete, repairing loose wrought iron railings; pourable cement that sets in 10-30 minutes and expands as it hardens.

Base coat stucco: For use as the scratch and/or brown coat in 3-coat stucco application; used with finish coat stucco.

Reinforced stucco: Glass fiber reinforced stucco for use as a 1-coat stucco over exterior insulation board or wall panel systems.

Glass-block mortar: White mortar for laying glass blocks for interior and exterior walls.

Sand mix: for pouring overlays less than 2" thick; patching and topping concrete surfaces; underlayment for brick pavers and flagstone.

Masonry coating: for painting masonry and concrete walls; interior and exterior use, above and below grade.

FOOTINGS

Footings for small structures typically are cylindrical in shape, between 8 and 14 in. in diameter, and they extend past the frostline in the ground. Rectangular concrete slabs that support brick or block walls also are classified as footings: see the section beginning on page 26.

In most cases, you'll find it easiest and most efficient to use tubular forms when pouring footings—See below. You can dispense with them and simply dig holes of the appropriate width and depth to accept the concrete, but this is only effective in fairly hard, compacted soils. Whether you use a tubular form or not, most codes require that footings have a "bell" at the bottom so they're a few inches wider at the base, which makes them more stable. If using tubular forms, the bell is created by widening the footing hole at

Options for connecting posts to footings

Set a J-bolt into the freshly poured concrete footing, centered with the threaded end sticking up. After the concrete cures, insert metal post anchor hardware over the J-bolt and thread a washer and nut to secure the anchor to the J-bolt.

Set posts directly into concrete. This is a little risky—if you manage to keep the post immobilized as the concrete sets up, you can end up with an almost-indestructible bond. But if the post slips, gaps are created and a loose fit (and water penetration) can result.

Post anchors with preattached corrugated fins can be inserted directly into the fresh concrete. Do your best to level the post anchors as you insert them. Do not disturb the anchors until the concrete has cured.

Tubular Forms

Tubular forms are available at most building centers in 4-foot lengths. The two most common sizes are 8-in. dia. (used mostly for small decks and light-weight building projects) and 12-in. dia. Some store will carry 10-in.-dia. forms. Other widths may be ordered. After placing the footing in the hole, pour and tamp compactible gravel in the base for drainage, then cut the tubular form to length (because the form needs to be raised off the bottom and extend above ground, you can cut the form to the full depth of the hole, then simply raise it up. On very flat ground, use batter boards and strings to lay out the locations and level the tops of the tubular forms. If the worksite has an uneven terrain, an easier approach is to pour the footings so each sticks up a few inches above ground, then cut each post to the necessary height to hit your level mark. In some cases, though, you can pour the footings so they extend as much as a couple of feet above ground, with the above-ground section functioning as a post (See next page).

Even if you don't use tubular forms for the body of your footings, you can create smooth, symmetrical appearance on the exposed portion of the footing by setting a 3 to 4 in. high section of tubular form on top of the loosely poured footing, then filling the form section and striking it off with a screed board.

the bottom, then raising the form a few inches above the bottom of the hole before the pour. This allows the concrete to spill out underneath the form, creating the bell. The tops of footings should extend a few inches above ground level to minimize the risk of ground or water contact at the point where the post or beam rests on the

footing. The tops should be crowned slightly so they shed water.

If you prefer to work by hand, use a shovel or posthole digger to make the footing holes. You can also rent a one or two man, gas-powered auger to dig round footing holes. These tools can make fast work of excavations, but if you've never used one before try to

find an experienced person to help you: power augers can be difficult to control, which can affect the layout of your post locations. The auger blades also have a tendency to catch and stick in larger roots, and extracting them usually requires you to disengage the blade from the machine and crank it backward by hand.

Check with your local building department to learn the footing requirements in your area. They will give you specifications on the diameter, depth, spacing and the size of the bell. Most building codes require that footing holes for load-bearing structures be inspected before they're filled. Don't forget to acquire a permit and schedule an inspection. The inspector may ask for up to a one-week notice— don't schedule concrete delivery until the footing holes are approved.

Amount of Concrete Needed for round footings				
No. of footings (8 in. dia.)	Depth of Footings			
	1ft.	2ft.	3ft.	4ft.
2	¾ ft.³	1½ ft.³	2¼ ft.³	3 ft.³
3	1 ft.³	2¼ ft.³	3½ ft.³	4½ ft.³
4	1½ ft.³	3 ft.³	4½ ft.³	6 ft.³
5	2 ft.³	3¾ ft.³	5¾ ft.³	7½ ft.³

Footing options

In addition to the conventional method of pouring subterranean footings and embedding hardware into the fresh concrete, you may have other options for making deck footings.

Precast concrete piers. This method is commonly used in mild climates with stable soil. When frost lines are not an issue, you can simply pour shallow concrete footings, then set precast concrete piers on top of the footings after they cure. At the footing locations, dig 12-in.-deep holes (or as required by local codes) that are 3 in. wider in dimension than the base of the pier block (pier blocks are normally 12 × 12 in.). Tamp loose soil in the bottom of the hole, then shovel in a 2-in. layer of coarse gravel and tamp firmly. Pour concrete into the holes, filling them to within 3 to 4 in. of ground level. While the concrete is still plastic, but strong enough to support the pier, embed the pier about 1 in. deep into the concrete footing. Use a plumb bob to align the center of the pier block with the post centers marked on the guide strings. The top of the pier block should be level and at least 3 in. above ground. After the concrete cures, simply set 4 × 4 posts on-end into the recess at the top of each pier.

Above-ground tube footings. You can extend tubular forms one or more feet above grade to double as posts or columns to support structural beams (common on hillside decks). If the tubes extend 2 ft. or more above the ground, you'll need to brace them with 1 × 4 or 2 × 4 braces as you would for a fence post. Insert a No. 5 reinforcing rod (rebar) into the footing after you've poured in the concrete, to prevent it from cracking. Because you'll be attaching the beams directly to the poured-concrete columns with metal connectors, you'll also need to make sure the tops of the form tubes are level to each other. Do this by attaching a string between the tops of the tubes, then leveling the string with a line level; or you can place a long, straight 2 × 4 on-edge across the tops of the tubes, and set a carpenter's level on top of the 2 × 4. Make any minor height adjustments when you install the tubes. Also run leveled strings out from the bottom of the ledger, centered over the post locations. Position the strings above the tubes to indicate the width of the beam, then measure down from the string to the tops of the tubular forms to indicate the beam width plus ½ in. Set the tubes to this height.

NOTICE: Before you locate footings, make sure you know the exact locations of any underground electrical, gas, telephone, sewer and water lines within the project area. Utility companies can provide you with this information; some offer a free locating service. Also check the original plot plans for your house, if you have them.

CONCRETE SLABS

Pouring a small concrete slab is not an especially difficult task, and you may even find it a rewarding experience. Start with smaller projects, though, such as short walkways or floors for outbuildings.

If you've never poured a concrete slab, be sure to get plenty of how-to information before you start. If the slab will be part of a habitable structure, get a permit and have the site inspected and approved before you pour.

Steps for pouring slabs:
• Identify the thickness of the slab and drainage base, along with the location of forms, reinforcement and isolation joints.
• Excavate the site, allowing for a layer of compacted gravel that's at least 2 inches thick—check with your local building department.
• Install and compact the drainage base (compactible gravel).
• Install and level concrete forms (2 × 4 or 2 × 6, depending on the thickness of the slab—most slabs are 4 inches thick).
• Install re-bar or re-wire reinforcement (See next page).
• Install isolation boards around structures (See next page).
• Prepare for delivery, making sure you have enough wheelbarrows, trowels, floats (and helpers) on hand.
• Fill the forms with concrete and immediately screed it to level with the tops of the forms.
• Once the bleed water forms on the surface, float it with a floating tool that's appropriate for the function and finish of the project.
• Tool the edges as desired and cut control joints (typically at 3-or-4-ft. intervals).
• Texture surface if desired.
• Cover surface with plastic or burlap as it cures (if using burlap, dampen it with water a couple of times a day.
• After curing (at least three days, but cure time varies according to the product and the weather condition) strip off the form and backfill around the new slab.

Finishing is an extremely important part of the slab-pouring process. It's important to determine the type of finish you want beforehand, and make sure you have the correct tools for applying it (such as the bull float seen above). Take care not to overwork the surface during finish, as this will draw too much water to the surface, weakening the concrete.

CUBIC YARDS OF CONCRETE FOR SLABS								
Slab Area	Slab Thickness, inches							
Sq. ft.	2	3	4	5	6	8	10	12
10	0.1	0.1	0.1	0.2	0.2	0.3	0.3	0.4
50	0.3	0.5	0.6	0.7	0.9	1.2	1.4	1.9
100	0.6	0.9	1.2	1.5	1.9	2.5	3.0	3.7
300	1.9	2.8	3.7	4.7	5.6	7.4	9.4	11.1
500	3.1	4.7	6.2	7.2	9.3	12.4	14.4	18.6

Pouring masonry footings

Vertically stacked masonry structures require a sturdy concrete footing. Local codes govern the required size and depth of the footing. Generally, the footing should be at least two to four inches wider than the structure at the base. Use forms to create a footing that's exactly level, and be sure the concrete is smoothed with a float after the pour. In most cases, you'll need to reinforce the footing with re-bar or re-wire (See next page).

Tips for pouring concrete slabs

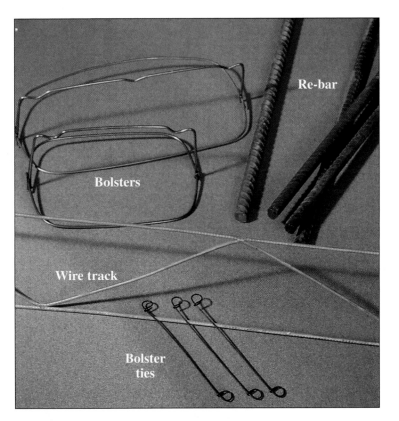

Above. Install reinforcement in the pour area as required (check with your local building department for allowable reinforcement sizes, types and spacing). Make sure the reinforcement is raised off the base of the site. Bolsters designed to supported rebar are shown in use above. The rebar should be positioned roughly midway through the thickness, and make sure it does not come within an inch or so of the surface. Fasten the rebar to the bolsters with bolster ties or wire to prevent it from slipping during the pour.
Right. Common concrete reinforcement products include re-wire mesh (not shown), metal re-bar, and ladder or track-style reinforcement strips that are set into the mortar when stacking block walls.

Avoid spilling and overfilling. Use a 5-gallon bucket (above) or a spade (below) to pour concrete into small forms or tight areas (don't try to "precision-dump" a wheelbarrow load).

Install isolation boards if the new slab will abut a permanent structure (it is important that the two structures be able to move independently). Building boards impregnated with asphalt often are used as isolation boards. Make sure the isolation board extends down past the drainage base and is slightly higher than the tops of the forms.

CUBIC YARDS OF CONCRETE FOR FOOTINGS/WALLS				
Depth or height (in.)	Width/thickness (inches)			
	6	8	12	18	24
8	.012	.017	.025	.037	.049
12	.019	.025	.037	.056	.074
24	.037	.049	.074	.111	.148
72	.111	.148	.222	.333	.444
96	.148	.198	.296	.444	.593
(Cubic yards per linear foot)				

BRICK & BLOCK

Concrete block and bricks (often classified as "masonry units") come in a very wide assortment of styles, sizes and shapes. The actual dimensions of each masonry unit are ⅜ in. less than the nominal (stated) size to allow for the mortar joint required between units when laid.

Bricks. *Modular* and *queen size* bricks are the most common shapes you'll find. Their sizing, when ordering, reads *T, H, L* (thickness, height and length). The actual size of a standard modular brick is 3⅝ × 2¼ × 7⅝ in, and the actual size of a queen brick is 3 × 2¾ × 7⅝ in. Queens are often used because they are higher (thicker), which means you'll need fewer bricks per square foot. Queens have become so common that some masons will not lay modular bricks, due to the extra work it will involve in a large project. Brick is graded and put into three categories, according to its *freeze/thaw capacity*. Throughout most of the U.S., the *SW* (severe weather) grade is required or recommended.

Blocks. The nominal sizes of concrete blocks range from 4 to 12 in. in width and they are typically 8 in. high and 16 in. long. The ⅜ in. allows for a mortar joint. Their sizing, when ordering, reads *W, H, L* (width, height, and length).

Bricks typically have a two-or-three-hole core that reduces the weight and makes a stronger mortar bond. Selection of size and color varies regionally, but you're likely to find a much better selection at a masonry products supplier than at a general home center.

Concrete blocks come in a much larger variety of shapes and sizes than bricks. Most blocks fall into one of three categories: stretchers, which are the field blocks in a structure; end and corner blocks; and solid cap blocks for laying the top course on a block wall.

Essential brick style options

Smooth-faced   **Textured-face**   **Tumbled**

Brick bond patterns

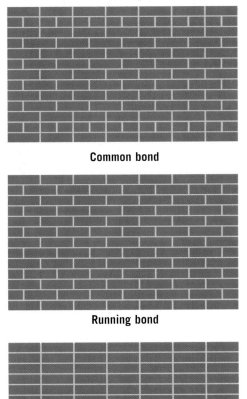

Common bond

Running bond

Stack bond

Brick-veneer walls

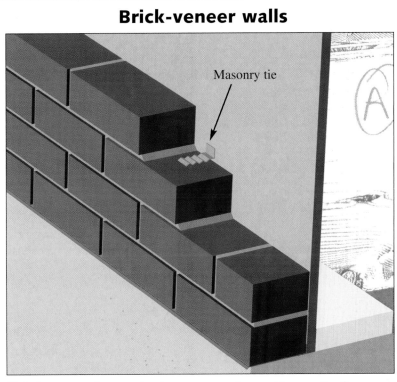

Masonry tie

Brick veneer is attached to an exterior wall, mostly for decorative effect. Brick veneer walls are constructed using most of the same mortaring and bricklaying techniques as a regular, single-wythe wall. The main difference is that the first course is supported by a concrete or metal ledger, and the wall is tied to the wall framing at regular intervals with masonry ties.

Concrete block walls

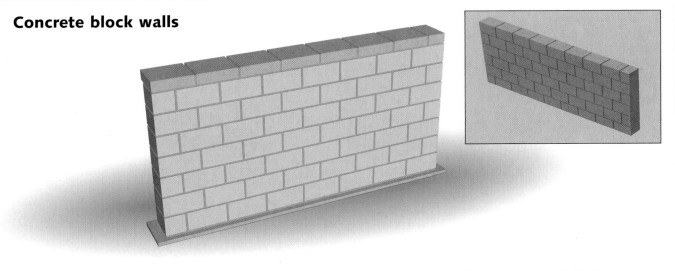

Solid block walls. Blocks are laid end-to-end with the vertical mortar joints staggered. Ends are formed from half and full-length end blocks, the field blocks are stretchers. Top of wall is made with cap blocks if top will be exposed (larger drawing). For foundation walls that will be built upon (smaller illustration), wall tops can be created with top-fill blocks formed with cores that extend three-fourths of the way through the unit, giving it a solid top surface.

Working with block

Mortar Options:
When laying brick or block, you can either use premixed, dry mortar mix (Photo A) or make your own from the constituent ingredients (Photo B). Using premixed powder is more convenient, but usually costlier. Mixing your own allows you to adjust the mixing ratios.

Finishing Options:
Concrete blocks walls are not attractive, for the most part. You can dress up your completed wall by applying a decorative topcoat. Stucco (Photo C) is a traditional product you can use, but it is fairly time-consuming to apply and requires different material layers. An alternative is a brush-on wall skimming compound (Photo D) that is applied in one coat.

Working with mortar

When mixing mortar, first dampen the mixing container (a mortar tub is shown here), then pour in the contents of one bag of dry mortar mix, along with any additives or fortifiers. Add clean, fresh water until the mixture attains a plastic-like consistency, blending with a masonry hoe. To test the consistency, slice into the mortar with a trowel—the product should hold its shape and cling to the trowel without crumbling or running off. Some brands of mortar will suggest a general water-to-mortar ratio, but for best results rely on a visual inspection of the first batch you mix, adding incremental amounts of water until the proper consistency is achieved. Keep track of how much water you add to ensure following batches are uniform.

GLASS BLOCK

Glass blocks are typically considered to be masonry units, although they have more differences with than similarities to brick and concrete block. Primarily, glass block cannot be used in locations where it must do any structural bearing. Yet, it's a versatile, highly decorative building material that is laid in much the same manner as other masonry units.

One easy glass-block project you might wish to consider is use it to build a room divider wall. When made with glass block, a room divider partition divides a room into distinct areas, without seeming to make the room smaller. The block also has a clean, contemporary appearance and is relatively easy to build with.

Building a glass block privacy panel is similar in many ways to building a brick or block wall. The blocks are laid in rows and set in a mortar bed, with metal reinforcement used between courses. The actual products used to build with glass block look a little different than the bricks, concrete blocks and rebar you may be accustomed to working with. But the function is essentially the same. The project wall illustrated here was built on a wood curb to protect it from impact at the busy floor level, then capped with two pieces of red oak to create handy ledges.

For more information on glass block see page 81

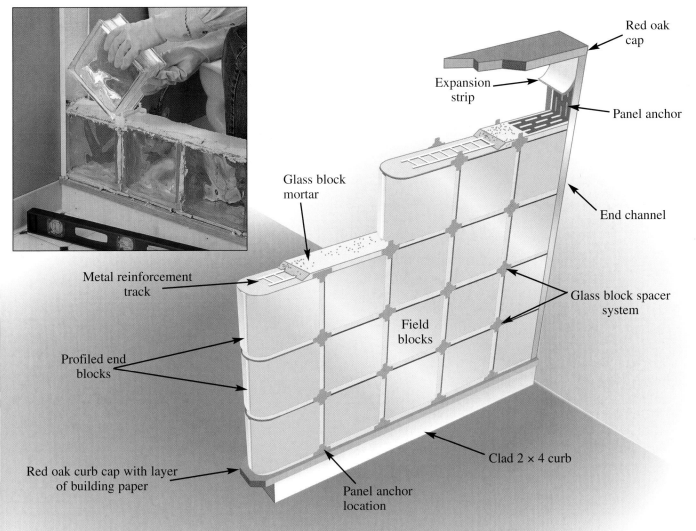

Red oak cap

Expansion strip

Panel anchor

End channel

Glass block mortar

Glass block spacer system

Metal reinforcement track

Field blocks

Profiled end blocks

Clad 2 × 4 curb

Red oak curb cap with layer of building paper

Panel anchor location

LANDSCAPING PAVERS

Concrete and brick pavers are used primarily as landscaping supplies to create patios and walkways. Landscape supply stores are the best source.

Paver shapes & patterns

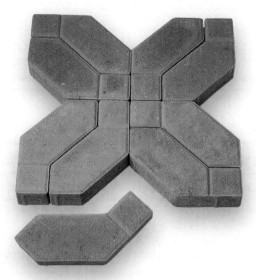

Cobblestones are noninterlocking square or rectangular pavers, typically antiqued using a tumbling process. The roundovers at the edges of the top surfaces create a quilted look when installed in groups.

Offset diamond shapes can be combined into dozens of pattern variations, especially when combined with square pavers. An X-shaped repeating medallion pattern is indicated above.

Zig-zag shapes have a larger amount of interlocking surface area, and are best used in running bond types of patterns.

Estimating Paver Quantities

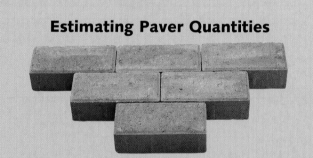

To estimate how many pavers you need to complete your project, the most accurate method is to arrange a handful of the pavers you'll be using into a small section of the pattern, then measure the total length and width of the section. Divide the measurements by the number of pavers it contains for an average per-unit length and width that allow for the gaps between pavers. Divide the planned width and length of the patio or walkway by the average unit dimensions and add 10% to the total for waste.

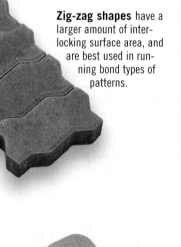

Split octagon with offset square ends can be combined to form any of the most common patterns. Note that the pavers are arranged in mirror-image pairs.

Popular paver layout patterns

Standard Basketweave

Running Bond

Offset Basketweave

Herringbone

Two-to-one Basketweave

Running Stack

Chapter Contents:

LUMBER &
FRAMING MATERIALS

Once the foundation is established, the framing of your structure can begin. The elements of house framing include wall studs, joists, rafters, beams, posts, cap and sole plates, and a few miscellaneous parts such as headers and blocking. In most cases, these parts are built with wood, although steel studs and channel tracks are becoming more popular.

Particularly in do-it-yourself projects, dimensional lumber is easily the most common framing material. But along with the advent of steel framing, advancing technology in wood engineering is resulting in more and more nontraditional building framing products. Engineered beams, for example, are formed largely from wood by-products but pack greater strength into smaller sizes than ordinary dimensional lumber: plus, they make much more efficient use of wood resources. For additions and outbuildings, many do-it-yourselfers also are turning to manufactured wood trusses for roof support, instead of conventional wood rafters. Floor truss systems are growing in popularity in new homes, as well.

Construction lumber, which is often referred to as "dimensional lumber," is cut from various species of softwood trees, including pine, spruce and fir. One of the very first things you need to know about construction lumber is that it's never as wide or thick as it appears from the size description. The "actual" size is between $\frac{1}{2}$ and $\frac{3}{4}$ in. smaller than the "nominal" size: thus a 2 × 4, for example, is really a 1$\frac{1}{2}$ × 3$\frac{1}{2}$. This difference must be taken into account when planning a project that makes use of construction lumber.

Framing material options

Dimensional lumber

Metal wall systems

Engineered beams

Truss systems for ceiling and floor support

CONSTRUCTION LUMBER

Construction lumber falls into three general categories of dimension: 1× ("one-by") stock, 2× stock and timbers, which are 4× and bigger.

There are a few common species of softwood used to make framing lumber for construction, each with its own advantages and disadvantages. Depending on your location, the time of year, environmental reasons or the dealer you go to, however, you may not have a choice as to which species you get. These species are then categorized into three groups: Western Lumber, Southern Pine and Canadian Lumber.

Western Lumber consists of:
• Douglas Fir, which is a straight-grained wood.
• Western Larch, which is also a strong, straight-grained softwood.
• Hem-Fir (hemlock and fir), which is a multi-species class of western lumber grown for appearance, versatility and performance. Hemlock is a strong wood and easy to work with, while the firs, composed of Pacific Silver Fir, White Fir, Grand Fir, California Red Fir and Noble Fir are some of the nations most versatile softwoods.

Southern Pine is a general group of longleaf, slash, shortleaf and loblolly species grown from Texas to Virginia. They tend to be strong, durable, and highly treatable with preservative.

Canadian Lumber is generally referred to as SPF lumber, which stands for "spruce, pine and fir." It is more plentiful in supply than lumber in the other categories, but its design values are generally lower.

(Continued on page 37)

Whitewood is a common term used to describe construction lumber. The term is sometimes misused, but actually is defined as a group of species that could include any of the true firs, Engelmann spruce, Hemlock or any of the pines. Generally, whitewood is relatively low in strength, but it is soft, workable and not prone to splitting.

Wood framing components

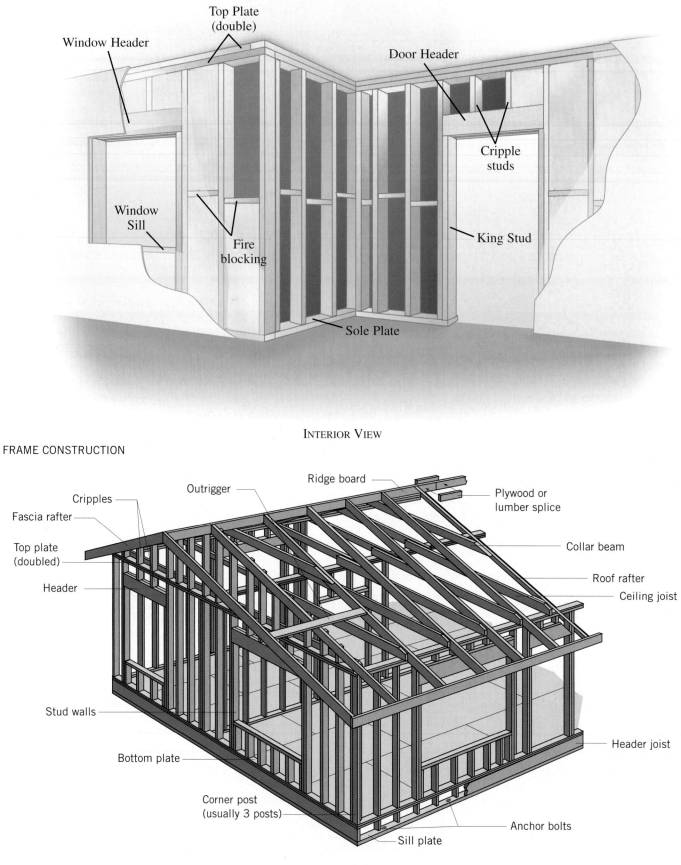

Window Header

Top Plate (double)

Door Header

Window Sill

Cripple studs

Fire blocking

King Stud

Sole Plate

INTERIOR VIEW

FRAME CONSTRUCTION

Cripples

Outrigger

Ridge board

Plywood or lumber splice

Fascia rafter

Top plate (doubled)

Collar beam

Header

Roof rafter

Ceiling joist

Stud walls

Bottom plate

Header joist

Corner post (usually 3 posts)

Anchor bolts

Sill plate

EXTERIOR VIEW

Construction Lumber Grades

Grade	Grading criteria
B Select and BTR	Highest quality lumber with few or no defects or blemishes. Nominal sizes may be limited.
C Select	Some small defects or blemishes permissible, but still largely clear and of high quality.
D Select	One board face usually defect-free.
Superior Finish	Highest grade finish lumber with only minor defects.
Prime Finish	High quality with some defects and blemishes.
No. 1 Common	Highest grade of knotty lumber; usually available by special-order.
No. 2 Common	Pronounced knots and large blemishes permissible.

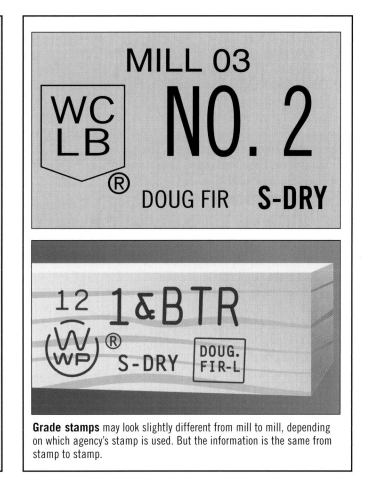

Grade stamps may look slightly different from mill to mill, depending on which agency's stamp is used. But the information is the same from stamp to stamp.

(Continued from page 35)

Grading. All construction lumber is stamped with a grade that informs the buyer of how it falls into certain uniform standards. Although there are several grading agencies, they have all adopted the standards set by the *American Lumber Standards Committee,* which is part of the U.S. Department of Commerce. Grade stamps include the mill number, certification agency, species, grade number and moisture content. Deciphering the information on the grade stamp can help you determine if the lumber in question will meet your needs. It will also give you clues to defects the lumber may carry.

Categories of lumber

Boards. In the realm of rough carpentry, the term "board" generally refers to softwood lumber with a nominal thickness of one inch. In construction, boards are commonly used as furring strips and bracing. This would include 1 × 2, 1 × 3, 1 × 4-in. and wider. NOTE: If you're using boards to fur-out a wall that will support wallboard, use nothing smaller than 1× 4 to provide an adequate surface for driving wallboard screws.

Dimensional lumber is divided into four sub-categories: *structural light framing; light framing; studs;* and *structural joists and planks.*

Structural light framing (2 to 4-in. thick, 2 to 4-in. wide). These members are used for a variety of purposes in framing, including plates and blocking.

• No. 1: General utility and construction, good appearance suitable for visually-exposed purposes.

• No. 2: Suitable for all types of construction, allows for well spaced knots of any quality.

Engineered Wood Products

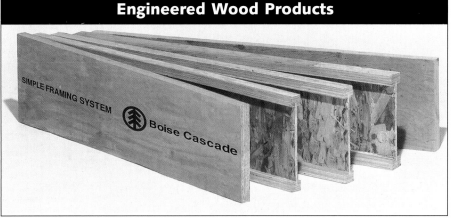

Laminated lumber is an engineered wood product made by gluing-up combinations of lumber, plywood and oriented strand board to form structural beams. These laminated beams and I-Joists are stronger than standard dimensional lumber and easier to manufacture in longer lengths and widths. They are specially engineered to carry loads over spans, such as garage doors and floors.

• No. 3: Suitable for general rough-construction purposes.

Light Framing (2 to 4-in. thick, 2 to 4-in. wide, 8 to 16-ft. long).

• Construction grade: For general framing purposes, good appearance, strong.

• Standard grade: Allows larger defects than Construction grade.

• Utility and Economy grades: For noncritical purposes only, where strength and appearance are not controlling factors, such as blocking, plates and bracing.

Studs (2 to 4-in. thick, 2 to 6-in. wide, 10-ft. and shorter). These framing members are the vertical components of a wall frame. These are graded as a composite of No. 3 strength and No. 1 nailing edge characteristics. Studs are pre-cut to lengths that enable carpenters to build to standard wall heights without cutting the studs to length. The pre-cut stud lengths are: 92⅝ in. (for 8-foot walls) and 104⅝ in. (for 9-foot walls). It is also possible to find studs that are pre-cut to 94⅛ in. for walls that will have only a single top-plate (not a highly recommended construction practice). Seven-foot studs are generally used in basements with low ceilings.

Structural joists and planks. Joists and planks run perpendicular to the walls and support the weight of the building by holding up the floor. This category of lumber contains the larger sizes, from 2 × 6 to 4 × 16. These planks are cut from a variety of species to a variety of grades, just as structural light framing lumber is. Structural joists and planks are mainly used for floor joists, ceiling joists, rafters, headers, beams or any other load-carrying members.

Timbers (5-in. thick by 5-in. wide and larger). This category is broken

Spans and Load

To determine the required girth and grade of structural framing members (posts, beams, joists, rafters, headers), architects and inspectors use span charts. Although getting your hands on a span chart to look the information up yourself is easy, interpreting the charts is not.

To get an accurate reading from a span chart, you'll need the following information: the *live load* (he temporary load imposed on a building by occupancy and the environment) and *dead load* (the load imposed on a structure by the weight of the building materials only) to be borne by the structure, along with the *snow load* and *wind load;* the greatest distance the structural member will cover unsupported; and more. It is, to be sure, very confusing to most of us. With a good deal of study, however, it can be deciphered. But by far the safer, and easier, approach is simply to ask your inspector. He or she will be glad to let you know what structural requirements are.

Construction Lumber Dimensions & Availability

Nominal Size	Actual size	4'	6'	7'	92⅝"	8'	104⅝"	10'	12'	14'	16'	18'	20'	22'	24'
1 × 2	¾ × 1½	N	N	N	N	C	N	N	N	N	N	N	N	N	N
1 × 3	¾ × 2½	N	N	N	N	C	N	N	N	N	N	N	N	N	N
1 × 4	¾ × 3½	L	L	N	N	C	N	C	C	L	L	N	N	N	N
1 × 6	¾ × 5½	L	L	N	N	C	N	C	L	L	L	N	N	N	N
1 × 8	¾ × 7¼	L	L	N	N	C	N	C	L	L	L	N	N	N	N
1 × 10	¾ × 9¼	L	L	N	N	C	N	C	L	L	L	N	N	N	N
1 × 12	¾ × 11¼	L	L	N	N	C	N	C	L	L	L	N	N	N	N
2 × 2	1½ × 1½	N	N	N	N	C	N	N	N	N	N	N	N	N	N
2 × 3	1½ × 2½	N	N	N	N	C	N	N	N	N	N	N	N	N	N
2 × 4	1½ × 3½	L	C	C	C	C	L	C	C	C	L	L	L	N	N
2 × 6	1½ × 5½	L	L	N	C	C	L	C	C	C	C	L	L	L	L
2 × 8	1½ × 7¼	L	L	N	N	C	N	C	C	L	C	L	L	L	L
2 × 10	1½ × 9¼	L	L	N	N	C	N	C	C	L	C	L	L	L	L
2 × 12	1½ × 11¼	L	L	N	N	C	N	C	C	L	C	L	L	L	L

KEY: NA = Not widely available **C** = Common **L** = Limited availability (hit-or-miss)

down into two subcategories: beams and stringers, and posts and timbers. Beams and stringers are 5-in. thick and thicker, and the width must be at least 2 inches greater than the thickness (for example, 6 × 10). Posts and timbers are 5-in. and larger, with the width no more than 2inches greater than the thickness (for example, 5 × 6 or 6 × 6). NOTE: There are important differences between landscape timbers and construction-grade timbers. Landscape timbers do not have to be cut to standard sizes and they do not need to conform to any structural properties. Construction-grade timbers are graded, cut to standard sizes and have structural properties that will meet local building codes.

Treated Lumber

If your building project will be subject to weather or moisture exposure, you may be required by code to use pressure treated lumber in some of the more vulnerable areas. Pressure treated lumber has been subjected to chemicals that help repel moisture, postpone decay and inhibit insect infestation. You may notice that some treated lumber is green and some is dark brown. The color difference stems from the differences in treatment processes, and do not bear on the qualities of the lumber. The green color, by far the most common, comes from copper, which is an element in the prevalent CCA treatment. The brown color is created by a tinting oil added to the treatment process for appearance.

Pressure-treated Construction Lumber

Nominal size*	8'	10'	12'	14'	16'	18'	20'
1 × 2	C	N	N	N	N	N	N
1 × 4	C	L	C	L	L	N	N
1 × 6	C	L	C	L	L	N	N
1 × 8	L	L	L	L	L	N	N
2 × 2	C	N	N	N	N	N	N
2 × 4	C	C	C	C	C	L	L
2 × 6	C	C	C	C	C	L	L
2 × 8	C	C	C	C	L	L	L
2 × 10	C	C	C	O	L	L	L
2 × 12	C	C	C	C	L	L	L
4 × 4	C	C	L	L	N	N	N
4 × 6	C	C	L	N	N	N	N
6 × 6	C	C	L	N	N	N	N

KEY: **NA** = Not widely available **C** = Common
L = Limited availability (hit-or-miss)
* For actual dimensions, see chart on previous page

Softwood Lumber Characteristics

Species	Hardness	Strength	Workability	Decay Resistance	Uses
Red Cedar	Soft	Low	Easy	Very High	Exterior construction
Redwood	Soft	Low	Easy	Very High	Exterior construction
Cypress	Soft/Med.	Medium	Medium	Very High	Exterior construction
Western White Pine	Soft/Med.	Low	Medium	Low	Millwork & trim
Southern Yellow Pine	Med./Hard	High	High	Medium	Framing & plywood
Fir	Med./Hard	High	Hard	Medium	Framing, millwork, plywood
Spruce	Medium	Medium	Medium	Low	Siding & subfloor
Sugar Pine	Soft	Low	Easy	Low	Millwork
Ponderosa Pine	Medium	Medium	Medium	Low	Millwork & trim
Western Larch	Med./Hard	High	Medium	Medium	Framing
Hemlock	Medium	Low/Med.	Medium	Medium	Framing

Depending upon your location, any of a variety of pressure treatments are used. The most common are *ACA and ACZA* (Ammoniacal Copper Zinc Arsenate), *ACQ* (Ammoniacal Copper Quat), *CCA* (Chromated Copper Arsenate) and *Borates.*

When choosing pressure treated lumber, make sure to pick that which contains the proper amount of treatment for your project. All treated lumber is graded to specifications and will give the information necessary, such as: year, preservative used, retention of treatment level, treatment plant, and the exposure to which it can be subjected.

All treatments are done after lumber is cut and dried to its nominal dimension, to ensure the whole piece is saturated to the required specifications. If the wood will be used above ground for decks, fences or foundation plates on a masonry slab, you should purchase members that have .25 lbs. of the preservative per cubic foot. This means, for example, that ¼ lb. of a preservative like *CCA* is retained in one cubic foot of wood. If it will come into ground contact in applications such as posts and retaining walls it should contain at least .40 lbs. per cubic feet. If a wood foundation will be built in-ground, .60 should be used to ensure stability and prevent decay. Most home centers will usually only carry .25 and maybe .40. To purchase other concentrations, you may have to contact a local lumberyard.

Treated lumber does not have to be painted or stained, but if a different color is desired, there should be a waiting period one to two months to let the wood to dry.

Because treated wood contains waterborne arsenical preservatives, care must be taken when handling and disposing of it. Proper safety precautions include goggles, dust mask and long clothing to avoid skin contact. Treated lumber should not be used where it could come in contact with food, drinking water or animal feed. It should also not be burned, but disposed of according to local regulations.

Wood expands and contracts in response to changes in moisture and temperature. Tangential movement (A) occurs parallel to the growth rings, while radial movement (B) happens across the rings. Wood moves very little along its length (C). Generally a board's tangential movement is about double its radial movement.

Moisture & Wood Movement

Even though construction lumber is kiln-dried, it will continue to seek what is known as equilibrium moisture content (EMC): it will absorb moisture or dry out until its moisture content matches the relative humidity in the surrounding air. A kiln-dried board will never absorb as much moisture as it initially had when it was green, but its sponge-like qualities cannot be stopped, even when a wood finish or primer and paint are applied.

The amount of moisture a board contains at the lumberyard is measured in percentages, which range from 6%

A moisture meter will tell you immediately the moisture content of a board. The red glowing light on this meter indicates the moisture content in this board to be 10%, an acceptable level for cutting and for project use. Be sure to test the wood on a fresh-cut edge or end—old edges dry quickly and will not provide an accurate reading.

to more than 20%. Framing lumber should be less than 18% moisture when purchased (about 14% is ideal). In comparison, stock destined for furniture or casework should be down around 6 to 8%. Moisture percentages are measured in terms of water weight vs. wood weight, not according to volume.

The only accurate way to check this is with a moisture meter (See Evaluating Moisture Content, below). A moisture meter is a small electronic tool with two sharp pins that are inserted into a freshly cut surface of the wood (old cuts dry quickly and give a false reading, so a fresh cut is essential).

As wood absorbs moisture from the air, it expands, and as the moisture evaporates, the wood will contract. You may be surprised to learn that wood basically moves parallel to the growth rings (tangentially) and across the rings (radially), but almost never along it (longitudinally). Therefore, in a standard plain-sawn board, expansion or contraction essentially occur in just two directions: width and thickness. Movement across the width is normally about twice that in thickness. The "greener" the board, the more it will move. It is important, as you make your plans, to consider how these forces of expansion and contraction will affect your project.

Lumber Distortion & Defects

Major defects. Often, lumber will not expand and contract uniformly, causing it to distort. Four types of distortion, caused largely by improper kiln drying, are cupping, crooking, bowing and winding. Cupping is where the two long edges of the board begin moving toward each other, while the middle remains flat. A cupped cross section resembles the letter C. Crooking is evident when a board's faces are flat but it warps from side to side. Bowing occurs when a board cups along its length and resembles a very wide rocking chair runner. Twisting is a case when the ends of a board will twist in opposite directions. Distortions can be spotted easily at the lumberyard by simply sighting down the edges and faces of each board before you buy.

Minor defects. Defects like pitch pockets, spalling or loose knots are easy to spot if you look carefully. Boards with these defects are salvageable by simply cutting away the bad areas. One defect that can't always be seen until after the lumber is rip-cut is a condition called case-hardening. Case-hardening occurs when the outside faces of the board dry quickly while the center remains wet, causing tremendous internal stresses. Telltale signs of case-hardening are checks (small cracks), shakes (large cracks, most often radiating out from the center across the grain), and a problem referred to as honeycombing: when the board is ripped, the inside looks just like the inside of a beehive, full of tiny honeycombs. To safeguard against case-hardening, check boards along their edges and ends, paying close attention to honey-combing, the worst kind of case-hardening. If one board in a pile is affected, chances are several more from the same batch will have the same defect

Let your lumber acclimate

Once you have purchased lumber for a project, allow it to acclimate to its new environment for a few weeks before building with it. If your shop is particularly damp, insert sticking between each board so that the air can surround it evenly on all sides.Or wrap it completely in 6 mil plastic until you need to use it, then machine and finish the lumber immediately.

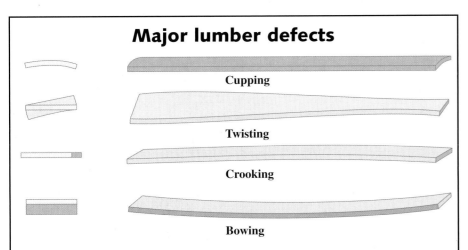

Major lumber defects

Cupping

Twisting

Crooking

Bowing

Boards distort in four primary ways, due to how internal stresses are released when it is machined as well as how the board absorbs and releases moisture. Moisture distortion is largely a measure of how the wood was dried at the mill. Wood that bows is flat across its width but the faces curve lengthwise. A crooked board is flat across the face but curves along the edges in one direction or the other, like the rocker on a rocking chair. Cupping occurs when a board is flat along its edges but curls across its width. Twist is the condition where one or both ends of a board twist so the board faces are no longer flat.

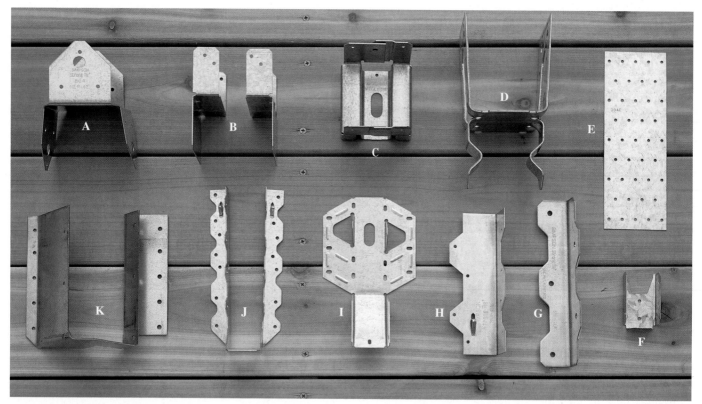

Galvanized metal connectors include: (A) one-piece post cap (4 × 4); (B) two-piece adjustable post cap; (C) stand-off post anchor; (D) post anchor with concrete fins; (E) tie plate; (F) fence hanger; (G) staircase angle bracket; (H) right-angle connector; (I) skewable joist hanger; (J) joist hanger; (K) angled joist hanger.

Fastening & Joining Lumber

The fundamental choice you'll need to make when assembling the framework of your project is whether to use fasteners (nails and screws) or metal connectors to make the joints. This can be achieved using a couple of complementary methods, such as nailing and metal lumber connectors. Building codes require specific nailing schedules for certain areas of a structure. The most common nails that are used in rough carpentry are 16d and 8d common nails. These can be driven manually or with air power. Pneumatic framing nail guns, powered by either an air compressor or a battery and fuel cells make building efficient. With a free hand to hold your work, two pieces of wood can be joined together with a pull of a trigger. If you do not own a framing nail gun or air compressor, they are usually available at rental centers. Renting one of these for a larger job will definitely save time and energy.

There are also a wide variety of other fasteners that are used in rough carpentry. Bolts and lag screws play a vital role. Galvanized nails also play an indispensable role in construction. They are used in locations where the nails will be exposed to the elements and could rust, such as decks, siding and door jambs. The use of galvanized nails will prevent the bleeding of rust onto the framing member.

When it comes to actually fastening the members together, there are two common methods: face nailing and toenailing. Face nailing is when a nail is driven through the cross grain of one

Pneumatic nail guns

Pneumatic nail guns, powered by compressed air, offer several advantages over driving screws or hammering nails. A squeeze of the trigger both drives and countersinks the nail, and you usually can keep one hand free to hold your work. A variety of nail options are  available for these tools so you can drive everything from brads to heavy framing nails. You'll need an air compressor to power most guns, but cartridge-style nailers are also available and require no compressor. Pneumatic nailers and compressors are expensive to buy but widely available to rent.

piece of wood into the end grain of another. Toenailing is driving a nail at a 45° angle through one piece of wood into another.

Lumber connectors, such as braces, straps and brackets are convenient, sturdy devices for joining two pieces of wood together. With their different shapes, sizes and uses, you can find a metal lumber connector for just about any imaginable construction purpose. While the number of hangers, strap and brackets number is in the hundreds, most home centers carry only a few of the more popular sizes and styles. Other styles can be found by contacting the manufacturers. Ask for more information at your lumberyard or building center.

The staple of metal lumber connectors are joist hangers. These U-shaped brackets come in just about every possible size to hold perpendicular framing members together. The various types, ranging from top-mount hangers to welded-steel hangers and everything in-between, can hold just about every size of dimensional lumber, I-joists, beams, trusses or purlins. Joist hangers come with nailing tabs to hold the workpiece steady while hanger nails are driven through pre-drilled holes. By driving nails into each available opening, the shear strength is increased, ensuring structural integrity.

Brackets and braces are also available to help construct decks and fences. These special connectors and shaped and styled to assist assembly.

Angles and straps are used to anchor studs, plates, mudsills and trusses. These connectors are often used in hurricane or seismic zones or to reinforce areas that could be affected.

If metal lumber connectors are used, the proper nails should also be used. They typically can be installed with 6d × 1½ in. long, hot-dipped galvanized joist hanger nails that are structurally rated for 2× applications. Some connectors require nails as large as 20d × 2½ in. long. Others require bolts and nuts. IMPORTANT: Never use deck screws to install metal connectors: the shear strength is only a fraction of what is required.

Making Framing Connections

MUDSILL TO FOUNDATION WALL

The mudsill is created with 2× dimension lumber that's laid onto the top of the foundation wall to serve as a building base for the walls. Typically, the mudsill is connected to the wall with J-bolts set into the concrete at regular intervals. In seismic zones, or just to strengthen new construction and help distribute the weight of the structure more evenly, you can install 90° angled connectors that bond the mudsill to the foundation wall. The connector shown here is attached to the foundation wall with masonry anchors and nailed to the mudsill.

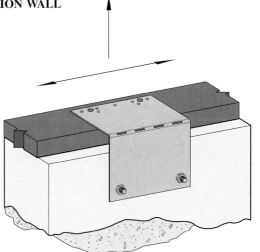

POST TO FOOTING

Metal post anchors are a convenient and sturdy method for attaching posts to concrete footings. While they do not provide significant side-to-side strength (and thus aren't great for anchoring unsupported posts, such as fence posts) they do keep the post stationary and aligned. Most post anchor systems have a metal "standoff base" that rests inside the connector's frame, providing clearance from the top of the J-bolt used to secure the post anchor. The platform also elevates the bottom of the post to eliminate ground contact, which can cause the post to rot.

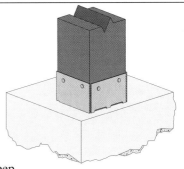

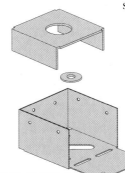

TIP FOR PNEUMATIC TOOL LOVERS

Look for joist hangers and connectors with extra wide flanges that make them accessible to bulky pneumatic nail guns. Use 0.105-in.-dia. × 1⅜ in. round-head pneumatic nails.

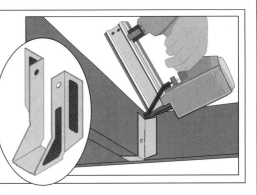

Making Framing Connections

PURLINS TO RAFTERS

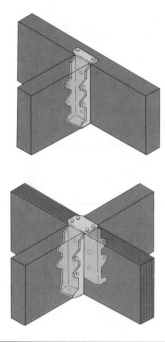

Panel roof systems require the installation of purlins at regular intervals between the rafters. The purlins provide support for the panels, which are too flimsy to span even a 16 o.c. rafter cavity. But installing them with nails or screws gets tricky, since they must be aligned so the ends of adjoining purlins are directly opposite one another on each side of the rafter. Purlin hangers like those shown here solve the access problem this arrangement creates.

JOIST TO BEAM OR LEDGER

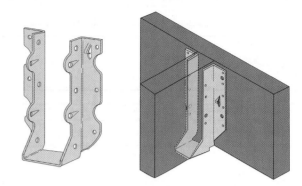

The most common situation for using joist hangers (and the one from which they derive their name) is for attaching joists to horizontal bearing members such as beams or ledgers. When installed correctly, the single joist hanger and the double-joist hanger create a connection that's many times stronger than simply nailing or screwing.

WALL STUDS TO PLATES

When building stud walls on site, most do-it-yourselfers toe-nail the studs into the sole plate and cap plate with 8d common nails. Structurally, this does not present an issue, other than making it a little tough at times to get the stud exactly where you want it. But on harder wood species, like red pine, toe-nailing close to the end of the stud often causes cracks or splits in the lumber. To avoid this, you can drill pilot holes for the nails. Or, use metal framing angles to make the connection cleanly and accurately.

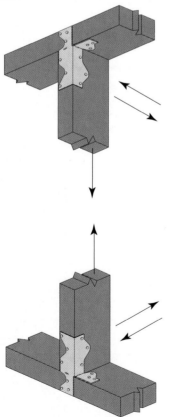

LAMINATED BEAM TO LAMINATED BEAM

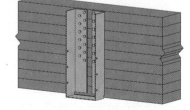

Laminated or engineered wood structural beams generally require special connectors, like the beam hangers shown here. The heavy-gauge hangers are attached to the edge-grain on laminated beams with 3-in.-long ring shank nails. Sizing of the hangers is designed to conform to typical laminated beam sizes. For best strength, drive nails in the upper area of the hanger on the supporting beam, and in the lower area only on the supported beam.

HEADER INSTALLATION

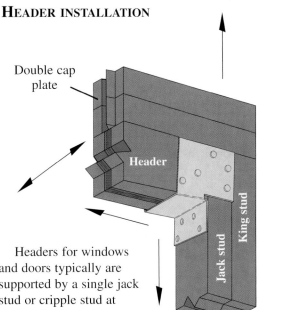

Double cap plate

Header

Jack stud

King stud

Headers for windows and doors typically are supported by a single jack stud or cripple stud at each end. The jack or cripple is face-nailed to a king stud. This connection is fairly susceptible to movement because many stresses work against it from several directions. Minor movement isn't structurally dangerous, but it can cause wall surfaces to crack at the corners around windows and doors. Adding a header hanger is one way to reinforce and stabilize the connection. Using a header hanger also allows you to cut the jack stud to the same length as the king so you can adjust and level the header without shimming or trimming—even in more typical applications than the one shown here, where there is space between the header and the wall cap plate.

BRIDGING FLOOR JOISTS

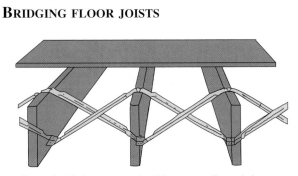

Cross-bridging is required between floor joists to help prevent the joists from moving. Traditionally, the bridging is accomplished with chunks of 2 × 4 or 1 × 4 scrap wedged into the joist openings. Another way is to install metal tension bridging, as shown above, prior to installing the subfloor.

TRUSS TO TOP PLATE

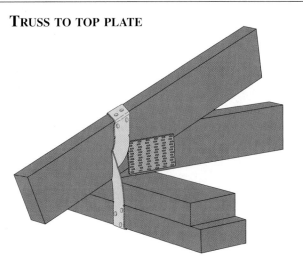

The bottom chord of a roof truss rests flat on the top plate of the wall supporting the truss. The presence of a metal gusset at the joint between the bottom chord and the rafter chord of the truss makes driving fasteners through the wood a bad idea. In this instance, a metal connector is pretty much your only option for joining the truss to the plate. Metal twist straps like the one shown above are designed exactly for this purpose.

RAFTER TO TOP PLATE

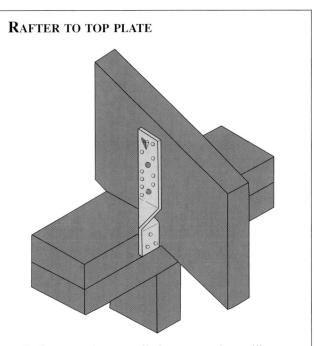

Rafters may be toe-nailed or screwed to ceiling plates. But the joint is not especially strong and, in hurricane-prone areas, it does not meet building codes. A hurricane tie is a metal twist strap that reinforces this joint and meets with most building codes.

INSTALLATION TIP: TOP-MOUNT HANGERS

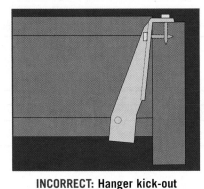

INCORRECT: Hanger kick-out

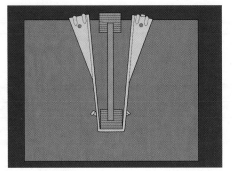

INCORRECT: Hanger overspread

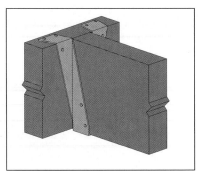

CORRECT: Framing is flush

Perhaps the most common installation error when using joist hangers is failing to get the hangers square to both members. This is especially true with top-mounted hangers. The illustrations above show two examples of out-of-square installations of top-mounted hangers. In the first, the hanger is not flush against the header beam, causing it to be out of plumb (also known as "hanger kick-out." In the second illustration, the legs of the hanger are too far apart at the top. This condition, called "overspread", can create problems if sheathing or decking is installed over the framing members. The overspread has the effect of shortening the hanger, which can cause the joist to be raised past the point where it is flush with the header. In the third illustration, the top-mount hanger is installed correctly.

INSTALLATION TIP: AVOID NAILING ERRORS

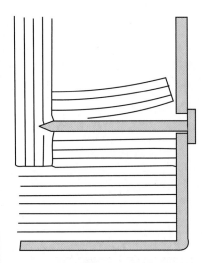

INCORRECT: Nails driven into framing members at a straight angle can cause splitting, especially on laminated I-beams like the one shown above.

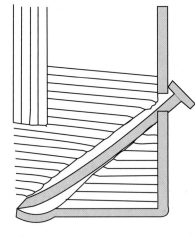

INCORRECT: Use the correct sized joist hanger nail. Nails that are too long, as shown above, can damage the hanger and unseat the framing member it holds. Connector manufacturers publish very specific recommendation for fastener use with each type and size connector they make.

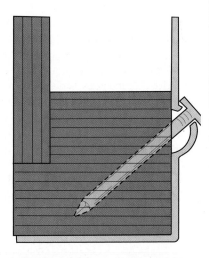

CORRECT: Joist hanger nails should be driven downward at a 45° angle to the framing member, as shown above. Some connector manufacturers punch dimples at each nail hole to serve as nailing guides.

Illustrations on pages 43 to 46 courtesy of USP Lumber Connectors

Wallcoverings are attached to steel studs in the same way they are attached to wood studs: by power-driving screws. For steel studs, however, you need to use "Type S" screws (the "S" stands for "steel"), not "Type W", which are normally used for fastening wallboard to wood.

METAL FRAMING SYSTEMS

In recent years, metal framing has become more popular among do-it-yourselfers, due to some of the benefits it has over lumber, such as non-combustibility, decay resistance and consistent sizing and grading. It is also used where there is declining availability of wood or regular price fluctuations, making it more affordable than wood in many cases. In commercial applications, many codes require the use of steel framing in partition walls as a fire-prevention measure.

Most home centers carry steel studs and the channel that is used as the sole and top plates—but only for interior, non-load bearing walls. The standard size used for this application is 25 gauge. (27 mil). Both channel and studs are sold in 2½ in. and 3⅝ in. widths. Channel pieces are sold in 10-foot lengths, while studs lengths include 8, 9, 10 and 12 feet. Home centers also carry the No. 7 × ⁷⁄₁₆ in. pan-head screws that are used to fasten the members together, as well as the plastic bushings that shield plumbing pipes and wires from the sharp punch-out edges that are stamped into every stud (See page 48).

One consideration when using steel studs is which type of wall covering to use. Gypsum board attaches easily to steel studs using self-tapping, Type S screws. But products, such as paneling, that typically are nailed on may require alternative methods of attachment, such as panel adhesive.

Lumber and steel studs are subject to pretty much the same building codes, since they perform the same function. Both may be spaced at either 16 and 24 in. on-center, depending on the installation circumstances. But for interior, non-load bearing walls, steel can be spaced at 24 o.c. in some cases where wood may not because of the added strength.

While most of us are more accustomed to working with all-wood framing members, steel studs are growing in popularity. Although they can be a little harder to use than plain old 2 × 4's, steel studs offer a few advantages: they're lightweight and easy to transport; they're fire-resistant; they're relatively inexpensive; and they're less likely to bow, warp or suffer movement than wood studs. And by inserting blocking (like a scrap of wood 2 × 4) near a cutting line, you can eliminate one of the biggest complaints about metal studs: that they twist, bend and vibrate when they're cut.

Metal framing systems

Material	Gauge	Size / Length
Metal channel	25 ga.	3⅝ in. ×10 ft.
"	"	2½ in. × 10 ft.
Metal Stud	25 ga.	2½ in. × 8 ft.
"	"	2½ in. × 10 ft.
"	"	3⅝ in. × 8 ft.
"	"	3⅝ in. × 9 ft.
"	"	3⅝ in. × 10 ft.
"	"	3⅝ in. × 12 ft.
Pan-head framing screws		No. 7 × ⁷⁄₁₆ in.

Steel vs. wood framing

There are a few pros and cons to consider when comparing steel studs to wood framing:

• Steel studs are generally cheaper than wood, but must be fastened with screws, which cost more than nails.

• Steel is more consistent in size and shape, with no knots, twists, bows or other defects to deal with.

• Steel is lighter than wood, but takes longer to install because they are put up one at a time, whereas lumber-framed walls can be built on the ground and then raised.

• With steel, greater strength may be obtained by switching to heavier gauge studs, as opposed to using lumber studs that are larger and occupy more space.

• When running electrical, plumbing and mechanical services, steel lets you work faster (once you get the hang of it), because the studs are pre-punched with holes at regular intervals and need only be lined with a bushing.

A hand seamer is one of the few new tools you may need to purchase to work with metal framing.

• Obtaining the tools needed to construct a steel-framed structure may result in additional costs. To cut the metal framing members efficiently, you'll need an abrasive blade for your power miter saw or circular saw. You can use aviation snips to cut the studs and channels, however. Other tools that are needed include: a hand seamer or "duck-billed pliers" to bend members for blocking or flanges; a hole-punch to punch out utility holes; and a drill/driver or screw gun to fasten steel-framed components.

Tips for installing metal framing

Heavy-gauge steel framing for constructing load-bearing walls is available, although typically not at your local home center. You'll need to obtain it from a steel products distributor. The lighter (25 gauge) steel studs sold at home centers are far too weak for load-bearing situations.

Attaching nailing strips to steel framing members if you want to install wall products that are not suitable for fastening with screws. Use Type S screws to attach the strips.

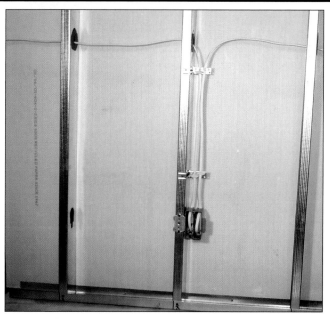

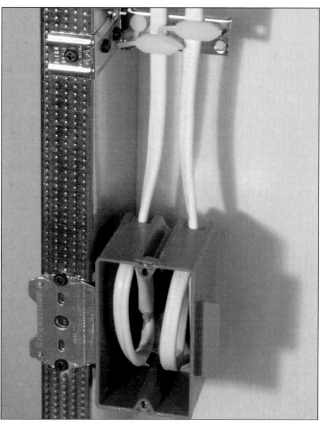

Pipes and tubing are fed through knock-out holes in metal studs. You'll find knockouts located at regular intervals on each stud so they should automatically align. Use a hole punch or an old screwdriver to remove the metal from the knock-out. Before feeding the pipes through the holes, insert a bushing in the opening.

Sheathed cable is fed through knock-out holes in metal studs just as pipes are (See photos, left). To secure the cable near electrical boxed, use cable stapling accessories designed for metal studs—regular wire staple cannot be driven into steel studs.

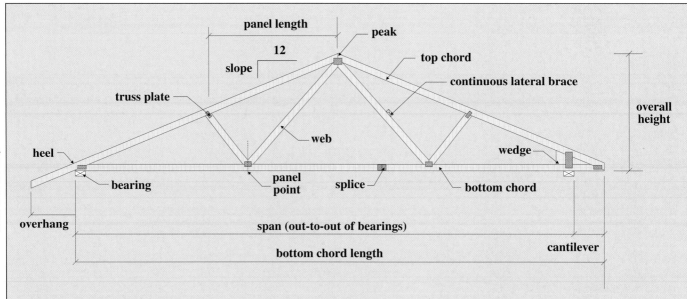

Illustration courtesy of Wood Truss Council of America

The parts of a metal-plate connected wood truss are labeled above. The critical dimensions are also indicated. You'll need to know this terminology when ordering a custom truss system for your building project.

TRUSS SYSTEMS

A truss is a metal-plate-connected structure, usually made individually at the manufacturing facility to meet the specifications of your project. There are two basic types of trusses. The *pitched* or *common* truss is characterized by its triangular shape and is used in roof construction. The *parallel chord,* or *flat truss,* is normally used for floor construction.

There are definite advantages for choosing truss framing over conventional, site-built wood rafters, especially for a larger structure. For one, there is no wasted lumber at the job-site. Trusses are simply ordered from a local truss manufacturer, home center or lumberyard. Having them ordered to the specifications of your project will ensure the structural integrity of your building. It will also simplify meeting the requirements of your local building code, not to mention saving a lot of time. Usually in about a week, manufacturers will build your trusses with the proper web configuration, using quality lumber that will meet building codes. Building with a truss system will also eliminate guesswork and the need to demonstrate your construction techniques to a building inspector.

For truss and rafter systems, the spans they are capable of supporting are dependent on the species and grade of wood used, whether the members are 2 × 4 or 2 × 6, the live and dead load and the pitch of the roof. Standard truss and rafter systems are built to be spaced at 24 in. on-center.

Larger building centers often maintain inventory of some of the more common sizes and pitches. Designing your project to use stock products can potentially save you some money, while eliminating the waiting time and the paperwork that come with custom products.

A truss is a highly engineered structure. To be effective at bearing loads, it depends on tension and even distribution of the load. Consequently, making even small cuts in a truss can greatly diminish its load-bearing capability and should never be done. Also avoid drilling through trusses: use nailed metal connectors to secure them (See page 45). When splicing trusses, you'll need to drill guide holes for bolts, however (See next page).

Photo courtesy of Wood Truss Council of America

Facilities for manufacturing and assembling trusses to your specifications are located all over the country, which helps to keep typical turnaround time when ordering trusses to about a week.

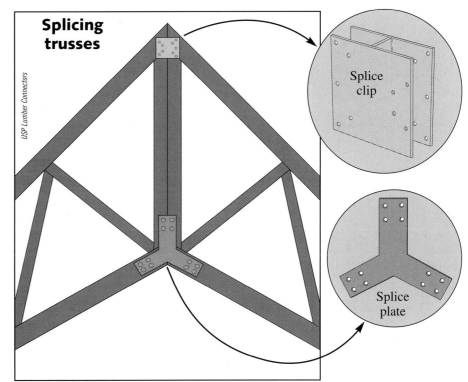

Splicing trusses

USP Lumber Connectors

Splice clip

Splice plate

Parallel-chord trusses (shown above) are becoming more popular for building floor systems in residential construction.

Splicing. In larger truss roof systems, it's sometimes necessary to splice together two trusses at the peak. The hardware shown above is designed for splicing scissors-style trusses on-site. The upper inset diagram shows a splice clip that's used to make the top connection (fasten it with 10d × 1½ in. nails). The splice clip is also intended to be used as a template for drilling bolt guide holes through the truss at the bottom of the joint to fasten the splice plate (lower inset photo).

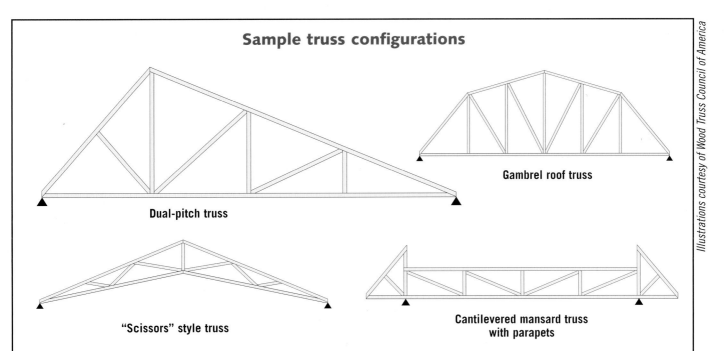

Sample truss configurations

Illustrations courtesy of Wood Truss Council of America

Dual-pitch truss

Gambrel roof truss

"Scissors" style truss

Cantilevered mansard truss with parapets

Trusses can be used to build in just about any building style. Manufacturers have dozens if not hundreds of configuration plans in stock, and they can also work with you to engineer a completely customized truss system for unusual rooflines. In addition to the four samples shown above, existing configurations can be found for vaulted ceilings, clerestory roofs, arched roofs, coffered ceilings, and many more.

Sheet goods is a broad term that describes many varieties of panels, including wall sheathing, decking for floors and roofs, and even hardwood-veneer plywood used in furnituremaking.

SHEET GOODS

Sheet goods fall into two basic categories: *construction panels,* which are used for building construction purposes, and *nonrated panels,* which are used for general purpose building, woodworking and lighter duty applications, but are not suitable for walls, floors or roof decks. This chapter will focus primarily on construction panels, but you'll find some useful information on nonrated panels as well.

The two most common structural panels used for floors, walls and roofs are plywood and oriented strand board (OSB). Plywood is made from thin sheets (plies) of wood veneer bonded in an odd number of layers and oriented with the grains perpendicular to

each other. It is suitable for subflooring, underlayment, single-layer flooring (Sturd-I-Floor), wall and roof sheathing and siding. Because the best veneers are oriented along its length, plywood is somewhat stronger when applied perpendicular to joists and rafter—an important consideration for floors and roofs but less of an issue with wall sheathing.

OSB is a composite panel consisting of strands of wood arranged in a cross-oriented pattern. It is less expensive than plywood, produces a stronger shear wall, is free of internal voids and does not delaminate. OSB is only marginally stronger along its lengthwise axis. It is widely used for wall and roof

sheathing, subflooring, underlayment and single-layer flooring.

On the downside, OSB is more vulnerable to moisture damage than plywood—as it absorbs water, OSB swells permanently. Because horizontal surfaces are most susceptible to standing water during construction, some builders prefer plywood for floors. Georgia-Pacific, a leading manufacturer of construction panels, generally recommends plywood rather than OSB for floors.

Consider the application
Although strength is important, don't waste money by using costly materials where they aren't needed. By

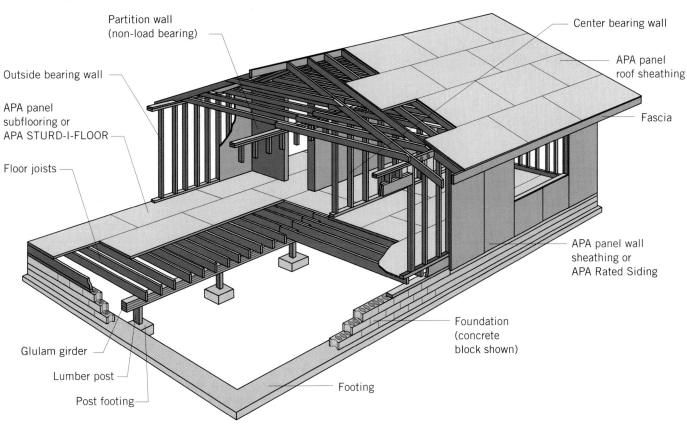

Partition wall
(non-load bearing)

Center bearing wall

APA panel
roof sheathing

Outside bearing wall

Fascia

APA panel
subflooring or
APA STURD-I-FLOOR

Floor joists

APA panel wall
sheathing or
APA Rated Siding

Foundation
(concrete
block shown)

Glulam girder

Lumber post

Post footing

Footing

the same token, don't skimp and sub-stitute inferior panels that aren't engi-neered for the application.

A panel must be strong enough for the span between framing members and have the proper exposure durabil-ity rating. Rated structural panels are described according to their intended use, such as sheathing. Some plywood is identified only by its front and back veneer grades (A-C, for example). Because these panels lack a structural application rating, you should consult standard span tables to determine how they can be used. Span tables are avail-able at lumberyards and government building departments and in architec-tural reference books.

The type of panel is just one com-ponent of a building's floor, wall or roof system. Consult the panel manu-facturer's installation literature and product specifications before selecting

panels or choosing an installation method. Consider what you will apply over the panels. For instance, some types of siding require a continuous nailing surface, and certain types of flooring cannot be installed over OSB.

Panel size and thickness

Besides choosing the best material for your project, you must pick the right size. While 4 × 8 panels are widely used in construction, they are not always the best choice. For example, 4 × 9-ft. or 4 × 10-ft. sheathing installed vertically can tie the stud wall to the rim joist, eliminat-ing the need for a separate filler strip and enhancing structural sta-bility.

Thickness is also important. Rated sheathing is measured in $\frac{1}{32}$-in. incre-ments rather than the usual $\frac{1}{8}$-in. increments. While the difference between a $\frac{15}{32}$-in. panel and a $\frac{1}{2}$-in. panel may seem slight, that extra $\frac{1}{32}$-in. can prevent a roof from warp-ing during rapid temperature swings.

A structural rating means nothing if the panel is improperly installed. Typi-cally, you nail 6 in. OC on edges and 12 in. OC in the field, but for panels that are $\frac{3}{8}$ in. thick or thin-ner, you may need to nail 3 and 6 in. OC.

Construction panels are sheet goods that are manufac-tured to perform specific jobs in construction. Rated plywood and oriented strand board (examples shown at right) represent most of the construction panel category.

Tongue-and-groove designs and glue-and-nail application always yield a stiffer floor and reduce floor squeaks.

Most plywood and OSB panels require ⅛-in. spacing between panels, except in dry climates, and some are specially sized for this reason. Particleboard underlayment, on the other hand, is installed so the edges touch lightly.

Floor systems

Floor sheathing and underlayment panels form the structural skin of joist/panel flooring systems, transferring loads to the walls. Traditional two-layer systems, which consisted of sheathing and underlayment throughout the house on joists spaced 16 in. OC, have given way to single-layer tongue-and-groove floors. Relatively thin underlayment is then applied only

(Continued page 56)

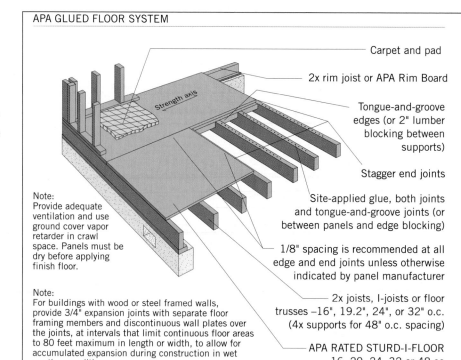

APA GLUED FLOOR SYSTEM

Strength axis

- Carpet and pad
- 2x rim joist or APA Rim Board
- Tongue-and-groove edges (or 2" lumber blocking between supports)
- Stagger end joints
- Site-applied glue, both joints and tongue-and-groove joints (or between panels and edge blocking)
- 1/8" spacing is recommended at all edge and end joints unless otherwise indicated by panel manufacturer
- 2x joists, I-joists or floor trusses –16", 19.2", 24", or 32" o.c. (4x supports for 48" o.c. spacing)
- APA RATED STURD-I-FLOOR 16, 20, 24, 32 or 48 oc

Note:
Provide adequate ventilation and use ground cover vapor retarder in crawl space. Panels must be dry before applying finish floor.

Note:
For buildings with wood or steel framed walls, provide 3/4" expansion joints with separate floor framing members and discontinuous wall plates over the joints, at intervals that limit continuous floor areas to 80 feet maximum in length or width, to allow for accumulated expansion during construction in wet weather conditions.

Sheathing & Sheet Goods Availability by Type & Size

Type	Size	Type	Size
PLYWOOD SHEATHING		*STRAWBOARD*	
ACX Superply	¼ × 4 × 8	Strawboard	½ × 4 × 8
Moisture-Resistant Lauan	¼ × 4 × 8	Strawboard	⅝ × 4 × 8
BL Pine	¼ × 4 × 8	Strawboard	¾ × 4 × 8
BL Pine	⅜ (¹¹⁄₃₂) × 4 × 8		
BL Pine	½ (¹⁵⁄₃₂) × 4 × 8	*MEDIUM DENSITY FIBERBOARD (MDF)*	
BL Pine	⅝ (¹⁹⁄₃₂) × 4 × 8	MDF	½ × 49 × 97 in.
BL Pine	¾ (²³⁄₃₂) × 4 × 8	MDF	¾ × 49 × 97 in.
CDX	⅜ (¹¹⁄₃₂) × 4 × 8		
CDX	½ (¹⁵⁄₃₂) × 4 × 8	*HARDBOARD*	
CDX	⅝ (¹⁹⁄₃₂) × 4 × 8	Standard	⅛ × 4 × 8
CDX	¾ (²³⁄₃₂) × 4 × 8	Standard	¼ × 4 × 8
T&G* *Sturd-I-Floor*	¾ × 4 × 8	Tempered / Perforated	¼ × 4 × 8
Russian Birch	¼ × 42 × 60 in.	Tempered	⅛ × 4 × 8
Underlayment (Multi-ply)	¼ × 4 × 4	Tempered	¼ × 4 × 8
CDX Treated: *Exp. 1*	¾ × 4 × 8		
Treated Plywood .40 Exp. 1	½ × 4 × 8	*MELAMINE*	
		Melamine (white)	¾ × 4 × 8
ORIENTED STRAND BOARD (OSB)			
OSB	¼ × 4 × 8		
OSB T&G*	¾ × 4 × 8		
OSB Exp. 1	½ × 4 × 8		
OSB Exp. 1	⅝ × 4 × 8		
OSB Exp. 1 Wall Only	¹⁵⁄₃₂ × 4 × 9	*** T&G = Tongue and groove**	

Grade Stamps & Ratings

Structural panels are grade-stamped on the face. The wood species and grade of interior plies determines the strength of the glue bond and its ability to withstand exposure to weather or moisture. EXTERIOR grade is for permanent exposure. EXPOSURE 1 is for protected applications temporarily exposed during construction (sheathing) or permanently exposed applications under overhangs. EXPOSURE 2 is for protected applications subject to high humidity or water leakage. INTERIOR grade is for interior applications only. EXPOSURE 2 and INTERIOR grades are rarely available.

Span ratings for sheathing assume that plywood panels are applied with the long dimension of the panel perpendicular to the joists and extending over at least three framing members. Permissible spans are greater for roofs than floors because floors typically support greater loads.

Span ratings do not directly apply to wall sheathing. If nailable wall sheathing is required for siding, a roof span rating of 24 in. is usually code-required for 16- or 24- in. stud spacing. In areas subject to earthquakes, or for very large walls or large walls with many openings, an engineer may need to specify the type or size of sheathing, nailing schedule or other requirements, such as additional bracing or tie-downs.

Unless otherwise specified by the manufacturer, spacing between panels is required to prevent buckling at the seams. Panels that are "sized for spacing" actually measure 47⅞ x 95-⅞ in. to allow the recommended ⅛-in. spacing and yet still have panel edges fall over the center of framing members installed 16 or 24 in. O.C.

Since wood panels can be composed from over 70 species of wood, including hardwood and softwood, panels are categorized by species group. The five groups are divided by their structural characteristics. Group 1 is the strongest and stiffest, while Group 5 is the weakest.

Installation practices. To achieve the panels' rated performance, they must be installed as directed. Application of construction adhesive and either spiral-shank nails or screws are critical to avoid squeaky floors.

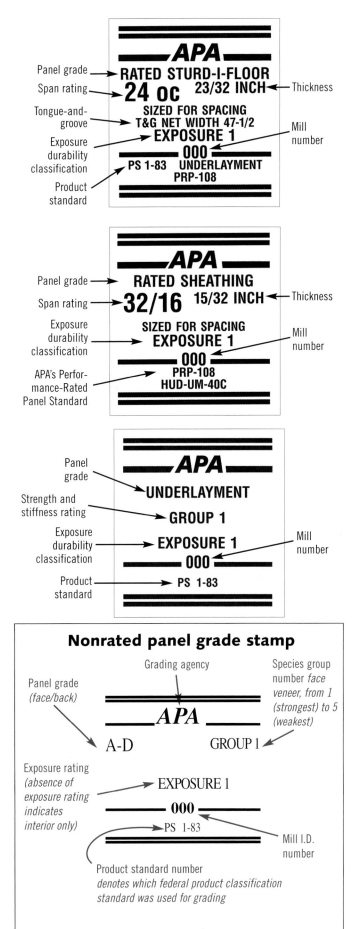

(Continued from page 54)

as required by certain finish floors. In determining the performance of the floor, installation details are as important as panel characteristics.

After meeting structural and exposure requirements, consider special needs, such as sound-deadening and finish-flooring requirements. Most manufacturers of solid-wood nail-down floors recommend a minimum ⅝-in.-thick plywood subfloor or ¾-in. OSB. Single-layer floors are also suitable for most carpeting. However, a separate underlayment is recommended for tile, resilient flooring, and fully adhered thin carpeting. Underlayment is rated to produce a smooth, dimensionally stable, flat and void-free base required by these floors.

Wall systems

Stud walls must be braced to resist the forces of wind, earthquakes and other loads. In most cases, plywood or OSB sheathing serves this purpose. Less often, plywood siding may serve the dual purposes of sheathing and siding. Wood shingles and stucco need a stiff base. Vertical board sidings require a minimum ⅝-in.-thick sheathing nailing base or horizontal nailing strips. However, assuming that a specific siding does not require a plywood or OSB nailing base, structural sheathing may not be necessary.

Applying structural panels at the corners or using diagonal let-in bracing may satisfy lateral bracing requirements. This may permit installation of a less expensive or more energy-efficient panel, such as rigid foam or paper-based fiberboard.

Roof systems

With a few exceptions, roof sheathing is structural and provides a nailing base for roofing materials. Choose a panel with a span rating that meets the minimum requirement for a given rafter or truss spacing. To avoid the poor appearance of sags between rafters, upgrade to the next higher span rating.

Typically, you must use tongue-and-groove panels for spans greater than 24 in. or install lumber blocking or panel-edge clips at edges between supports. Clips are a good idea in all cases. They not only help to align the panels but also ensure proper joint spacing. Although some building codes permit ⁵⁄₁₆-in.-thick roof sheathing for 16-in.-OC rafters, shingle nails and staples hold better in the thicker sheathing.

When installing OSB on a roof deck, be sure to stagger the panels from course to course, always making sure that the ends and edges fall over rafter locations.

ORIENTED STRAND BOARD (OSB)

The staple of sheathing products is OSB (oriented strand board). It is composed of wood strands that are ⅜ to 2½ inches wide, laid in three or more directionally-oriented layers that are at right angles to one another. OSB is twice as strong as waferboard and is commonly used for roof and wall sheathing. OSB is also available with tongue-and-groove joints and in versions that are graded to meet structural subfloor requirements.

When used as roof sheathing, the side seams are held together with clips and nailed with 8d nails or 1½ in. staples. End seams should meet over a rafter to maintain rigidity. The standard thickness of OSB for roof and wall sheathing is ¹⁵⁄₃₂ in. All types of OSB come in 4 × 8 sheets; OSB specifically graded for use as wall sheathing is also available in 9-foot length. The extra

Per-panel weights of common sheet goods (4 × 8 panels)	
TYPE	*WEIGHT*
Veneer core plywood (softwood face)	65 to 70 lb.
Veneer core plywood (hardwood face)	55 to 60 lb.
MDF	105 to 110 lb.
Particleboard	90 to 100 lb.
Composite-core plywood	80 to 85 lb.
Lumber-core plywood	55 to 65 lb.

Which face goes out? (Right) OSB panels intended for use as sheathing are textured on one side to provide a slip-resistant surface for roof sheathing installation. The other face is smooth. If you're sheathing a wall with OSB, you can put either side facing out, although the stud-alignment marks are on the rough surface, so most builders choose to install it smooth-face-in. One exception might be in cases where you suspect the sheathing will be exposed to the elements for a significant period of time after it is installed. The smooth face is more slick and, while not water repellent, will shed moisture better than the rough face.

Smooth surface

Rough surface (anti-skid)

foot allows you to install the sheathing so it runs all the way from the rim joist of the house to the cap plate of the first floor. This is an effective way to help tie the walls together, and allows you to skip patching in spacer strips on the rim before siding.

To help the builder fasten panels to wall framing, OSB sheets are printed with full-length lines spaced at 8-in. intervals. These lines help you find the studs when you're fastening the sheathing (because they're 8 inches apart, they'll be right-on with either 16 or 24 OC walls).

Most manufacturers now seal the edges of OSB. In addition, Louisiana-Pacific and other manufacturers offer premium OSB products identified for use in extreme wet conditions; and these products offer no-sanding warranties.

Flakeboard, an OSB look-alike, and special utility grades of OSB are neither exposure- nor span-rated. As such, they are appropriate for only interior, nonstructural applications.

9-foot-long OSB wall sheathing panels allow you to install a single piece of sheathing that runs all the way from the rim joist to the cap plate of the first-story wall.

Lines printed at 8-in. intervals on wall sheathing help you to locate studs when nailing (they work for both 16 and 24 OC walls).

Tongue-and-groove sheathing panels (plywood and OSB alike) often have drainage holes in their tongues to prevent puddles during construction.

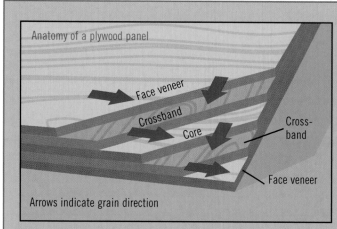

Plywood is manufactured in several thicknesses, using many different materials and processes to create the core, but ¾-in.-thick laminated veneer-core plywood with smooth hardwood veneer faces is the type used most frequently for woodworking and household building projects.

PLYWOOD

Perhaps no building material has brought about greater changes in the way building tradesmen work than plywood. Originally developed for use as decking and subfloors (still its main usage), plywood quickly gained acceptance in the years immediately following World War II, where it was ideally suited for the mass-production demands that accompanied the post-war housing boom. Due to its ease of use and versatility, plywood soon found its way into the lumber yards and building centers, where it was instantly popular with weekend do-it-yourselfers as well.

Initially, nearly all plywood was fashioned from sheets of softwood veneer—primarily, pines and fir. By orienting the wood grain of each laminated sheet so adjacent sheets are perpendicular, the product was able to withstand greater stress than construction lumber of the same thickness. In addition, it was (and is) more dimensionally stable. The only real drawback to plywood was aesthetic: scarred with plugs and cracks on the outer faces and filled with voids on the edges, it simply wasn't much to look at. But since its arrival on the market, new grades of plywood with hardwood face veneer and a range of core options have essentially eliminated this drawback. Today, plywood is a favored working material for many designers and builders of fine furnishings, and it has become a standard for use in building custom cabinetry, not to mention a multitude of general building projects around the house.

Anatomy of a plywood panel

Face veneer

Crossband

Core

Cross-band

Face veneer

Arrows indicate grain direction

Traditional veneer-core plywood gets its strength from the perpendicular arrangement of the wood grain direction in alternating plies. The grain in the veneer on each face always runs lengthwise.

Manufacturing plywood

Although it is only within the last 50 or 60 years that plywood has become a common building material, the concept of face-gluing multiple sheets of thin wood together to create a panel is centuries old. Naturally, the process has become more sophisticated as various mass-production manufacturing processes have arisen. The end result is an inexpensive, versatile building material that makes efficient use of our dwindling forest resources.

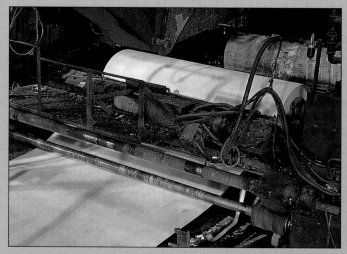

Logs are peeled of bark, steamed or soaked, then trimmed to just over 8 feet in length before they're chucked into a rotary veneer slicer. The slicer shaves the log into long, continuous veneer ribbons. Softwood veneer for the core and crossbands is sliced to a thickness of .1 to .25 inches. Face veneers generally are sliced to about .03 in. (¹⁄₃₂). The rotary slicer can produce up to 600 lineal feet of veneer per minute.

The plywood manufacturing process starts with the selection and separation of suitable logs. The logs are peeled of bark, cut to length, then usually soaked or steamed before being mounted in a rotary cutter that slices them into sheets of veneer. The veneer sheets are dried, trimmed, sorted,

Nonrated plywood thickness guide

Thickness (nominal/actual*)	Uses
¼ in. / ⁷⁄₃₂ in.	Back panels, drawer bottoms, frame-and-panel inserts
½ in. / ¹⁵⁄₃₂ in.	Small cabinet carcases, drawer sides
¾ in. / ²³⁄₃₂ in.	Structural components, large cabinet carcases, doors, drawer fronts, face frames, stretchers

* Actual thickness varies by type and grade: read grade stamp or take measurements to find individual panel thickness.

Plywood core types

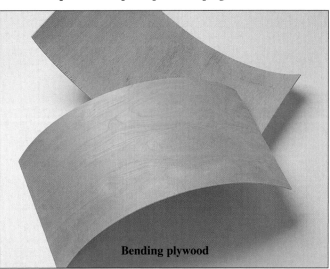

The most common plywood core types are:
(A) Combination core (wood veneer and composition board) has smooth surfaces and holds screws well; **(B) solid core** (MDF) resists warping and has smooth surfaces: good choice for tabletops in low-moisture areas; **(C) veneer core** has all-wood plies with alternating grain direction for light weight and high strength; **(D) lumber core** plywood is made by bonding face veneer to edge-glued strips of solid lumber; very rigid, good screw-holding capability, but has less dimensional stability than other core types.

Sheets of green veneer are fed into a dryer for the curing process that reduces their moisture content to about 5%. The dried sheets are sorted and graded, then glued, heated to about to about 270°, and pressed into plywood panels under as much as 200 pounds of pressure per square inch. The pressed panels are then sanded, graded and trimmed to size.

plugged or patched if needed, glued, then arranged by hand into multiple-ply "sandwiches" with cross-directional grain. The sandwiches of veneer are hot-pressed into plywood, some grades are sanded, then each panel is individually graded and stamped.

Special-purpose plywood

Bending plywood

Exterior plywood

Bending plywood (above) has a single-ply core (often lauan plywood) with face veneer (maple is shown above); some types have multiple plies laminated with the same grain direction to allow flexing;

Exterior plywood (left) is made with water-resistant glue and is used for cabinetry in high-moisture areas; choose panels with one **B** or better face.

APA A-A
Typical Trademark (mark on panel edge)

| A-A • G-1 • EXPOSURE 1-APA • 000 • PS1-95 |

Use where appearance of both sides is important for interior applications such as built-ins, cabinets, furniture, partitions; and exterior applications such as fences, signs, boats, shipping containers, tanks, ducts, etc. Smooth surfaces suitable for painting BOND CLASSIFICATIONS: Interior, Exposure 1, Exterior COMMON THICKNESSES 1/4, 11/32, 3/8, 15/32, 1/2, 19/32, 5/8, 23/32, 3/4.

APA A-B
Typical Trademark (mark on panel edge)

| A-B • G-1 • EXPOSURE 1-APA • 000 • PS1-95 |

For use where appearance of one side is less important but where two solid surfaces are necessary. BOND CLASSIFICATIONS: Interior, Exposure 1, Exterior COMMON THICKNESSES: 1/4, 11/32, 3/8, 15/32, 1/2, 19/32, 5/8, 23/32, 3/4.

APA A-C
Typical Trademark

APA
THE ENGINEERED
WOOD ASSOCIATION
A-C GROUP 1
EXTERIOR
000
PS 1-95

For use where appearance of only one side is important in exterior or interior applications, such as soffits, fences, farm buildings, etc.[f] BOND CLASSIFICATION: Exterior. COMMON THICKNESSES: 1/4, 11/32, 3/8, 15/32, 1/2, 19/32, 5/8, 23/32, 3/4.

APA A-D
Typical Trademark

APA
THE ENGINEERED
WOOD ASSOCIATION
A-D GROUP 1
EXPOSURE 1
000
PS 1-95

For use where appearance of only one side is important in interior applications, such as paneling, built-ins, shelving, partitions, flow racks, etc.[f] BOND CLASSIFICATIONS: Interior, Exposure 1. COMMON THICKNESSES 1/4, 11/32, 3/8, 15/32, 1/2, 19/32, 5/8, 23/32, 3/4.

APA B-B
Typical Trademark (mark on panel edge)

| B-B • G-2 • EXT-APA • 000 • PS1-95 |

Utility panels with two solid sides. BOND CLASSIFICATIONS: Interior, Exposure 1, Exterior COMMON THICKNESSES: 1/4, 11/32, 3/8, 15/32, 1/2, 19/32, 5/8, 23/32, 3/4.

APA B-C
Typical Trademark

APA
THE ENGINEERED
WOOD ASSOCIATION
B-C GROUP 1
EXTERIOR
000
PS 1-95

Utility panel for farm service and work buildings, boxcar and truck linings, containers, tanks, agricultural equipment, as a base for exterior coatings and other exterior uses or applications subject to high or continuous moisture.[f] BOND CLASSIFICATION: Exterior. COMMON THICKNESSES 1/4, 11/32, 3/8, 15/32, 1/2, 19/32, 5/8, 23/32, 3/4.

APA B-D
Typical Trademark

APA
THE ENGINEERED
WOOD ASSOCIATION
B-D GROUP 2
EXPOSURE 1
000
PS 1-95

Utility panel for backing, sides of built-ins, industry shelving slip sheets, separator boards, bins and other interior or protected applications.[f] BOND CLASSIFICATIONS: Interior, Exposure 1. COMMON THICKNESSES: 1/4, 11/32, 3/8, 15/32, 1/2, 19/32, 5/8, 23/32, 3/4.

Continued on next page

GUIDE TO APA SPECIALTY PLYWOOD PANELS[a]

APA DECORATIVE
Typical Trademark

```
APA
THE ENGINEERED
WOOD ASSOCIATION
DECORATIVE
GROUP 2
EXPOSURE 1
000
PS 1-95
```

Rough-sawn, brushed, grooved, or striated faces. For paneling, interior accent walls, builtins, counter facing, exhibit displays. Can also be made by some manufacturers in Exterior for exterior siding, gable ends, fences and other exterior applications. Use recommendations for Exterior panels vary with the particular product. Check with the manufacturer. BOND CLASSIFICATIONS: Interior, Exposure 1, Exterior. COMMON THICKNESSES: 5/16, 3/8, 1/2, 5/8.

APA HIGH DENSITY OVERLAY (HDO)[b]
Typical Trademark (mark on panel edge)

HDO • A-A • G-1 • EXT-APA • 000 • PS 1-95

Has a hard semi-opaque resin-fiber overlay on both faces. Abrasion resistant. For concrete forms, cabinets, countertops, signs, tanks. Also available with skid-resistant screen-grid surface. BOND CLASSIFICA-TION: Exterior. COMMON THICKNESSES: 3/8, 1/2, 5/8, 3/4.

APA MEDIUM DENSITY OVERLAY (MDO)[b]
Typical Trademark

```
APA
THE ENGINEERED
WOOD ASSOCIATION
M. D. OVERLAY
GROUP 1
EXTERIOR
000
PS 1-95
```

Smooth, opaque, resin-fiber overlay on one or both faces. Ideal base for paint, both indoors and outdoors. For exterior siding, paneling, shelving, exhibit displays, cabinets, signs. BOND CLASSIFICATION: Exterior. COMMON THICKNESSES: 11/32, 3/8, 15/32, 1/2, 19/32, 5/8, 23/32, 3/4.

APA MARINE
Typical Trademark (mark on panel edge)

MARINE • A-A • EXT-APA • 000 • PS 1-95

Ideal for boat hulls. Made only with Douglas-fir or western larch. Subject to special limitations on core gaps and face repairs. Also available with HDO or MDO faces. BOND CLASSIFICATION: Exterior. COMMON THICKNESSES: 1/4, 3/8, 1/2, 5/8, 3/4.

APA PLYFORM CLASS I[b]
Typical Trademark

```
APA
THE ENGINEERED
WOOD ASSOCIATION
PLYFORM
B-B CLASS 1
EXTERIOR
000
PS 1-95
```

Concrete form grades with high reuse factor. Sanded both faces and mill-oiled unless otherwise specified. Special restrictions on species. Also available in HDO for very smooth concrete finish, and with special overlays. BOND CLASSIFICATION: Exterior. COMMON THICKNESSES: 19/32, 5/8, 23/32, 3/4.

APA PLYRON
Typical Trademark (mark on panel edge)

PLYRON • EXPOSURE 1 • APA • 000

Hardboard face on both sides. Faces tempered, untempered, smooth or screened. For countertops, shelving, cabinet doors, flooring. BOND CLASSIFICATIONS: Interior, Exposure 1, Exterior. COMMON THICKNESSES 1/2, 5/8, 3/4.

(a) Specific plywood grades, thicknesses and bond classifications may be in limited supply in some areas. Check with your supplier before specifying

(b) Can also be manufactured in Structural I (all plies limited to Group 1 species).

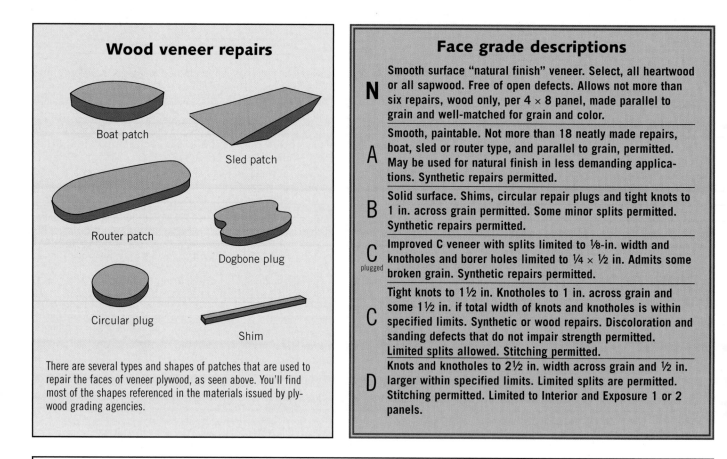

Wood veneer repairs

Boat patch

Sled patch

Router patch

Dogbone plug

Circular plug

Shim

There are several types and shapes of patches that are used to repair the faces of veneer plywood, as seen above. You'll find most of the shapes referenced in the materials issued by plywood grading agencies.

Face grade descriptions

N Smooth surface "natural finish" veneer. Select, all heartwood or all sapwood. Free of open defects. Allows not more than six repairs, wood only, per 4 × 8 panel, made parallel to grain and well-matched for grain and color.

A Smooth, paintable. Not more than 18 neatly made repairs, boat, sled or router type, and parallel to grain, permitted. May be used for natural finish in less demanding applications. Synthetic repairs permitted.

B Solid surface. Shims, circular repair plugs and tight knots to 1 in. across grain permitted. Some minor splits permitted. Synthetic repairs permitted.

C plugged Improved C veneer with splits limited to ⅛-in. width and knotholes and borer holes limited to ¼ × ½ in. Admits some broken grain. Synthetic repairs permitted.

C Tight knots to 1½ in. Knotholes to 1 in. across grain and some 1½ in. if total width of knots and knotholes is within specified limits. Synthetic or wood repairs. Discoloration and sanding defects that do not impair strength permitted. Limited splits allowed. Stitching permitted.

D Knots and knotholes to 2½ in. width across grain and ½ in. larger within specified limits. Limited splits are permitted. Stitching permitted. Limited to Interior and Exposure 1 or 2 panels.

Selecting plywood for woodworking & furniture building

Choosing the right plywood for your project is an important task that can get complicated pretty quickly. In addition to the various core, thickness and face veneer options, you'll also need to make a decision on the plywood grade, as it pertains to finished appearance (See page 55 for more information on grading plywood for structural purposes).

Despite the fact that trade-association sponsored plywood grading systems are clearly established, their application isn't always universal. This can complicate the task of ordering plywood, and can lead to costly miscommunication. Basically, there are two grading systems in use today. The one most people are familiar with is administered by the *APA* (Engineered Wood Association, formerly the American Plywood Association). The *APA* grade stamps are found on sanded plywood, sheathing and other construction panels.

Many hardwood-veneer sanded plywood panels (those you'd typically use for furniture building) are graded by the Hardwood Plywood and Veneer Association (*HPVA*). Both grading organizations are trade groups whose stamps are used only by manufacturers who are members of that respective group). The *HPVA* grading numbers are similar to those employed by *APA*: they refer to a face grade (from A to E) and a back grade (from 1 to 4). Thus, a sheet of plywood that has a premium face (A) and a so-so back (3) would be referred to as "A-3" by *HPVA* (and AC by *APA*).

When ordering some species of hardwood plywood, you'll find you have more than one option for veneer grain pattern. Most plywood has rotary-cut veneer, which is the most economical type. But to obtain finished surfaces that more closely resemble solid hardwood, look for sliced veneer faces that have strips of veneer, usually less than 1 ft. wide, that are laid edge to edge. The strips may be plain-sawn (also called face-sawn) or quarter sawn. If ordering from a mill, you can specify that the veneer strips be applied in the same order they're cut from the log.

MDF

Medium-density fiberboard (MDF) is quickly becoming the industry standard for many woodworking and carpentry activities that involve sheet goods. It's similar to particleboard in constitution, as it's created by hot-pressing wood fibers and resins into dense sheets that are trimmed to size. But the main difference is that MDF is formed from wood and wood pulp that has been pulverized into individual wood fibers, rather than chips or flakes. The individual fibers fit together much more tightly than odd-shaped chips and flakes, creating a smooth, dense material that can be edge-shaped with a router. The difference between standard particleboard and MDF is a little like the difference between concrete and mortar: Mixed with large aggregate, concrete surfaces and edges tend to exhibit popouts and voids, whereas mortar mixed with fine sand is smooth on the surface, edges and throughout.

The smoothness and density of MDF make it a good substrate choice for veneered projects: the rougher surfaces of particleboard and most plywoods do not bond as cleanly with thin wood veneer. You can even laminate layers of MDF to create table legs and other structural components that can be veneered or painted. MDF is also increasing in popularity as a trim molding material.

Like particleboard, MDF does not have a great deal of stiffness, and tends to sag if not adequately supported. It also tends to be fragile around the edges, swells and degrades from constant moisture contact, and it does not hold screws well (although coarse-threaded wallboard screws can be reasonably effective). If you are using it to build structural project parts, try to use mechanical knockdown fasteners wherever possible, and don't skimp on the wood glue. MDF costs a little more than particleboard, and is comparable in price to construction-grade plywood.

Medium-density fiberboard (MDF) is growing in popularity as a veneer substrate, paintable surface and as a raw material for mouldings.

Composite board thickness

Unlike most plywood, which is typically undersized in thickness by $1/32$ in., composite boards such as particleboard and MDF are manufactured within .005 in. of their nominal thickness. When designing your woodworking project, be sure to use the actual thickness of sheet goods, especially on finer projects with little tolerance for error.

Manufacturing MDF

The process of forming MDF begins with the heating and grinding of white softwood until it is broken down to individual wood fibers no more than $1/8$ in. in length. The fibers are coated with resin and (in some cases) additives and formed into a mat that's about 18 in. thick. The mat is hot-pressed at about 350°, using 350 pounds per square inch of pressure to compress it to finished thickness (from $1/4$ to $1 1/4$ in.). The continuous webs of MDF are cut to rough size then loaded into cooling racks (See photo, right). Then, the sheets are sanded lightly, cut to finished size, inspected and given appropriate grade stamps.

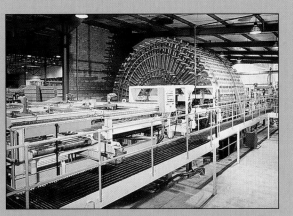

Cooling wheels are used to cool composite panels (both MDF and particleboard) as they begin to dry and cure after hot-pressing. The cooling wheel lets air circulate across both faces of the panel before it is processed further.

PARTICLEBOARD

Particleboard has developed a dubious reputation over the years, perhaps in part because it is used so extensively in the manufacture of low-grade, knock-down furniture that's mass-marketed through discount store chains. While it certainly has its limitations in woodworking pursuits, it also possesses several unique qualities that might make it just the right sheet-good choice for your next project—particularly if the project includes a counter or tabletop. Particleboard is very dimensionally stable (it stays flat and isn't likely to be affected by wood movement issues); it has a relatively smooth surface that provides a suitable substrate for plastic laminate; it comes in a very wide range of thicknesses and panel dimensions; and it is inexpensive. In addition, particleboard makes efficient use of wood chips that might otherwise be wasted, helping to conserve forest products.

But particleboard does have some drawbacks: it lacks stiffness and shear strength; it has poor screw-holding ability; it degrades quickly when exposed to moisture; it's too coarse in the core to be shaped effectively; it's heavy; and it's made with bonding agents that release potentially dangerous or irritating chemical vapors.

In some woodworking applications, particleboard can be used for purposes other than as a substrate for plastic laminate. It is used occasionally to build carcases and doors for light-duty cabinets in low-moisture areas, and it is often employed as an inexpensive shelving material (although it tends to sag as spans get longer).

In woodworking, particle-board is used almost exclusively as a substrate for plastic laminate.

NOTICE

Particleboard and MDF usually contain urea formaldehyde resins that continue to emit low levels of formaldehyde gas for at least six months as they cure. People with high sensitivity to chemical vapors should limit the number of composite panels added to a room at one time. Always wear a particle mask or respirator as required and provide adequate dust collection and ventilation when cutting or shaping these products.

Manufacturing particleboard

Particleboard is made by using heat and pressure to fuse wood chips, shavings, resins and bonding agents into dense, continuous panels (up to 2¼ in. thick) that are trimmed to standard panel dimensions. The wood ingredients on better grade panels are distributed so the larger flakes and chips are at the core of the panel, and the finer shavings and sawdust are closer to the faces. This arrangement increases the stiffness and strength at the core, while creating surfaces that can be sanded to a reasonably smooth texture.

In some cases, additives are included in the particleboard recipe to create special-purpose wood panels. Among them are fire retardants and exterior-grade resins for moisture-resistance.

Because the wood particle used to make particleboard can be as large as ¼ in., the finished product

Particleboard moves along a conveyor belt from the sander, past the blow bar (which checks for delaminations) and to the stacker, which stacks the boards into units.

is generally coarser and less dense than other types of composite board, such as medium-density fiberboard.

MISCELLANEOUS SHEET GOODS

The universe of sheet goods is growing larger all the time, with new-and-improved and special-purpose products constantly added to manufacturer inventories. Most of these products have little application in woodworking, but some, when used creatively, can provide an interesting or unique touch to your project. A few of the more useful types are shown here.

Textured plywood. Designed to be used as exterior siding, textured pine plywood can be used as a back panel on open cupboards, or even as a cabinet carcase material on informal projects. The channel-groove surfaced plywood shown here is readily available with grooves that are either 4 in. or 8 in. apart. Rough-sawn and brushed textures (with or without kerfs or channel grooves) can provide interesting surfaces for rustic or country-style projects.

Glue-up panels. Fashioned from strips of solid pine, these panels offer the benefits of solid wood: superior nail and screw holding, and ease of sanding and shaping. They do not require edge-taping or filling. The strips are finger-jointed together at the ends and edge-glued into ¾-in.-thick panels sold in a variety of sizes, ranging from 12 to 30 in. wide and 36 to 96 in. long. As a woodworking material, glue-up panels cost more per square inch than most plywoods, but are cheaper and more convenient to use than solid lumber. Higher-end versions are made from strips of select clear pine that are laminated together to increase thickness, finger jointed to length, then edge-glued into prefabricated panels.

Tempered hardboard. Hardboard is used in woodworking mostly to make inexpensive panel parts that will not have high visibility: drawer bottoms and cabinet backs are two of the most common usages. It also makes good templates and patterns for project parts you may want to duplicate many times or make again in the future. Tempered hardboard (avoid the softer, non-tempered hardboard) can also be used as a bending plywood in areas that will not receive high stress or be exposed to moisture. It can be used as a veneer substrate in low-stress areas.

Perforated hardboard. Known commonly as "pegboard" or "perfboard", perforated hardboard is simply hardboard (tempered or untempered) that is machined with ¼-in.-dia. holes every 1 in. on-center. For woodworking applications, perfboard may be used as a back panel material for cabinets that require ventilation, but it is commonly used as drilling guide material for locating shelf-pin holes in cabinet sides and standards.

Chapter Contents:

WINDOWS & DOORS

Windows and doors are a part of the essential structure of your house. Because they operate and contain moving parts, they require maintenance and occasional replacement. Installing new windows or doors is often done for reasons of general repair, but aesthetics and energy effi-

ciency are also leading reasons homeowners choose to replace them.

Any major remodeling project or addition will almost certainly involve windows and doors. They will be one of the major expenses, and they will have a dramatic effect on the final appearance of the room. So choosing

Window & Door Framing

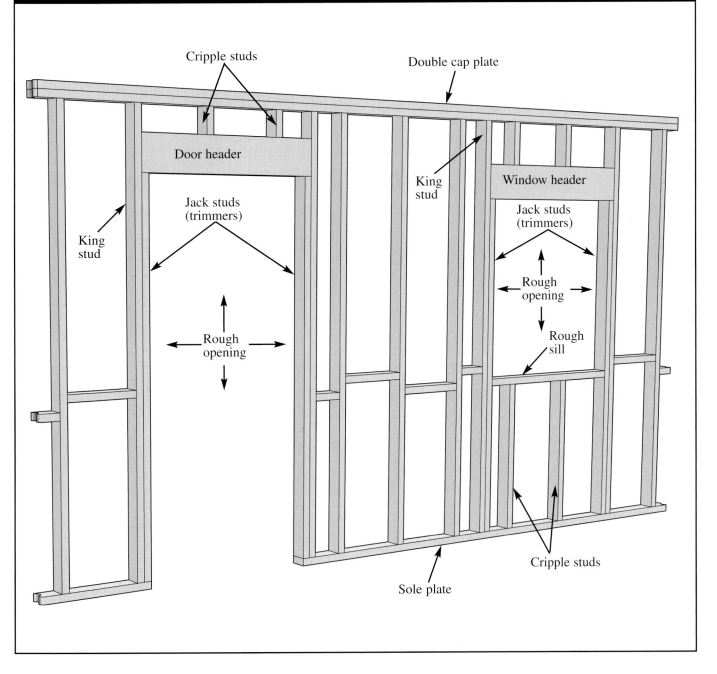

Cripple studs

Double cap plate

Door header

King stud

Jack studs (trimmers)

King stud

Window header

Jack studs (trimmers)

Rough opening

Rough opening

Rough sill

Cripple studs

Sole plate

them wisely is an important responsibility.

Even more than most other building materials, windows and doors are manufactured in a very wide spectrum of quality levels. Most of the variance in cost is attributable to basic material selection, but craftsmanship and detailing also come into play.

When choosing the right windows and doors for your project, start by assessing the wall framing, room size and exterior exposure. If you're replac-

ing old with new, remove the case molding that trims out the door or window on the interior and take careful measurements of the rough openings. Whenever possible, purchase a new unit that fits into the old opening—you'll save a lot of work. In older houses, the rough opening is more likely to be "nonstandard," especially in the case of doors where the standards are more consistent. To avoid the chore of increasing the rough opening size, you may have to purchase a new

unit that's slightly smaller than the original window or door, then decrease the rough opening size with shims or trimmers. It is certainly possible, and not really that difficult, to replace an old unit with a larger one, however. In fact, increasing the amount of sunlight that can enter the room or making access easier with a wider door are very good reasons for a replacement. Be aware, though, that to enlarge a rough opening you'll generally need to remove at least one wall stud, which can mean a considerable amount of demolition and mess, along with the necessity of providing temporary support then a new header and, in many cases, obtaining a building permit.

If you're planning an addition or a down-to-the-studs remodel, it's not a bad idea to choose your windows and doors early on in the planning process. That way, you can create a framing plan that easily accommodates your choices. If you have the time, a good way to save money is to shop around at liquidators and salvage yards and watch for sales, then buy windows and doors as the good deals pop up. Then, work them into the framing plan. Keep in mind, however, that there's a good chance salvaged materials won't meet your local energy efficiency requirements, and any up-front costs savings may be consumed quickly by the higher energy loss of an older unit. As a rule, choose reclaimed products only for their architectural uniqueness and, even then, take some time to tighten the unit up by upgrading the weatherstripping. In some cases, you can "graft" an old sash together with a newer, more efficient window (often a storm window) to get the best of both worlds.

Installation process. There is quite a bit of sameness in the techniques used to install windows and doors. The rough openings are framed in much the same way, the chief difference being that window rough openings generally have a lower sill, whereas door rough openings extend all the way to the floor.

Both types of openings will almost always contain a header: the horizontal

Header construction

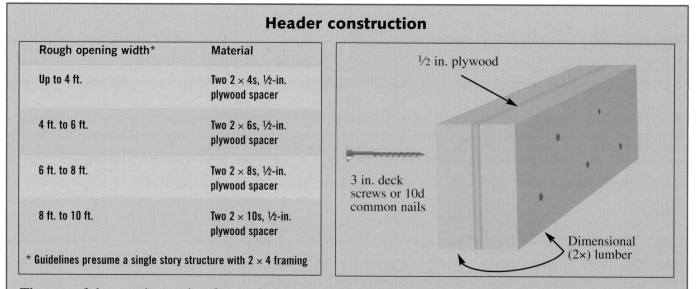

Rough opening width*	Material
Up to 4 ft.	Two 2 × 4s, ½-in. plywood spacer
4 ft. to 6 ft.	Two 2 × 6s, ½-in. plywood spacer
6 ft. to 8 ft.	Two 2 × 8s, ½-in. plywood spacer
8 ft. to 10 ft.	Two 2 × 10s, ½-in. plywood spacer
* Guidelines presume a single story structure with 2 × 4 framing	

½ in. plywood

3 in. deck screws or 10d common nails

Dimensional (2×) lumber

The top of the rough opening for a window or door must include a header to direct the pressure of the overhead wall studs onto the jack studs at the sides of the opening. The size of the header is determined by the span of the opening. Some general guidelines are listed above, but be sure to check with your local building inspector to confirm your plans. Typically, headers are constructed by sandwiching a strip of ½-in. plywood between two pieces of dimensional lumber. The plywood increases the actual thickness of the header to 3½ in. so the faces will be flush with both edges of the 2 × 4 support studs. For 2 × 6-framed walls, you can add a third length of dimensional lumber and a second ½-in. plywood spacer, or install 2½-in. blocking at the top and bottom of the header (this conserves lumber and creates a void that can be packed with insulation). Use construction adhesive and 3-in. deck screws driven through both faces to join the parts of the header.

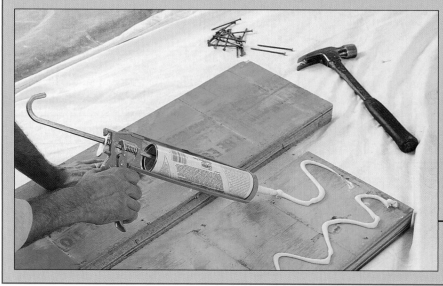

Apply construction adhesive or panel adhesive between the plywood spacer and both pieces of dimensional lumber before assembling a header.

framing member that distributes the weight from above the opening onto wall studs at either side of the opening. Building codes are very specific about the required size of headers. The chart below gives some general guidelines as to what you can expect, but be sure to check with your local building department early on in the project planning stage. You'll likely find that allowable span issue has an impact on your design choice: you don't want to purchase a 72-in.-wide double patio door only to find that the width of the required header will reduce the rough opening height enough that the door won't fit.

Once the rough opening is framed and square, the installation process become mostly an exercise in centering the new unit squarely in the opening and fastening it to the framing members.

NOTE: In addition to the suitability of the window or door units themselves, building codes also regulate the number, size and positioning of windows and doors.

Glazing

All windows and many doors are glazed: that is, they function largely as frames for glass panels. Tougher minimum standards of energy efficiency and safety have taken quite a bit of the guesswork out of assessing glass quality: basically, if a new window or door is available for purchase at a reputable building center you can be confident it will meet at least the most basic quality standards. But beyond the basics, you'll find plenty of glazing options.

Three main types of glass are used in residential construction: *float glass, plate glass* and *tempered glass.*

Float glass has replaced sheet glass, because it is much flatter. It comes in a standard size of ⅛ in. thick. Plate glass has a ground and polished surface that makes it the most suitable for large picture windows. Tempered glass is produced by rapidly cooling the glass to achieve unrelieved tension in its surfaces. This process gives it five times the impact strength. It is generally reserved for full-glass exterior doors.

Float and plate glass can be treated to increase energy efficient. The energy efficiency of a window or door lite is measured by how well it resists heat passing through the frame and glass and how well it keeps air from leaking around it. These measurement are stated in *R-values,* the same way insulation is. Typical R-values for windows range from R-1 to R-5. The higher the value, the more efficient it is.

To make a glazing panel more efficient, there are three things that can be done: add more layers of glass with air or inert gas between them; coat the glazing with compounds that reflect heat and absorb light; or tint the glass to reflect heat and light. If glass is insulated by adding more layers, each pane will provide an additional R-1. If gas,

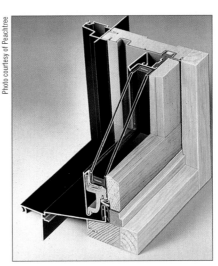

Photo courtesy of Peachtree

Better quality windows and glazed doors are equipped with multi-pane "insulated glass units" (IGU's) that are assembled and sealed at the factory then installed in the frame.

such as argon or carbon dioxide, is injected between panes, the R-value increases by R-2.

If you want to reduce light, then tinted glass is for you. Tinted glass works by filtering all or some of the spectrum of light, including ultraviolet light and infra-red radiation. Tinted glass is mainly used in warmer climates to keep heat out. Tinted glass can also be used in combination with *Low-E* or insulating glass.

Polycarbonate or plexiglass panels can be substituted in windows or doors where breakage is a concern.

Low-E Glass
For maximum insulation capability, look for Low-E *window and door glass. The "E" in Low-E glass stands for "emissivity", which is basically the ability of a material to impede heat flow—the lower the "E" number the better the insulating power. Increasingly common,* Low-E *glass is coated with a metallic compound so it will reflect the sunlight and impede the escape of radiant heat from the interior.*

Code issues related to windows

• **Energy efficiency:** Codes in most colder climates require that new windows have "Low-E" glazing and meet minimum thermal insulation standards.

• **Ventilation:** Spaces that will be inhabited require specific minimum amounts of ventilation, based on a percentage of total floorspace. Keep in mind that only half of the wall space occupied by doublehung and sliding windows counts against the requirements, since they are not fully vented.

• **Light:** Similar standards as those for ventilation may apply to the introduction of natural light.

• **Egress:** Bedrooms require an emergency exit, usually in the form of a window, that must be large enough to pass through.

• **Structural integrity:** Areas with high wind exposure may have more stringent requirements for resistance to wind load.

Windows

Few components can so drastically change the curb appeal of a house as the addition of new windows. Ordinary windows over the kitchen sink can be replaced with box windows that can hold potted plants; double-hung bedroom windows can be replaced with a bay window and a window seat, or the ho-hum picture window can be replaced by a bank of windows or a large bay unit. New windows are not only more energy efficient than older models, but also can provide an exterior face-lift. Fitting Colonial-style muntin windows to a tract home, for example, can visually transform the ordinary house into a charming Cape Cod colonial.

Windows can be purchased in stock sizes or you can have them custom-made. Custom-made windows are ordered to your specifications and usually take between two and six weeks for delivery. The cost is higher, but the options are almost unlimited.

To ensure the windows you choose will fit into your design, there are two measurements that you should take. First, there is the unit dimension. This is the overall size of the window itself, measured from the outside of the frame, top-to-bottom and side-to-side.

(Continued, page 72)

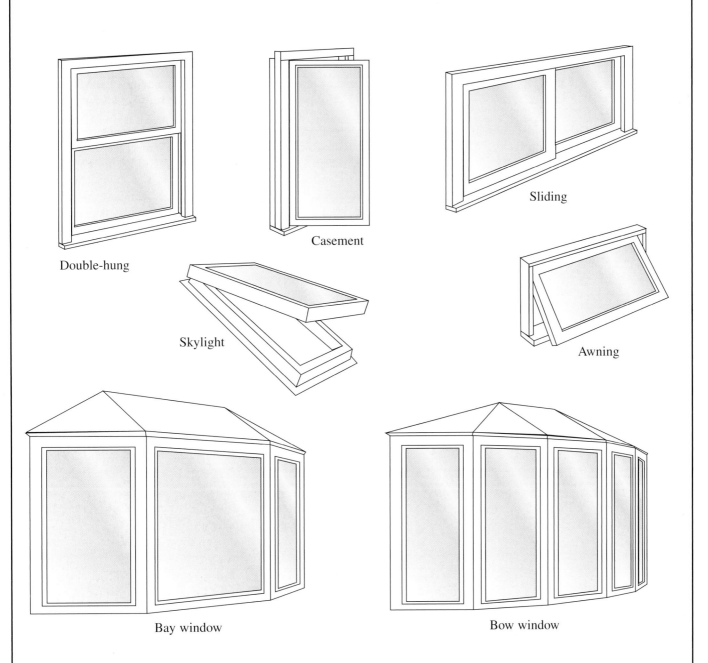

Double-hung

Casement

Sliding

Skylight

Awning

Bay window

Bow window

The most common operating window types are double-hung windows and casement windows. The frames and sashes may be wood, steel, aluminum or vinyl-clad, or any combination of these. Other less-common operating windows include sliding windows, awning windows (used mostly in basements) and skylights. Skylights, sometimes called roof windows, can be operating (that is, they can be opened for ventilation) or fixed.

Bay windows and bow windows are larger banks of windows that project from the house. The windows themselves are usually double-hung or casement types. Narrow side windows in bays and bows, however, frequently are fixed windows.

(Continued, page 70)

The second is the rough opening where the window will be installed. Most window manufacturers recommend that rough openings be ½ to 1 in. wider and ½ to 1 in. taller than the unit dimensions. This extra clearance around the window will allow it to be shimmed and leveled.

Cladding. Cladding refers to the material the frame of the window is made of. Most windows are clad with wood, vinyl or aluminum.

Wood is the traditional material that window frames are made from and clad with. Wood windows are more expensive than vinyl or aluminum and they generally require more maintenance, but they have a warm, natural appearance that is especially appropriate for older homes. Some wood windows today come pre-treated from the manufacture to help prevent weather dam-

age. If, however, wood windows are left untreated, they will eventually decay and leak. Despite this downfall, wood is very durable, easy to work with, and the best insulator for windows.

Vinyl can be used in three ways to clad windows. It can cover the entire frame of a wood-framed window; it can cover only the exterior portion of a wood framed window; or, it can compose the entire frame by itself. The main advantage to vinyl is that it does not rot and therefore requires very minimal maintenance—just wash the exposed vinyl surfaces every couple of years with soap and water. Vinyl-framed and vinyl-clad windows have reasonably good insulating properties. On the down side, vinyl is weaker than wood and is prone to swelling and shrinking with changing temperatures. It is also susceptible to cracking in sub-freezing temperatures and it's

unsuitable for painting.

Aluminum has a number of disadvantages as a cladding material. First of all, it is a soft metal that doesn't grip fasteners well and can be dented pretty easily. It is also a poor insulator, offering just a tiny fraction of the insulating benefits of wood. On the plus side, however, aluminum-clad windows are the least expensive type, generally costing less than half the price of wood windows of comparable size and style. Aluminum frames can be painted.

Window Types. The simplest windows are fixed-sash types that cannot be opened. A familiar example of a fixed-sash window is the picture window. Others include barn sash and utility sash windows, which are simply plain window sash sold unframed. Fixed-sash windows may be flanked by operating windows (windows that open). Common operating windows include: *Double-hung* windows that

Recommended window sill heights

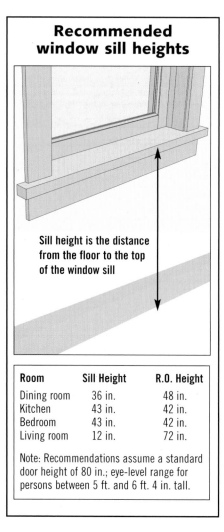

Sill height is the distance from the floor to the top of the window sill

Room	Sill Height	R.O. Height
Dining room	36 in.	48 in.
Kitchen	43 in.	42 in.
Bedroom	43 in.	42 in.
Living room	12 in.	72 in.

Note: Recommendations assume a standard door height of 80 in.; eye-level range for persons between 5 ft. and 6 ft. 4 in. tall.

Ordering windows

Different window manufacturers and distributors use different methods for pricing custom-sized windows. Many base their cost on the rough opening size. If the window you want does not conform to one of the "stock" rough opening sizes they make, they'll likely add an upcharge to the order, so it pays to check into the stock sizes carried by the manufacturer you're intending to buy from before you do your framing.

A few manufacturers use a system called "united inches" to determine the cost of each window unit—especially in window styles that are less popular, like sliding windows. In this system, the total height of the unit is added to the total width to obtain the united inches measurement. Then, the measurement is compared against a pricing chart to see which prince range the window fits into: for example, windows that are 175 to 200 united inches may be sold for the same price. If you do a little price checking in advance of ordering, you can maximize the amount of window you get for your money by planning your rough opening to accommodate a unit at the upper end of the price range.

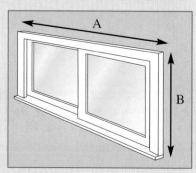

"United inches" is one one system used to price custom windows: you add the width of the window (A) to the height (B) and the sum determines which price range the window fits into.

have two movable sash that bypass one another as they open vertically (single-hung windows are a cheaper version of the double-hung, with one fixed sash and one movable sash); *Casement* windows that are operated with a hand crank and open outward; *Awning* windows that swing outward on top-mounted hinges and hopper windows that swing inward on bottom-mounted hinges; *Sliding windows* that open by sliding horizontally on tracks fastened to the sill and header jamb; *Skylights* (also called roof windows), which can be either fixed or operating; and *bay* and *bow* windows.

Screens are often included as options with modern windows. The screens are attached to the exterior frame on double-hung windows, and are attached to the interior frame for sliding, casement or awning windows.

Other options to consider include sashes that tilt in without disconnecting for ease of cleaning, prefinished frames and sash, and decorative cross-hatch grids.

Sizing a rough opening

Rough openings, (shaded here in red), should be ½ to 1 in. larger than the outside dimensions of the window unit in each direction. This will create gaps of ¼ to ½ in. on all sides, which should be enough room to adjust the window so it's square in the rough opening. Window manufacturers specify the required rough opening for framing a window in the installation instructions.

Grids are decorative options that give any window the appearance of a multi-lite window panel. Some grids are snap-in cross-hatch moldings that fit over the glazing. Others, like the one above, are installed between the glazing panels when the window unit is built.

Window Installation Methods

NAILING FLANGES

Windows with nailing flanges around the perimeter of the window unit are best suited for new construction. Attach them to the framing members inside the wall sheathing using 2-in. roofing nails driven at 6 in. intervals.

NAIL THROUGH BRICKMOLD

Windows that are attached by nailing through the exterior brickmold are best for retrofit jobs. In most cases, you'll need to trace around the brickmold with the new window in the opening, then trim off the siding in that area so the inside of the brickmold fits against the wall sheathing.

MASONRY CLIPS

Windows in masonry-framed openings can't be attached directly to the exterior framing. You'll need to attach masonry clips to the window before positioning it in the opening, then attach the clips to the interior side of the framing.

Parts of a Window (Double-hung)

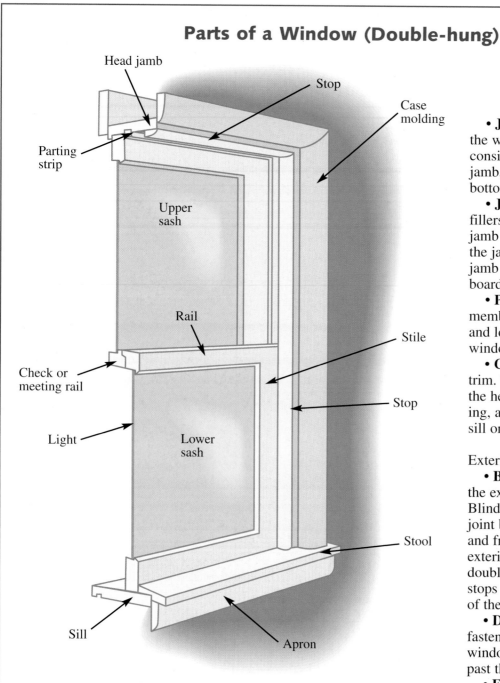

Head jamb

Stop

Case molding

Parting strip

Upper sash

Rail

Stile

Check or meeting rail

Stop

Light

Lower sash

Stool

Sill

Apron

To follow maintenance or installation instructions you must understand the terminology of window construction. The names of window parts are:

• **Sash** is the window frame.
• **Rails** are the top and bottom horizontal members.
• **Stiles** are the vertical side members of the sash.
• **Muntins** are the narrow wood strips that separate the glass or lights of a multi-pane sash. Muntins may be actual separation strips or may be a wood or plastic grid that is fitted over a single-pane sash to create the appearance of a multi-pane sash.
• **Lights** (lites) are the glass members of the sash.

• **Jamb** is the inside portion of the window frame. The frame consists of the top or header jamb, the side jambs, and the bottom jamb.
• **Jamb extensions** are wood fillers nailed to the edges of the jamb if the wall is thicker than the jamb. Extensions furr out the jamb so it is flush with the wallboard or plaster wall surface.
• **Parting strip** is the narrow member that separates the upper and lower sash on a double-hung window.
• **Case molding** is the window trim. The exterior casing includes the header casing, the side casing, and the bottom casing is the sill or stool.

Exterior window parts:
• **Blind stops** are attached to the exterior edge of the jambs. Blind stops weatherproof the joint between the exterior casing and frame, and provide stops for exterior screen or storm sash. On double-hung windows the blind stops also serve as the outer side of the sash channel.
• **Drip edge** is the metal cap fastened to the top edge of the window casing to divert water past the window.
• **Flashing** may be a metal or vinyl strip. The vertical or top side of flashing extends about two inches up the wall above the window. The bottom or horizontal side of the flashing is bent over the top of the header casing, then is bent down about $1/4$-in. over the casing face.
• **Finish** on a window as shipped may be primer, or may be low maintenance aluminum or vinyl cladding in a choice of colors.

Tips for Installing Windows

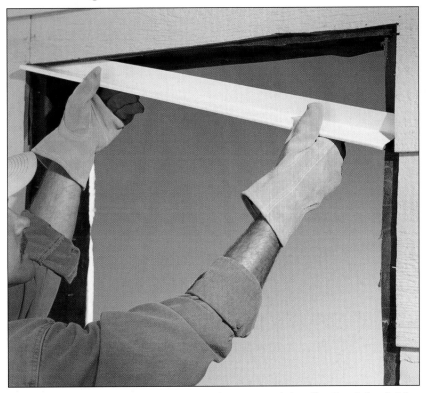

Cover the rough-opening framing members with an impermeable material, such as building paper. Make sure any seams overlap from above and that the edges of the material are tucked cleanly behind the siding.

Install drip edge above the window opening before permanently installing the window. Cut the drip edge to length and tuck it up between the siding and the sheathing. Don't use fasteners to attach drip edge: the siding pressure should hold it in place (if not, it's all right to use a little caulk to secure the drip edge until the window is installed and caulked.

Safety tip

Apply wide masking tape diagonally across window sashes before removing or installing a window. In the event the glass should break, the tape will help contain the broken glass, minimizing the risk of cuts.

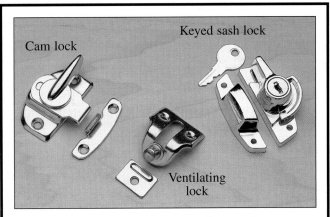

SECURITY TIP: Sash Locks

Window sash locks are available in three common styles: *cam locks* lock upper and lower sashes together by means of a swiveling thumbturn; a sliding button on *ventilating locks* limits the distance a lower sash can be opened for ventilation by obstructing its travel past the upper sash or it can be slid out of the way to open the window fully; *keyed sash locks* operate the same way cam locks do, but the thumbturn is locked in the open or closed position until a key is inserted.

TILT-WASH DOUBLE-HUNG WINDOWS

Widths and heights are rough opening dimensions.
To calculate unit dimension, subtract 1/2" from width and 3/8" from height.

Exterior View Shown — Tilt-To-Clean Mode

UNIT	WIDTH	HEIGHT	UNIT	WIDTH	HEIGHT	UNIT	WIDTH	HEIGHT	UNIT	WIDTH	HEIGHT	UNIT	WIDTH	HEIGHT
TW18210	22 1/8" x	37 1/4"	TW20210	26 1/8" x	37 1/4"	TW24210	30 1/8" x	37 1/4"	TW26210*	32 1/8" x	37 1/4"	TW28210	34 1/8" x	37 1/4"
TW1832	22 1/8" x	41 1/4"	TW2032	26 1/8" x	41 1/4"	TW2432	30 1/8" x	41 1/4"	TW2632*	32 1/8" x	41 1/4"	TW2832	34 1/8" x	41 1/4"
TW1836*	22 1/8" x	45 1/4"	TW2036*	26 1/8" x	45 1/4"	TW2436*	30 1/8" x	45 1/4"	TW2636*	32 1/8" x	45 1/4"	TW2836*	34 1/8" x	45 1/4"
TW18310	22 1/8" x	49 1/4"	TW20310	26 1/8" x	49 1/4"	TW24310	30 1/8" x	49 1/4"	TW26310*	32 1/8" x	49 1/4"	TW28310	34 1/8" x	49 1/4"
TW1842	22 1/8" x	53 1/4"	TW2042	26 1/8" x	53 1/4"	TW2442	30 1/8" x	53 1/4"	TW2642*	32 1/8" x	53 1/4"	TW2842	34 1/8" x	53 1/4"
TW1846	22 1/8" x	57 1/4"	TW2046	26 1/8" x	57 1/4"	TW2446	30 1/8" x	57 1/4"	TW2646*	32 1/8" x	57 1/4"	TW2846	34 1/8" x	57 1/4"
TW18410*	22 1/8" x	61 1/4"	TW20410*	26 1/8" x	61 1/4"	TW24410*	30 1/8" x	61 1/4"	TW26410*	32 1/8" x	61 1/4"	TW28410*	34 1/8" x	61 1/4"
TW1852	22 1/8" x	65 1/4"	TW2052	26 1/8" x	65 1/4"	TW2452	30 1/8" x	65 1/4"	TW2652*	32 1/8" x	65 1/4"	TW2852	34 1/8" x	65 1/4"
TW1856	22 1/8" x	69 1/4"	TW2056	26 1/8" x	69 1/4"	TW2456	30 1/8" x	69 1/4"	TW2656*	32 1/8" x	69 1/4"	TW2856	34 1/8" x	69 1/4"
TW18510*	22 1/8" x	73 1/4"	TW20510*	26 1/8" x	73 1/4"	TW24510*	30 1/8" x	73 1/4"	TW26510*	32 1/8" x	73 1/4"	TW28510*	34 1/8" x	73 1/4"
TW1862	22 1/8" x	77 1/4"	TW2062	26 1/8" x	77 1/4"	TW2462	30 1/8" x	77 1/4"	TW2662*	32 1/8" x	77 1/4"	TW2862	34 1/8" x	77 1/4"
TW210210	36 1/8" x	37 1/4"	TW30210	38 1/8" x	37 1/4"	TW34210	42 1/8" x	37 1/4"	TW38210	46 1/8" x	37 1/4"			
TW21032*	36 1/8" x	41 1/4"	TW3032	38 1/8" x	41 1/4"	TW3432	42 1/8" x	41 1/4"	TW3832	46 1/8" x	41 1/4"			
TW21036*	36 1/8" x	45 1/4"	TW3036*	38 1/8" x	45 1/4"	TW3436*	42 1/8" x	45 1/4"	TW3836*	46 1/8" x	45 1/4"			
TW210310*	36 1/8" x	49 1/4"	TW30310	38 1/8" x	49 1/4"	TW34310	42 1/8" x	49 1/4"	TW38310	46 1/8" x	49 1/4"			
TW21042*	36 1/8" x	53 1/4"	TW3042	38 1/8" x	53 1/4"	TW3442	42 1/8" x	53 1/4"	TW3842	46 1/8" x	53 1/4"			
TW21046*	36 1/8" x	57 1/4"	TW3046	38 1/8" x	57 1/4"	TW3446	42 1/8" x	57 1/4"	TW3846	46 1/8" x	57 1/4"			
TW210410*	36 1/8" x	61 1/4"	TW30410*	38 1/8" x	61 1/4"	TW34410*	42 1/8" x	61 1/4"	TW38410*	46 1/8" x	61 1/4"			
TW21052*	36 1/8" x	65 1/4"	TW3052	38 1/8" x	65 1/4"	TW3452	42 1/8" x	65 1/4"	TW3852	46 1/8" x	65 1/4"			
TW21056*	36 1/8" x	69 1/4"	TW3056	38 1/8" x	69 1/4"	TW3456	42 1/8" x	69 1/4"	TW3856	46 1/8" x	69 1/4"			
TW210510*	36 1/8" x	73 1/4"	TW30510*	38 1/8" x	73 1/4"	TW34510*	42 1/8" x	73 1/4"	TW38510*	46 1/8" x	73 1/4"			
TW21062*	36 1/8" x	77 1/4"	TW3062	38 1/8" x	77 1/4"	TW3462	42 1/8" x	77 1/4"	TW3862	46 1/8" x	77 1/4"			

*Available in white only.

TILT-WASH DOUBLE-HUNG TRANSOM WINDOWS

Widths and heights are rough opening dimensions.
To calculate unit dimension, subtract 1/2" from width and 1/2" from height. Transom units shown are the most common Andersen sizes.

Exterior View Shown

UNIT	WIDTH	HEIGHT	UNIT	WIDTH	HEIGHT	UNIT	WIDTH	HEIGHT	UNIT	WIDTH	HEIGHT	UNIT	WIDTH	HEIGHT
DHT2010	26 1/8" x	12 1/2"	DHT2410	30 1/8" x	12 1/2"	DHT2810	34 1/8" x	12 1/2"	DHT3010	38 1/8" x	12 1/2"	DHT3410	42 1/8" x	12 1/2"
DHT2015	26 1/8" x	19 7/8"	DHT2415	30 1/8" x	19 7/8"	DHT2815	34 1/8" x	19 7/8"	DHT3015	38 1/8" x	19 7/8"	DHT3415	42 1/8" x	19 7/8"
DHT2017	26 1/8" x	21 7/8"	DHT2417	30 1/8" x	21 7/8"	DHT2817	34 1/8" x	21 7/8"	DHT3017	38 1/8" x	21 7/8"	DHT3417	42 1/8" x	21 7/8"
DHT20111	26 1/8" x	25 7/8"	DHT24111	30 1/8" x	25 7/8"	DHT28111	34 1/8" x	25 7/8"	DHT30111	38 1/8" x	25 7/8"	DHT34111	42 1/8" x	25 7/8"
DHT2021	26 1/8" x	27 7/8"	DHT2421	30 1/8" x	27 7/8"	DHT2821	34 1/8" x	27 7/8"	DHT3021	38 1/8" x	27 7/8"	DHT3421	42 1/8" x	27 7/8"
DHT2023	26 1/8" x	29 7/8"	DHT2423	30 1/8" x	29 7/8"	DHT2823	34 1/8" x	29 7/8"	DHT3023	38 1/8" x	29 7/8"	DHT3423	42 1/8" x	29 7/8"
DHT2027	26 1/8" x	33 7/8"	DHT2427	30 1/8" x	33 7/8"	DHT2827	34 1/8" x	33 7/8"	DHT3027	38 1/8" x	33 7/8"	DHT3427	42 1/8" x	33 7/8"
DHT2031	26 1/8" x	39 7/8"	DHT2431	30 1/8" x	39 7/8"	DHT2831	34 1/8" x	39 7/8"	DHT3031	38 1/8" x	39 7/8"	DHT3431	42 1/8" x	39 7/8"

TILT-WASH DOUBLE-HUNG PICTURE WINDOWS

Widths and heights are rough opening dimensions.
To calculate unit dimension, subtract 1/2" from width and 3/8" from height.

Exterior View Shown

UNIT	WIDTH	HEIGHT	UNIT	WIDTH	HEIGHT	UNIT	WIDTH	HEIGHT	UNIT	WIDTH	HEIGHT	UNIT	WIDTH	HEIGHT
DHP10310*	12 1/2" x	49 1/4"	DHP30310	38 1/8" x	49 1/4"	DHP34310*	42 1/8" x	49 1/4"	DHP310310	47 7/8" x	49 1/4"	DHP42310	51 7/8" x	49 1/4"
DHP1042	12 1/2" x	53 1/4"	DHP3042	38 1/8" x	53 1/4"	DHP3442	42 1/8" x	53 1/4"	DHP31042	47 7/8" x	53 1/4"	DHP4242	51 7/8" x	53 1/4"
DHP1046	12 1/2" x	57 1/4"	DHP3046	38 1/8" x	57 1/4"	DHP3446	42 1/8" x	57 1/4"	DHP31046	47 7/8" x	57 1/4"	DHP4246	51 7/8" x	57 1/4"
DHP10410*	12 1/2" x	61 1/4"	DHP30410*	38 1/8" x	61 1/4"	DHP34410*	42 1/8" x	61 1/4"	DHP310410**	51 7/8" x	61 1/4"	DHP42410**	51 7/8" x	61 1/4"
DHP1052	12 1/2" x	65 1/4"	DHP3052	38 1/8" x	65 1/4"	DHP3452*	42 1/8" x	65 1/4"	DHP31052	47 7/8" x	65 1/4"	DHP4252	51 7/8" x	65 1/4"
DHP1056*	12 1/2" x	69 1/4"	DHP3056*	38 1/8" x	69 1/4"	DHP3456*	42 1/8" x	69 1/4"	DHP31056	47 7/8" x	69 1/4"	DHP4256	51 7/8" x	69 1/4"
DHP10510*	12 1/2" x	73 1/4"	DHP30510*	38 1/8" x	73 1/4"	DHP34510*	42 1/8" x	73 1/4"	DHP310510**	47 7/8" x	73 1/4"	DHP42510**	51 7/8" x	73 1/4"
DHP1062*	12 1/2" x	77 1/4"	DHP3062	38 1/8" x	77 1/4"	DHP3462*	42 1/8" x	77 1/4"	DHP31062**	47 7/8" x	77 1/4"	DHP4262**	51 7/8" x	77 1/4"
DHP410310	59 7/8" x	49 1/4"	DHP56310*	67 7/8" x	49 1/4"									
DHP41042	59 7/8" x	53 1/4"	DHP5642	67 7/8" x	53 1/4"									
DHP41046	59 7/8" x	57 1/4"	DHP5646	67 7/8" x	57 1/4"									
DHP410410*	59 7/8" x	61 1/4"	DHP56410*	67 7/8" x	61 1/4"									
DHP41052	59 7/8" x	65 1/4"	DHP5652*	67 7/8" x	65 1/4"									
DHP41056*	59 7/8" x	69 1/4"	DHP5656*	67 7/8" x	69 1/4"									
DHP410510*	59 7/8" x	73 1/4"	DHP56510*	67 7/8" x	73 1/4"									
DHP41062*	59 7/8" x	77 1/4"	DHP5662*	67 7/8" x	77 1/4"									

*These sizes may not be available in normal lead times.
**Available in white only. An optional wood interior trim kit is available.

CIRCLE TOP™ WINDOWS

Widths and heights are rough opening dimensions.
To calculate unit dimension, subtract 1/2" from width and 1/2" from height.

Exterior View Shown

UNIT	WIDTH	HEIGHT	UNIT	WIDTH	HEIGHT	UNIT	WIDTH	HEIGHT
CTN20	26 1/8" x	15 3/4"	CTN30	38 1/8" x	21 3/4"	CTN30-2	75 7/8" x	40 1/2"
CTN24	30 1/8" x	17 3/4"	CTN34	42 1/8" x	23 3/4"			
CTN28	34 1/8" x	19 3/4"	CTN28-2	67 7/8" x	36 1/2"			

NARROLINE® DOUBLE-HUNG WINDOWS   White Exterior Color Only.

Widths and heights are rough opening dimensions.
To calculate unit dimension, subtract 1/2" from width.

Exterior View Shown

UNIT	WIDTH	HEIGHT	UNIT	WIDTH	HEIGHT	UNIT	WIDTH	HEIGHT	UNIT	WIDTH	HEIGHT
18210	22 1/8" x	37 1/4"	20210	26 1/8" x	37 1/4"	24210	30 1/8" x	37 1/4"	28210	34 1/8" x	37 1/4"
1832	22 1/8" x	41 1/4"	2032	26 1/8" x	41 1/4"	2432	30 1/8" x	41 1/4"	2832	34 1/8" x	41 1/4"
18310	22 1/8" x	49 1/4"	20310	26 1/8" x	49 1/4"	24310	30 1/8" x	49 1/4"	28310	34 1/8" x	49 1/4"
1842	22 1/8" x	53 1/4"	2042	26 1/8" x	53 1/4"	2442	30 1/8" x	53 1/4"	2842	34 1/8" x	53 1/4"
1846	22 1/8" x	57 1/4"	2046	26 1/8" x	57 1/4"	2446	30 1/8" x	57 1/4"	2846	34 1/8" x	57 1/4"
1852	22 1/8" x	65 1/4"	2052	26 1/8" x	65 1/4"	2452	30 1/8" x	65 1/4"	2852	34 1/8" x	65 1/4"
1856	22 1/8" x	69 1/4"	2056	26 1/8" x	69 1/4"	2456	30 1/8" x	69 1/4"	2856	34 1/8" x	69 1/4"
1862	22 1/8" x	77 1/4"	2062	26 1/8" x	77 1/4"	2462	30 1/8" x	77 1/4"	2862	34 1/8" x	77 1/4"
30210	38 1/8" x	37 1/4"	34210	42 1/8" x	37 1/4"						
3032	38 1/8" x	41 1/4"	3432	42 1/8" x	41 1/4"						
30310	38 1/8" x	49 1/4"	34310	42 1/8" x	49 1/4"						
3042	38 1/8" x	53 1/4"	3442	42 1/8" x	53 1/4"						
3046	38 1/8" x	57 1/4"	3446	42 1/8" x	57 1/4"						
3052	38 1/8" x	65 1/4"	3452	42 1/8" x	65 1/4"						
3056	38 1/8" x	69 1/4"	3456	42 1/8" x	69 1/4"						
3062	38 1/8" x	77 1/4"	3462	42 1/8" x	77 1/4"						

A sample of commonly available window sizes and styles. See your local distributors for current information and options. *Courtesy of Andersen Corp.*

CASEMENT WINDOWS

Widths and heights are rough opening dimensions.
To calculate unit dimension, subtract 1/2" from width and 1/2" from height.

(L) (S) (R)

L = Venting unit hinged on left
S = Stationary, non-venting unit
R = Venting unit hinged on right

Exterior View Shown

UNIT	WIDTH		HEIGHT	UNIT	WIDTH		HEIGHT	UNIT	WIDTH		HEIGHT	UNIT	WIDTH		HEIGHT	UNIT	WIDTH		HEIGHT
CR12	17 1/2"	x	24 5/8"	CN12	21"	x	24 5/8"	C12	24 5/8"	x	24 5/8"	CW12	28 7/8"	x	24 5/8"	CXW13	36 1/2"	x	36 1/2"
CR125	17 1/2"	x	28 7/8"	CN125	21"	x	28 7/8"	C125	24 5/8"	x	28 7/8"	CW125	28 7/8"	x	28 7/8"	CXW135	36 1/2"	x	41 3/8"
CR13	17 1/2"	x	36 1/2"	CN13	21"	x	36 1/2"	C13	24 5/8"	x	36 1/2"	CW13	28 7/8"	x	36 1/2"	CXW14	36 1/2"	x	48 1/2"
CR135	17 1/2"	x	41 3/8"	CN135	21"	x	41 3/8"	C135	24 5/8"	x	41 3/8"	CW135	28 7/8"	x	41 3/8"	CXW145	36 1/2"	x	53 3/8"
CR14	17 1/2"	x	48 1/2"	CN14	21"	x	48 1/2"	C14	24 5/8"	x	48 1/2"	CW14	28 7/8"	x	48 1/2"	CXW15	36 1/2"	x	60 3/8"
CR145	17 1/2"	x	53 3/8"	CN145	21"	x	53 3/8"	C145	24 5/8"	x	53 3/8"	CW145	28 7/8"	x	53 3/8"	CXW155	36 1/2"	x	65 3/8"
CR15	17 1/2"	x	60 3/8"	CN15	21"	x	60 3/8"	C15	24 5/8"	x	60 3/8"	CW15	28 7/8"	x	60 3/8"	CXW16	36 1/2"	x	72 3/8"
CR155	17 1/2"	x	65 3/8"	CN155	21"	x	65 3/8"	C155	24 5/8"	x	65 3/8"	CW155	28 7/8"	x	65 3/8"				
CR16	17 1/2"	x	72 3/8"	CN16	21"	x	72 3/8"	C16	24 5/8"	x	72 3/8"	CW16	28 7/8"	x	72 3/8"				

DOUBLE CASEMENT UNIT

Widths and heights are rough opening dimensions.
To calculate unit dimension, subtract 1/2" from width and 1/2" from height.

Exterior View Shown

UNIT	WIDTH		HEIGHT	UNIT	WIDTH		HEIGHT	UNIT	WIDTH		HEIGHT	UNIT	WIDTH		HEIGHT
CR23	34 1/4"	x	36 1/2"	CN23	41 1/4"	x	36 1/2"	C23	48 1/2"	x	36 1/2"	CW23	57"	x	36 1/2"
CR235	34 1/4"	x	41 3/8"	CN235	41 1/4"	x	41 3/8"	C235	48 1/2"	x	41 3/8"	CW235	57"	x	41 3/8"
CR24	34 1/4"	x	48 1/2"	CN24	41 1/4"	x	48 1/2"	C24	48 1/2"	x	48 1/2"	CW24	57"	x	48 1/2"
CR245	34 1/4"	x	53 3/8"	CN245	41 1/4"	x	53 3/8"	C245	48 1/2"	x	53 3/8"	CW245	57"	x	53 3/8"
CR25	34 1/4"	x	60 3/8"	CN25	41 1/4"	x	60 3/8"	C25	48 1/2"	x	60 3/8"	CW25	57"	x	60 3/8"
CR255	34 1/4"	x	65 3/8"	CN255	41 1/4"	x	65 3/8"	C255	48 1/2"	x	65 3/8"	CW255	57"	x	65 3/8"
CR26	34 1/4"	x	72 3/8"	CN26	41 1/4"	x	72 3/8"	C26	48 1/2"	x	72 3/8"	CW26	57"	x	72 3/8"

TRIPLE CASEMENT UNIT

Widths and heights are rough opening dimensions.
To calculate unit dimension, subtract 1/2" from width and 1/2" from height.

Exterior View Shown

UNIT	WIDTH		HEIGHT
C33	72 3/8"	x	36 1/2"
C335	72 3/8"	x	41 3/8"
C34	72 3/8"	x	48 1/2"
C345	72 3/8"	x	53 3/8"
C35	72 3/8"	x	60 3/8"

CASEMENT / AWNING PICTURE WINDOWS

Widths and heights are rough opening dimensions.
To calculate unit dimension, subtract 1/2" from width and 1/2" from height.

Exterior View Shown

UNIT	WIDTH		HEIGHT	UNIT	WIDTH		HEIGHT	UNIT	WIDTH		HEIGHT	UNIT	WIDTH		HEIGHT
P3030	36 1/2"	x	36 1/2"	P4030	48 1/2"	x	36 1/2"	P5030	60 3/8"	x	36 1/2"	P6030	72 3/8"	x	36 1/2"
P3035	36 1/2"	x	41 3/8"	P4035	48 1/2"	x	41 3/8"	P5035	60 3/8"	x	41 3/8"	P6035	72 3/8"	x	41 3/8"
P3040	36 1/2"	x	48 1/2"	P4040	48 1/2"	x	48 1/2"	P5040	60 3/8"	x	48 1/2"	P6040*	72 3/8"	x	48 1/2"
P3045	36 1/2"	x	53 3/8"	P4045	48 1/2"	x	53 3/8"	P5045*	60 3/8"	x	53 3/8"	P6045*	72 3/8"	x	53 3/8"
P3050	36 1/2"	x	60 3/8"	P4050	48 1/2"	x	60 3/8"	P5050*	60 3/8"	x	60 3/8"	P6050*	72 3/8"	x	60 3/8"
P3055	36 1/2"	x	65 3/8"	P4055*	48 1/2"	x	65 3/8"	P5055*	60 3/8"	x	65 3/8"				
P3060	36 1/2"	x	72 3/8"	P4060*	48 1/2"	x	72 3/8"	P5060*	60 3/8"	x	72 3/8"				
P3530	41 3/8"	x	36 1/2"	P4530	53 3/8"	x	36 1/2"	P5530	65 3/8"	x	36 1/2"				
P3535	41 3/8"	x	41 3/8"	P4535	53 3/8"	x	41 3/8"	P5535	65 3/8"	x	41 3/8"				
P3540	41 3/8"	x	48 1/2"	P4540	53 3/8"	x	48 1/2"	P5540*	65 3/8"	x	48 1/2"				
P3545	41 3/8"	x	53 3/8"	P4545*	53 3/8"	x	53 3/8"	P5545*	65 3/8"	x	53 3/8"				
P3550	41 3/8"	x	60 3/8"	P4550*	53 3/8"	x	60 3/8"	P5550*	65 3/8"	x	60 3/8"				
P3555	41 3/8"	x	65 3/8"	P4555*	53 3/8"	x	65 3/8"								
P3560	41 3/8"	x	72 3/8"	P4560*	53 3/8"	x	72 3/8"								

* Andersen Art Glass® Collection panels are available for these units by special order ONLY.

AWNING WINDOWS

Widths and heights are rough opening dimensions.
To calculate unit dimension, subtract 1/2" from width and 1/2" from height.

(S)

(V)

S = Stationary, non-venting unit
V = Venting unit

Exterior View Shown

UNIT	WIDTH		HEIGHT	UNIT	WIDTH		HEIGHT	UNIT	WIDTH		HEIGHT	UNIT	WIDTH		HEIGHT	UNIT	WIDTH		HEIGHT
AR21	24 5/8"	x	17 1/2"	AN21	24 5/8"	x	21"	A21	24 5/8"	x	24 5/8"	AW21	24 5/8"	x	28 7/8"	AXW31	36 1/2"	x	36 1/2"
AR251	28 7/8"	x	17 1/2"	AN251	28 7/8"	x	21"	A251	28 7/8"	x	24 5/8"	AW251	28 7/8"	x	28 7/8"	AXW351	41 3/8"	x	36 1/2"
AR31	36 1/2"	x	17 1/2"	AN31	36 1/2"	x	21"	A31	36 1/2"	x	24 5/8"	AW31	36 1/2"	x	28 7/8"	AXW41	48 1/2"	x	36 1/2"
AR351	41 3/8"	x	17 1/2"	AN351	41 3/8"	x	21"	A351	41 3/8"	x	24 5/8"	AW351	41 3/8"	x	28 7/8"	AXW451	53 3/8"	x	36 1/2"
AR41	48 1/2"	x	17 1/2"	AN41	48 1/2"	x	21"	A41	48 1/2"	x	24 5/8"	AW41	48 1/2"	x	28 7/8"	AXW51	60 3/8"	x	36 1/2"
AR451	53 3/8"	x	17 1/2"	AN451	53 3/8"	x	21"	A451	53 3/8"	x	24 5/8"	AW451	53 3/8"	x	28 7/8"	AXW551	65 3/8"	x	36 1/2"
AR51	60 3/8"	x	17 1/2"	AN51	60 3/8"	x	21"	A51	60 3/8"	x	24 5/8"	AW51	60 3/8"	x	28 7/8"	AXW61	72 3/8"	x	36 1/2"
AR551	65 3/8"	x	17 1/2"	AN551	65 3/8"	x	21"	A551	65 3/8"	x	24 5/8"	AW551	65 3/8"	x	28 7/8"				
AR61	72 3/8"	x	17 1/2"	AN61	72 3/8"	x	21"	A61	72 3/8"	x	24 5/8"	AW61	72 3/8"	x	28 7/8"				

AWNING VENTING PICTURE WINDOWS

Widths and heights are rough opening dimensions.
To calculate unit dimension, subtract 1/2" from width and 1/2" from height.

AWNING 2 HIGH								AWNING VENTING PICTURE							
UNIT	WIDTH		HEIGHT	UNIT	WIDTH		HEIGHT	UNIT	WIDTH		HEIGHT	UNIT	WIDTH		HEIGHT
A32	36 1/2"	x	48 1/2"	AP321	36 1/2"	x	72 3/8"	AP32	36 1/2"	x	48 1/2"	AP321	36 1/2"	x	72 3/8"
A42	48 1/2"	x	48 1/2"	AP3521	41 3/8"	x	72 3/8"	AP352	41 3/8"	x	48 1/2"	AP3521	41 3/8"	x	72 3/8"
				AP421	48 1/2"	x	72 3/8"	AP42	48 1/2"	x	48 1/2"	AP421	48 1/2"	x	72 3/8"

A sample of commonly available window sizes and styles. See your local distributors for current information and options.
Courtesy of Andersen Corp.

Bay windows add a new dimension to any room in your home. They project out from your walls and bring a piece of the great outdoors inside. Simply by replacing a plain picture window with an elegant bay window, you can transform a flat view into a three-dimensional panorama that puts your indoor living in a whole new light.

Box Bay Windows

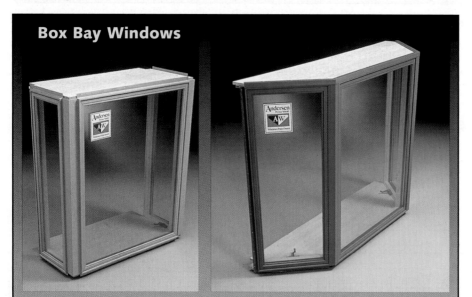

Windows with nailing flanges around the perimeter of the window unit are best suited for new construction. Attach them to the framing members inside the wall sheathing using 2-in. roofing nails driven at 6-in. intervals.

BAY & BOW WINDOWS

A bay window is a three-sided window structure with side sashes that project out from the exterior wall at an angle, then join with a larger picture window that's typically 15 to 24 in. away from the house. The individual sashes can be of just about any window type: casement, double-hung or fixed. The top of the bay window is treated in one of two ways: either a three-faced roof frame matching the profile of the window unit is added, or the window is connected directly to an overhanging soffit with vertical walls or trim boards. The area under the window unit can be treated with a short apron that covers a sturdy platform projecting out from the wall, or the apron may extend all the way or nearly all the way to the house foundation.

Window units that project out from the house in a smooth arc formed by multiple sashes are known as *bow windows*. Bow windows generally are longer than bays, but the installation techniques are nearly identical.

Specifications. True bay windows are generally at least 60 in. wide and a minimum of 42 in. high—most are in a horizontal configuration. The side sashes on shorter bay windows generally angle inward at 45° to maximize the size of the main window at the front of the unit, while still allowing for full projection away from the house. On longer bay windows, the side sashes project out at a shallower 30° angle and are usually closer in size to the main window, resulting in a more symmetrical window unit.

Support systems. Bay windows usually rely on the structural bearing of the wall they're installed into for support. Until recent years, the most common support method was to attach a sturdy platform with angled braces to the wall framing members or rim joist. Variations to this method included the use of heavy iron support braces bolted to the wall or rim joist, or extending the floor joists outward to support the unit from below. Today, however, professional window installers most often use a cable system to provide support to the unit from above.

Cable support systems. The cables are attached to the wall members above the window, then threaded through the front of the window inside the joints where the side sashes meet the front sash. The cable is then attached at the bottom of the window unit. Finding cable support systems for bay windows can take a little legwork, but most building centers that provide service to the building trades should be able to help out.

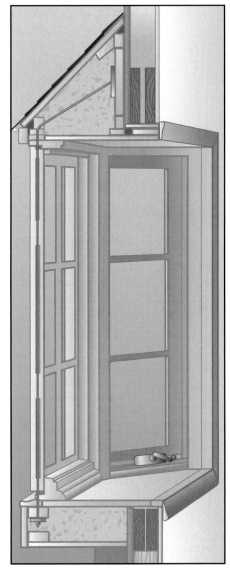

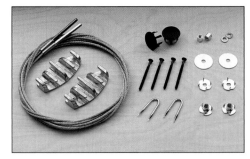

A roof structure is required for bay windows that aren't shielded by an overhanging roof soffit. Prefabricated roof frames are available in a variety of pitches from bay window manufacturers. Or, you can construct your own from dimensional lumber.

Cable kits for installing and supporting bay window units eliminate the need for structural framing underneath. Braided steel cables are threaded through concealed channels in the window framing and tie off to metal wall anchors that are attached to the wall studs. If the window is installed beneath a soffit or rafter overhang, you can attach the cables to the rafter ends, then install skirting between the top of the window and the soffit or rafter area.

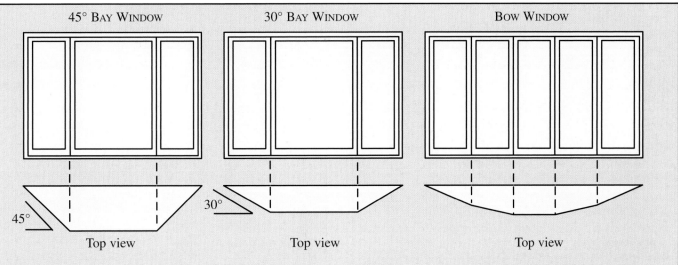

45° BAY WINDOW   30° BAY WINDOW   BOW WINDOW

45°   Top view   30°   Top view   Top view

Bay windows come in a variety of window sash configurations and styles to suit different installation requirements and house styles. Two common varieties are 45° bays (left) and 30° bays (center), that feature a large picture window in the center flanked by two narrower sashes that may or may not open for ventilation. These bay styles get their names based on the angle the side panes face away from the house. Bow windows (right) offer a slim overall profile that's popular in more contemporary homes.

Ordering a bay window

Bay windows are almost always special-order items that take two to four weeks for delivery. When ordering your bay window, you'll be asked to make some basic style choices, including: casement vs. double-hung, 30° vs. 45°, exterior trim color, whether to add grilles, and what type of glass to use. If you're replacing a picture window with a bay, take jamb-to-jamb and sill-to-header measurements of the existing window. Bay windows are manufactured in many sizes, but you may not be able to get one that fits the rough opening exactly. In such a case, order the closest smaller size and plan on adding framing to the rough opening to bring it to the correct size for the new window unit. Also make sure the clerk helping you with your order knows what kind of siding you have. If the window opening is framed with masonry veneer, the window should be sized somewhat smaller so the preattached brick molding can fit inside the masonry veneer—if you use the rough opening dimensions as a guide, you'll have to remove the molding before installation (a bad idea) or trim the bricks all around the window opening.

Bay window installation tip

Bay windows are very heavy. In addition to enlisting at least one helper, set the window into the opening and support it temporarily from beneath with 2 × 4 braces. A jack with a wood post and T-brace can be used to adjust the height of the window easily. Make sure the T-brace is centered.

Options for bracing a bay window from below

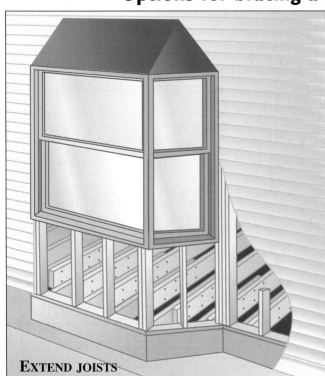

EXTEND JOISTS

One method for supporting a bay window from below is to extend the floor joists out from the house and under the new window to serve as the base for a support platform. The joist extensions overlap the joists and are bolted to them—called "sistering"—and a skirt is framed up to the window from the extended joists (similar to a short wall).

BRACE FROM BELOW

Another option for supporting bay windows from beneath is to attach angled braces, made from dimension lumber, that extend from the bay to the rim joist of the house. A framed skirt hides the braces and serves as a nailing structure for sheathing and siding.

MISCELLANEOUS WINDOW TYPES

Awning windows

Also called *hopper windows,* awning windows are used primarily in high-on-the-wall locations (over doors, for example) and in basements, where about 16 in. high by 32 in. wide is a common size.

Jalousie windows

Jalousie windows are constructed of horizontal glass louvers, joined together at the metal frames. The slats are pitched to overlap each other when the window is closed—the same way mini-blinds or venetian blinds work. Jalousie windows are not designed to provide much protection from either the elements or insects, but they do provide excellent ventilation when opened, and just enough protection to keep larger pests out. They are used primarily in informal settings in temperate climates, such as porches and sunrooms.

Barn sash are fixed windows that are used as inexpensive light sources, generally for non-weatherized out-buildings. The 18 × 24 in., multi-lite unit shown here cost about ten dollars. It was installed in a frame made from left-over construction lumber, then shimmed and nailed into the window opening in this shed.

Barn Sash

Looking for a cheap but attractive window for a shed or garage, where an operating window is not required? Most building centers carry a selection of fixed windows, usually called *barn sash,* that are sized in roughly the same proportions as large picture frames. Many are multi-pane construction. To install them, build a frame from 1 × 4 or 2 × 4 and attach the frame in the opening.

Glass block

Glass block windows are most popular in two areas: as basement windows (ready-to-go, framed units are available) and in bathrooms. In bathrooms, they're typically used to replace operating windows over tub/shower areas. The most common block size is 8 × 8 × 4 in., although you'll find quite a bit of variety in size and style. You can also purchase glass block installation systems that make working with glass block a simple process. The top, right photo shows the basic components you'll need to build a mortared block panel. The lower right photo is a mortarless kit for framed panel installations made by *Pittsburgh Corning.* Vents designed to be mortared into the block panel are also available.

The crank-style casement window is the smallest window to meet the height, width and area requirements for egress windows.

All bedrooms, whether they're above or below grade, are required to have a code-approved egress window.

EGRESS WINDOWS

Generally, the more bedrooms a house has, the more it is worth. However, you can't call a room a bedroom unless it has a properly sized and installed egress window.

The need for a second means of escape is one of the most important fire protection provisions of the various model building and life safety codes. But it is often overlooked or misunderstood when homeowners convert basements or attics to living space without the proper permits.

The *Life Safety Code,* published by the National Fire Protection Association (NFPA), is the building industry's core reference on life/safety issues. The other document used is the CABO/ICC (Code Administrators & Building Officials/International Code Council) *One- and Two-Family Dwelling Code,* which is referenced by the three model building codes. The relevance of these documents and their requirements depend on the application by the appropriate fire or building official. Local fire marshals, meanwhile, enforce the Life Safety Code to the degree allowed by state law. When applied to single-family homes, that can be very little or not at all.

According to the *Life Safety Code,* all sleeping and living spaces in a home must have at least two means of escape. The primary one must be a door or stairs leading to the outdoors at ground level. Although the second one can be another door, stairs or an independent, unlockable passageway, the requirement usually is met by an *egress* (or rescue) window that is remote from the primary escape route.

The CABO/ICC secondary egress requirement applies solely to bedrooms, not other living spaces. As such, it would not apply to a family room in a finished basement or attic, even if the user was the sort of person who fell asleep on the sofa every night.

Whether or not a window constitutes an acceptable secondary form of egress depends on its size, shape and placement. The multiple specifications can be confusing. The *Life Safety Code* requires that egress windows "provide

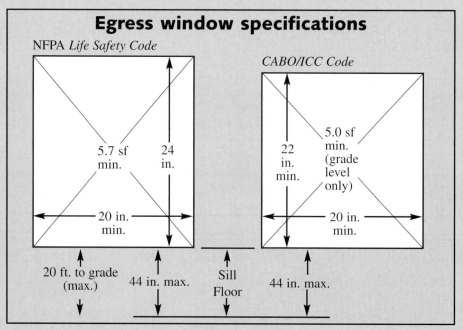

Egress window specifications

NFPA *Life Safety Code*

5.7 sf min.
24 in.
20 in. min.
20 ft. to grade (max.)
44 in. max.

Sill Floor

CABO/ICC Code

22 in. min.
5.0 sf min. (grade level only)
20 in. min.
44 in. max.

The *Life Safety Code* and the *CABO/ICC* requirements for egress windows differ. Check with your local code official to find out what your community prescribes.

a clear opening of not less than 20 in. in width, 24 in. in height and 5.7 s.f. in area. The bottom of the opening shall not be more than 44 in. off the floor." The window also must operate from the inside without the use of tools. And finally, it must be within 20 ft. of the ground or be directly accessible to fire department rescue apparatus or a balcony.

Again, *CABO* is more lenient. It reduces the minimum height from 24 in. to 22 in., and grade-level windows need be only 5.0 s.f. rather than 5.7 s.f. It also eliminates the above-grade height limitation altogether.

As with most building codes, you can't appreciate the importance of a requirement until you understand the thinking that went into its creation. In the case of secondary egress, the goal is to ensure another escape or rescue route if smoke or fire blocks the primary one.

The minimum width was originally established, in part, so a ladder could be set into the window and would not slip sideways. However, firefighters now are trained to place their ladders just beneath or to the side of a window.

Windows that must be opened with a special tool are unacceptable because even if the tool were attached to the window, the person may not be in a state of mind, or have the ability or time, to use it in an emergency.

Finally, 20 ft. is considered the maximum height from which someone could hang and safely drop to the ground. Most window manufacturers and code officials interpret the code to mean that a minimum legal opening must be provided when you simply open the window. Code officials differ on whether the popular "easy-clean" removable-sash windows satisfy egress requirements if you must pivot the sash out of the frame to gain the minimum height.

Although some roof windows are large enough and open wide enough to

Photos courtesy of Andersen Windows

Egress size is measured by the size of the opening, not the size of the window. Openings for the double-hung window (right) and the sliding window (above) need to be nearly twice as large as the minimum egress dimensions to meet the egress codes.

meet egress size requirements, they typically don't qualify as egress windows because they are installed more than 42 in. from the floor, even in the sloped ceiling of a finished attic.

No matter what the *Life Safety Code* or model building codes require, each state and even each municipality may have slightly different regulations. It is essential that you consult with your local building inspector to determine exactly what local laws require. Local laws take precedence, and codes are written to allow the local code enforcer to use considerable judgment in deciding how to satisfy the intent of a specific code. Together, you can choose an option that keeps you safe without unnecessary expense or modifications.

It is easier to incorporate adequate egress into rooms at the design stage. However, you can correct an existing hazard, often without much difficulty.

If you are replacing an old double-hung window that has a weighted balance system, you should be able to gain up to 5 in. on the width of the new double-hung window because it won't require the weight cavities. If that's not enough, you can nearly double the clear opening if you replace a double-hung with a casement window that opens fully.

In either case, you should be able to find a standard-sized window that will

fit the opening while increasing the clear space. You will need to install new trim inside. Outside, you may have to modify the casing or siding.

Enlarging a rough opening to accommodate a larger window is far more disruptive. You may have to support the load above the window when replacing the header. And you'll have to patch drywall and refinish walls in addition to the work previously described regarding the trim.

Installing a below-grade egress window begins with substantial excavation. You must dig out a hole about 18 in. below the new windowsill level and provide a drained gravel bed (protected with filter fabric) at the bottom. Additional excavation is required to run drainage tile from the base of the window well to a functioning footing drain, a sump pump or to grade (builders call this "daylight") if there's a significant slope away from the house. If you must make an opening in a poured concrete foundation, hire a specialist for this.

Modern skylights have made great strides in overcoming the reputation of older roof windows as being very susceptible to leaking. *Photo courtesy of Andersen Windows.*

SKYLIGHTS

Skylights, also called *roof windows,* provide extra light and added ventilation into a room. They are especially useful for use in rooms with no exterior walls or in rooms such as the kitchen or bath where maximum ventilation is desirable.

Modern skylights are operable (they can be opened), energy-efficient and weatherproof. Earlier models had a reputation for leaking, but many of those leaks were due to faulty installation. The key to a leak-proof skylight is to buy a quality unit and install it properly. Though the skylight unit may have a flange that is described as "self-flashing," it is best to install flashing on all sides of the window unit. This is especially true if you live in an area of high rain or snowfall. Optional flashing kits are available from the window manufacturer.

To minimize carpentry work, select and install a skylight unit that will fit between existing rafters or trusses. It is best to install a series of small skylights, rather than one large unit, to avoid having to cut away rafters. Most skylights are 21½-in. wide so they fit between roof trusses and rafters set 24-in. o.c. It's possible to order them wider, or as narrow as 15 in. for 16-o.c. framing.

If the skylight is installed in a cathedral or attic ceiling, where the bottom side of the rafters is finished with wallboard or plaster, no light shaft is required. If installed in a conventional roof, a light shaft must be built to connect the skylight opening to the ceiling opening. A light shaft can be straight with walls at right angles to the ceiling, or angled so the opening in the ceiling is larger than the skylight opening.

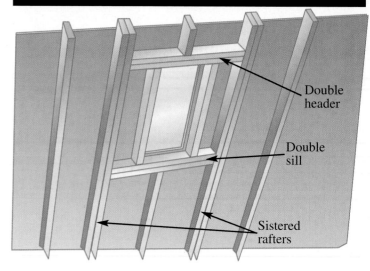

Double header

Double sill

Sistered rafters

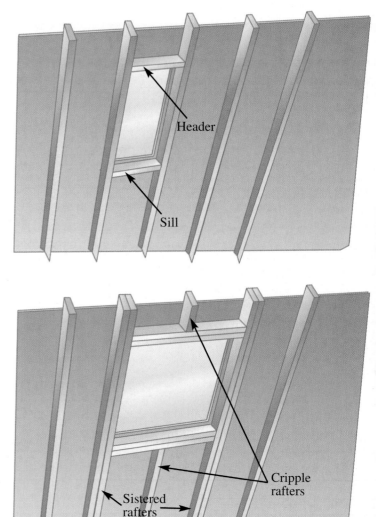

Header

Sill

Cripple rafters

Sistered rafters

Skylight framing varies depending upon the width of the skylight and the construction of the roof. In cases where a portion of a rafter must be removed (top and bottom drawings), a new rafter is fastened to the old rafter (called "sistering") on either side of the window. A header and sill are installed between the cut ends of the rafter, creating cripple rafters above and below the window. Narrow skylights (center) often are sized to fit between two rafters.

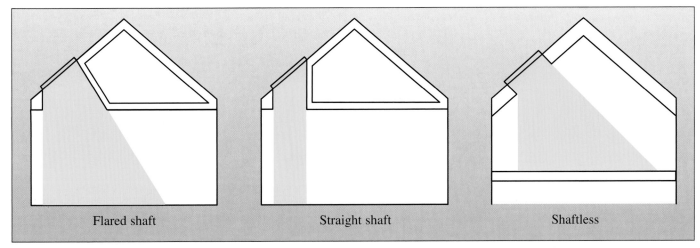

Flared shaft | Straight shaft | Shaftless

TUBULAR SKYLIGHTS

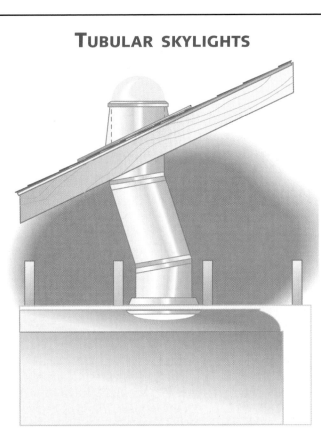

The tubular skylight is a close cousin to the conventional skylight. Like a skylight, it introduces natural light into a dark room. But unlike a skylight, the reflective tube that creates the "shaft" of these newer home improvement products can be twisted, bent or rerouted around obstructions in the attic area—with little or no loss of light intensity. If you've never seen one of these products in use, check one out at your local building center or home show—you'll be shocked at how much light they can bring into a room.

Light enters through a clear acrylic dome on the roof and passes through a reflective tube before diffusing into the room below. The tube can be angled as needed to accommodate the roof and ceiling framing.

DOORS

Regardless of the purpose your door will serve, there are a few basic styles that are used for both interior and exterior doors. These include a *slab door, panel door* and *sash door.* These doors may be made from a variety of materials, such as wood, wood veneer, hardboard, plastic laminate, steel or fiberglass and be either hollow (hollow-core, reserved for interior doors) or insulated (solid-core, used for exterior doors and interior doors where soundproofing is desirable). Most can be painted, wood and wood-veneer are suitable for staining or varnishing.

Most pre-hung doors are installed by driving casing nails or deck screws through the side jambs and head jamb,

and into the jack studs and header that frame the rough opening. Some exterior doors also require nailing through the preattached exterior brickmold trim. To prevent the door from bowing or sagging, a 3" long screw should be driven through one of the holes of the middle hinge.

To open, doors swing aside, slide or fold. Swinging doors are mounted with hinges on one side. Swinging doors must have sufficient free floor space to swing—an easy miscalculation to make when you're planning. Sliding doors may be two or more doors that are track mounted, and bypass each other as they slide to open. Some sliding doors slide into pockets built into the wall, and are

called pocket doors. Sliding doors have the advantage that they do not require free floor space, and are often used where there is not room to swing a hinged door. Folding doors are commonly used on closets. These doors pivot on anchors set at the top of the doors, and often are used as two pairs of narrow doors. For example, for a four-foot-wide closet opening, two pairs of 1-foot-wide doors may be hinged together, so that one pair folds to the left, the other pair folds to the right. Folding doors use little floor space to open, and offer the advantage that when open they permit full access to the entire closet.

Doors are made in a standard height of 6 ft. 8 in. (80 in.), but 7 ft.

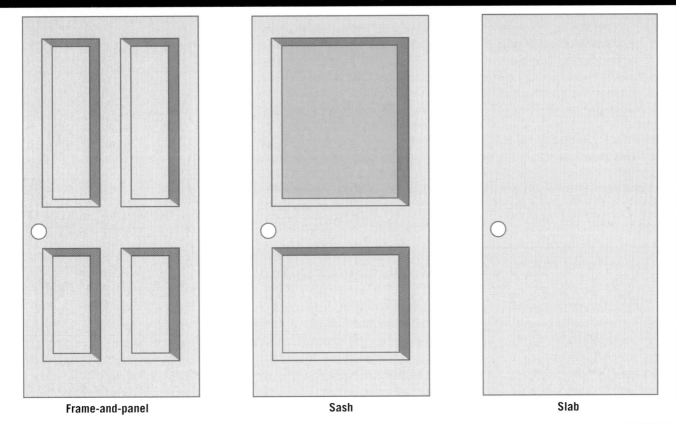

Basic door styles

Frame-and-panel   **Sash**   **Slab**

A *frame-and-panel door* is composed of horizontal rails and vertical stiles that provide frames for thin, inset panels. Some doors are manufactured to look like panel doors, but are actually made of one solid piece of material, generally steel or fiberglass. A *sash door* is simply a panel door, with glass panes used in place of wood panels. A *slab door* is built around an internal frame and is covered on the outside with a skin to give it a body. Interior slab doors are usually hollow-core doors, while exterior slab doors usually have a solid core.

Standard Door Widths

INDUSTRY NAME	WIDTH
2/0	24 in.
2/4	28 in.
2/6	30 in.
2/8	32 in.
3/0	36 in.

The most common door widths are 3/0 for exterior and 2/8 for interior. Heights are normally 80 in. (79¼ in. actual).

exterior entry doors are available. If you require a taller door, consult your millwork company. Any size door can be made on custom order. Folding doors for closets are available in 8-foot heights so that closet door openings may be built without need for framing headers. The doors thus offer full accessibility from floor to ceiling.

Exterior doors all function in pretty much the same manner but you'll find a huge assortment of materials, styles and accessories available.

Interior doors can be found in a wide range of types, from swinging to bi-fold, but there is less choice in styling within categories.

Photos courtesy of Premdor Inc.

The width of a main entry door should be at least 3 ft. (36 in.). Other swinging exterior doors may be as narrow as 2 ft. 6 in. (30 in.) wide. Interior doors are available in widths from 2 ft. to 3 ft. Whenever possible, install wider doors to make moving furniture easier, and to make the interior of the house barrier-free for easy entry via a wheelchair.

Entry doors are usually 1¾ in. thick, while interior doors are 1¼ to 1½-in. thick. Sliding or bifold closet doors that are used simply to provide a privacy screen are even thinner, and may be as thin as ¾-in. thick.

Choosing doors

When working with doors, observe these general precautions to ensure a proper installation and operation.

• First, when shopping sight wood doors along the edges to make sure the door is not bowed or warped. If the door is packaged, have a store associate open it for you.

• Have the doors delivered a few days in advance of the planned installation. Let the doors acclimate in a dry, well-ventilated room for a few days. Sight the door edges again prior to hanging them. If there is a slight bow,

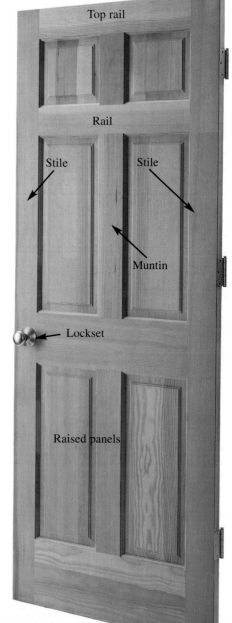

Pre-hung doors

Prehung door units are available both for interior and exterior installation. They are shipped with the jamb assembled, the door fitted and hung on the hinges, and with the holes bored for lock installation. The door trim is installed on one side of the jamb. Installation consists of shimming and plumbing the door frame in the rough opening, installing the trim on one side of the unit, and installing the lock. Prehung interior door units usually have two, 3½-inch butt hinges, while heavier exterior doors have three, 4-inch butt hinges.

Anatomy of a door

The horizontal members of a panel door are called rails: the top piece is the top rail, the center rail is called the lock rail, and the bottom member is the bottom rail. Other horizontal members are called intermediate rails. The vertical door members at each side are called the stiles. Vertical members between the stiles are called mullions. The panel door may have panels either of glass or wood. The glass panels are called lights; the wood members that separate the lights are called bars. Wood members are simply called panels.

Swing direction

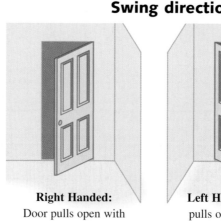

Right Handed: Door pulls open with right hand

Left Handed: Door pulls open with left hand

Swing direction is an important factor to consider when buying a prehung door (interior or exterior) because prehung doors are prebored for lockset installation. The easiest way to keep from confusing swing direction is to use your hands as a reminder: Right-handed doors are designed to pull open with your right hand, and left-handed doors naturally are pulled open with your left hand.

(RIGHT) Measure the rough opening to see what size door it will accommodate. The R.O. should be at least 1 in. wider and taller than the door jambs and header for interior doors and at least 2 in. for exterior doors.

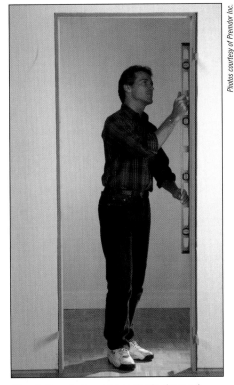

hang the door with the bowed (concave) side toward the stops. When the door is pulled shut and locked, the lock will hold the lock side of the door straight, while the hinges will hold the hinge side straight.

• Before hanging the door, seal all wood door edges with a clear wood sealer. To protect against moisture and warping, apply the paint or varnish finish as soon as the door is fitted.

• When choosing an interior door, consider the location of light switches, closet doors and potential obstacles.

• Exterior doors should swing into the building, interior door should do the same by swinging into a room to avoid opening to possible traffic.

Photos courtesy of Premdor Inc.

Check the studs and header in the rough opening to make sure they're level and plumb before you begin installing a new door.

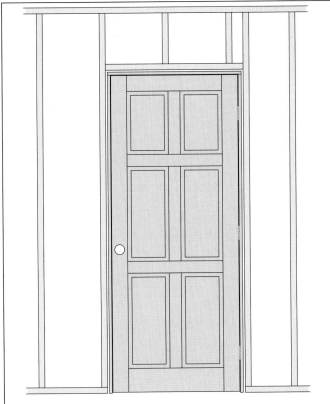

Door framing: There is more than one way to frame a rough opening for a door. Typically, shorter jack studs are butted up against the full-height studs at each side of the opening and support a 2 × 4 header at the top of the opening.

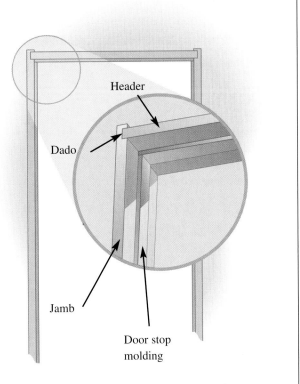

Header

Dado

Jamb

Door stop molding

Door jambs: A door is attached to a set of jambs, which in turn are attached to the framing members that form the door rough opening. The top, or "head" jamb is usually set into dadoes at the tops of the side jambs. A framework of door stop molding on the inside faces of the jambs creates a surface for the door to close against.

Exterior doors cover a wide range of styles, from fancy, multi-lite units with side lites and brass caming, to relatively inexpensive steel models.

EXTERIOR DOORS

Exterior doors come in a variety of styles and materials. They can be made of solid wood, foam-core steel, fiberglass or laminated wood clad with vinyl or aluminum. They can be highly decorative for front-entry use, or a basic slab door for a service entry, such as in a garage.

Exterior doors are usually pre-hung and come with an integrated weather-stripping and threshold to ensure a proper seal. Steel doors are sealed by using a magnetic strip, similar to a refrigerator gasket. Other doors use products such as brass, bronze, rubber, vinyl, foam and other materials to seal the gaps and crevices.

Options available for exterior doors include sidelights and transoms. These accessories can enhance both beauty and function by allowing more natural light to find its way into the entryway. Sidelights and transoms are available individually or as a system. Other options include etched, tinted, leaded or stained glass. Naturally, all of these accessories will increase the price of the door.

Comparing Exterior Door Types

| DOOR TYPE | SUSCEPTIBLE TO: | | | | | PAINTABLE? | STAINABLE? | FIRE RESISTANT? | LOW MAINTENANCE? |
	RUST?	CRACKS?	PEELING?	WARPING?	DENTS?				
WOOD	No	Yes	Yes	Yes	No	Yes	Yes	No	No
METAL	Yes	No	No	No	Yes	Yes	No	Yes	Yes
FIBERGLASS	No	No	No	No	Yes	Yes	Yes	No	Yes

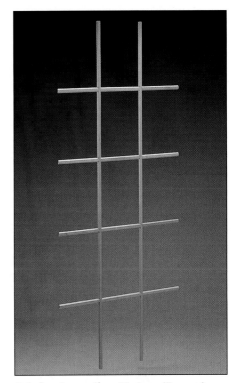

Exterior door styles: Full-view, pre-hung exterior door with overlaid multi-pane grilles.

Exterior door styles: Steel, insulated core, pre-hung exterior door with pressed frame-and-panel styling.

Exterior door option: Window grilles can be ordered from most door manufacturers. Overlaid on the glass panels, they fit into the door frame in one piece to create a French door appearance. These grilles simply snap into place with the use of small bullet clips.

Predrilled, double cutouts for the lockset and deadbolt save a considerable amount of installation work and increase accuracy.

Insulated cores make steel exterior doors extremely energy efficient.

Steel cladding tucks into channels in the wood door frame, protecting the frame while leaving the wood exposed for hinge installation.

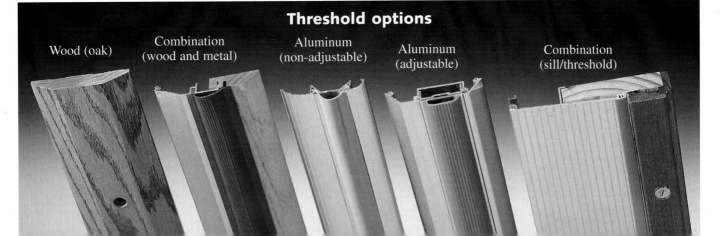

Threshold options

Wood (oak) Combination (wood and metal) Aluminum (non-adjustable) Aluminum (adjustable) Combination (sill/threshold)

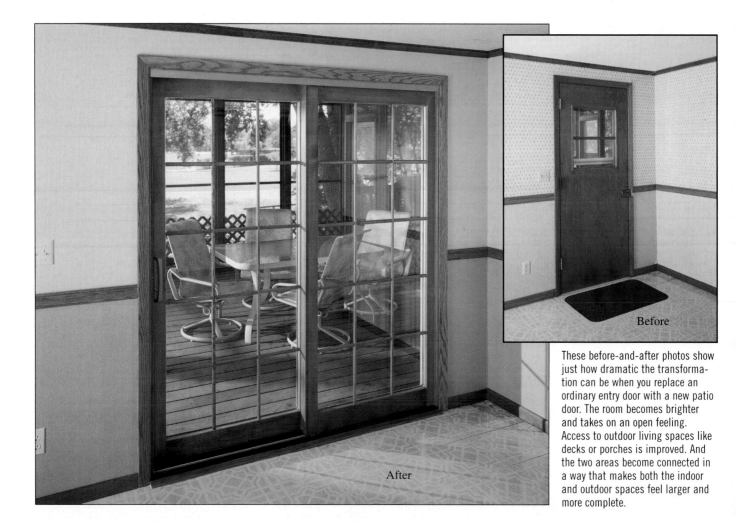

Before

These before-and-after photos show just how dramatic the transformation can be when you replace an ordinary entry door with a new patio door. The room becomes brighter and takes on an open feeling. Access to outdoor living spaces like decks or porches is improved. And the two areas become connected in a way that makes both the indoor and outdoor spaces feel larger and more complete.

After

PATIO DOORS

Perhaps more than any other home feature, patio doors effectively bring the outdoors into your home. Patio door glass area alone is double or triple the size of most windows and extends nearly from floor to ceiling. Yet today's glass technology and door design don't sacrifice comfort or energy dollars for a larger view. The popularity of patio doors means there is an array of styles and configurations to choose from.

Installing a sliding patio door is a job for two or more persons. The weight of the double doors makes these units too heavy for one person to handle. If necessary, remove the two doors from the frame until the frame is installed.

Patio doors are commonly fit with shatter-resistant, insulating glass. They come in two styles: sliding and swinging. Sliding patio doors are a good choice if the door will remain open for

periods of time to allow ventilation. Swinging patio doors, often called French doors, can be right or left-hinged and swing either inward or outward. They usually come in two-panel units, of which one or both panels can open. They also offer some advantages over sliders. Swinging patio doors are more energy-efficient because they seal tighter. They also can be fitted with a deadbolt making them more secure.

Models with two operating panels offer twice the access width of sliders, which you'll appreciate next time you're moving furniture.

Installing patio doors. Prepare the door opening to the proper size. Set the door unit into the opening and plumb and level the unit. Use wood shims placed under the bottom ends of the side jambs to level the unit.

Security

Patio doors, especially sliding patio doors, can be inviting entry points for uninvited guests. Products that increase the security of a patio door include: keyed patio

Keyed patio door lock

Security bar

Door pin

door lock that attaches to the frame of a fixed door panel; security bar that fits into the door track to prevent the sliding door panel from moving (or you can simply cut a piece of 2 × 2 to fit snugly between the sliding panel and the jamb); or a patio door pin that fits into aligning holes in the door frames, pinning them together so they can't slide.

Patio door styles

SLIDING   SWINGING

When selecting a patio door, a basic choice you'll need to make is whether you want a door with sliding glass panels or one with panels that swing open and shut. Sliding patio doors are a good choice if you plan to leave the door open for long periods of time to create ventilation, or if either side of the door is a high traffic area or likely to be obstructed. One other advantage to sliding doors is that both panels can be removed from the tracks to allow clear access to the full door opening. Swinging patio doors are generally more energy efficient and less prone to water leakage than sliding doors, and they pose less of a security risk. But the permanent jamb between the glass panels can get in the way when moving large objects in and out of the house, and the hinged doors are vulnerable to damage when left open.

Mark the outline of the door brick molding on the siding. Remove the door unit and use a circular saw, set just deep enough to cut through the siding, to remove the siding from under the brick molding. Use a wood chisel to cut away siding at the corners.

Cut the drip edge to the proper length, and slide the top edge of the drip edge between the siding and sheathing. Leave the drip edge unnailed so you can adjust it later.

Cut 8-in.-wide strips of building paper and insert one edge of the paper between the siding and sheathing on the outside of the door. Wrap the paper over the interior surface of the header and jack studs, insert the opposite edge of the paper around the inside edge of the framing. Staple the building paper in place.

Apply silicone caulk to the subfloor where the threshold will sit. Also caulk the front edge of the paper around the edge of the framing members.

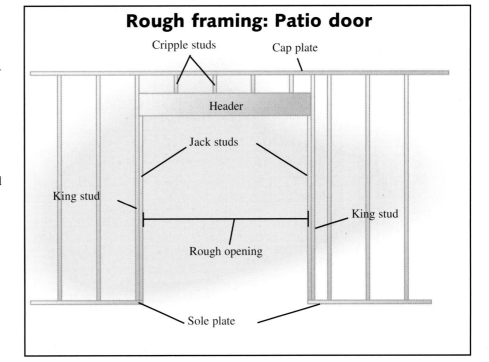

Rough framing: Patio door

Cripple studs

Cap plate

Header

Jack studs

King stud

King stud

Rough opening

Sole plate

The rough framing for a patio door is similar to the framing for any other door. Due to the width of the rough opening, however, a wide header made from built-up dimension lumber or even engineered beam material is often required. Before starting a patio door installation project, make sure that the required header is not so wide that the rough opening becomes too short for the patio door.

Center the door unit in the opening and have a helper hold the door in place until it is nailed.

If there are gaps between the threshold and the subfloor, coat wood shims with silicone caulk and insert them at six-inch intervals between the threshold and subfloor. Check the threshold for level as you shim it.

Shim between the door frame and the rough opening. Shim at lock location, at top and bottom corners, and at 12-in. intervals between.

Drive 10d casing nails through the exterior brick molding and into the jack studs and header. Also drive 10d casing nails on the inside of the jamb, at each shim location. Use a nail set to set the nails. Remove one screw from the threshold stop block and drive a three-inch screw into the hole, anchoring the threshold to the subfloor.

On the inside, cut off the shims so they are flush with the door jambs. Loosely pack fiberglass insulation into any open crack around the door frame.

Install sill nosing against the siding, under the threshold. Drill pilot holes in the nosing and secure with 10d casing nails. At the outside top of the unit, slip the drip cap down so it is tight against the top brick molding. Apply silicone caulk along the drip cap, and down both sides of the brick moldings to the door bottom. Caulk around the sill nosing to weatherproof any crack at that point.

Install the lockset, following the directions of the manufacturer.

Handling Patio Doors

Twin tapes. Enlist a helper and an extra tape measure when it's time to square the big door unit in the rough opening. Check the frame for square after shimming, comparing the diagonal measurements of the jamb as you make adjustments.

Give them enough rope. Patio door units are heavy, but two people can safely carry a bulky, 200-lb. door through a home to an elevated deck. Keep the door in its box and band it with ropes or moving straps (as shown) for ease of transport.

Swinging screens: A patio door accessory you'll appreciate

Can't decide whether to buy a swinging patio door or a slider? Here's something that might put a plus in the swinging door column for you: swinging screen doors. These useful accessories mount on the exterior of the swinging door frame. One of the screen doors stays fixed most of the time, but can be opened with a latch if need be. The other has a pneumatic closer, so you can travel through it the same way as any other screen door. You can get screens for sliding patio doors, but they also slide, which makes them harder to operate and they don't close automatically.

A full-view storm door offers excellent sight-lines and good energy efficiency, but can't be vented.

A double-hung combination storm door brings in plenty of light and offers ventilation when the movable sash is opened.

The cross-buck combination storm door has a classic design that's immediately recognizable and very popular.

COMBINATION STORM DOORS

A combination door has an operable glass sash and screen. These units can be adjusted so the door serves as a storm door in cold weather, and as a screen door in warm weather.

To install a combination door, set two sawhorses about six feet apart and lay planks across the tops of the saw-horses. Remove the carton and packing and lay the combination door unit flat atop the scaffold.

Use a T-bevel to check the slope of the entry door sill. Transfer this angle to the sides of the combination door frame, and use a hack saw to cut the side frames to the proper angle. Allow about ⅛-inch extra on the cut to ensure that the door frame will slide freely into the entry door jamb.

Set the door unit into the opening and plumb it. With the combination door frame tight against the brick molding on the hinge side, mark on the molding along the edge of the door

frame. Then slide the unit so the lock side of the door is tight against the brick molding. Make another pencil mark. Now measure between the first and second marks. If the distance is more than ⅜-in., nail wood spacer strips to the molding on the hinge side of the door. This will ensure a weather-tight fit between the combination door and the brick molding.

Position the door unit back in the entry door frame, and push it tightly against the brick molding on the hinge side of the door. Drill pilot holes in the side frame of the door and drive the mounting screws through the door frame and into the brick molding.

Center the top of the combination door frame over the side frames. Drill pilot holes and screw the top frame to the brick molding. Adjust the bottom door sweep via the adjustment screws. Install the lock and latch as per the manufacturer's instructions.

A new storm door can offer the benefits of increased energy efficiency and improved ventilation. If your entry door is old or out of style, think about adding an attractive new storm door to increase curb appeal instead of replacing the entry door.

Among the more elegant interior doors you'll find are French-style, swinging double doors.

Panel doors, or nonwood doors made to resemble panels doors, offer a more interesting appearance than plain, slab doors.

Cafe doors aren't the first types of interior door we tend to think of, but if the doorway connects two rooms that receive a lot of traffic between them, yet don't demand too much privacy, they are an excellent, inobtrusive solution with a definite sense of style.

INTERIOR DOORS

Interior door types include:

Flush doors: may be solid wood or have a solid core of particle board, or may be hollow core.

Paneled doors—have a wooden frame, with wood or glass panels inset into the wood frame. Doors with glass panels are called sash doors.

Louvered doors—have slanted slats instead of solid wood panels. The slatted panels provide a visual screen to ensure privacy, but permit air to circulate through the gaps between the slats. Louvered doors are often used on closets to act as screens while permitting air to flow into the closet space. If you have a stuffy or humid closet, replace the existing doors with louvered doors.

Pocket doors—make a great alternative where a small opening is need and there is no room for a swinging door.

When open, pocket doors are stored away in a special frame, which is built into the wall, forming a pocket. To install a pocket door in an existing wall, the studs, wiring and piping must be removed to make room for the frame. Before installation, check for obstructions within the wall.

Bi-fold doors—primarily used for closets. They are sold as single units or as a pair which includes a whole kit with all of the hardware. Styles range from slab, panel, louvered or mirrored models. They are hinged between the two halves, pivot at the jamb and slide along a top track.

Bypassing doors—another type that is commonly used for closets. There are usually two, and sometimes three, units that hang from a track and slide from side to side, while floor guides

hold the doors in their plane. They come as a kit in various styles and widths to accommodate different-sized closets. A downfall of bypassing doors is that access to the closet is always hindered by the width of one panel.

Hollow-core doors

In houses built prior to the 1950s, all doors were solid core—meaning they were built from solid lumber. For both economy and lightness of weight, interior doors sold today are most often hollow-core doors, and generally pre-hung and leveled in their jambs.

Hollow-core doors have a solid wood perimeter frame that provides sufficient rigidity and strength. The perimeter frame consists of side stiles that are a minimum 1-in. wide and can be mortised for hinges; and top and bottom rails that are a minimum 2¼-in. wide. They also have lock blocks located at the center of the door so they can be bored for locks.

The doors are faced with a thin wood veneer, which is reinforced by spacers installed between the veneer faces. These spacers may be a web of wood or cardboard that is glued to the face veneers. The lightweight hollow core doors are supported by two hinges. The top hinge is positioned about 6 in. down from the top edge of the door, and the lower hinge about 8 in. up from the floor. The door lock is located about 36 in. up from the floor.

Hollow-core interior doors are probably the best-selling type of doors for do-it-yourself installation. Their light weight and the fact that they're usually pre-hung makes installation about as simple as it can get; plus they are very inexpensive. Typically, a web of corrugated cardboard runs throughout the inside of the door, between the wood veneer skins.

TIP: How to trim a hollow-core door to length

1 Trim off the door bottom using a fine-tooth blade in a circular saw. To ensure a straight cut, clamp a straightedge cutting guide to the door to guide the saw cut. Scoring along the cutting line with a utility knife first will minimize tear-out from the saw.

2 The cutoff portion of the door will contain the bottom door rail, which must be reinserted into the door. Scrape the veneer and any glue residue off the rail with a chisel. Then slide it back into the bottom of the door.

3 Check the bottom rail for fit in the door bottom. Remove core filler, if the door contains any), from inside the door so the bottom rail fits completely into the cavity and is flush with the door bottom. Then glue it into place with wood glue. Apply two or three padded C-clamps to hold the rail in place while the glue dries.

Louvered (bi-fold) Doors

Louvered closet doors are installed like any other bi-fold door. Used mostly on closets, they allow airflow while still separating the room or closet area visually.

Louvered doors and other bi-folds are are available in widths to fit most closet door openings. To install them, first cut the top track to the right length to fit the door width. Install socket pins in the track and screw the track to the header or ceiling. Position the track on the header to fit your trim application.

Screw pivot pin sockets to the bottom end of the side jambs, aligned with the pin sockets in the header track. Insert pivot pins in the tops of the jamb-side doors, and guides in the holes in the adjoining doors.

Move the top pivot socket a few inches away from the jamb and insert the bottom pivot pin in the bottom socket. Then tilt the top of the door until the top pivot pin snaps into the top pin socket. Adjust the top and bottom pivot sockets until the gap between the door and jamb is uniform.

Insert the guide on the second door into the track. Following the same steps, install the second pair of doors on the open side of the jamb. Install the door pulls. The final step is to install metal door aligners near the bottom of the center doors where they meet. The aligners are needed to hold the faces of the meeting doors in line when the doors are closed.

Pocket Doors

You can buy pocket doors in pre-assembled frames, or you can buy a non-.pre-hung door

Bypass door hardware

and rig up a pocket for it using dimension lumber and bypass door hardware. Either way, you'll need a pair of wood frames, one on each side of the door pocket. The door slides along an overhead track between the frames. A steel channel at the bottom of the unit serves as a spacer to hold the frames apart, and anchors the bottom of the door when the channel is attached to the floor. The frames consist of a ladder-like set of horizontal wood nailers, and the wallboard is attached to these wood members.

Inexpensive bi-pass door hardware kits (inset photo) include: a length of metal track that attaches to the closet header; roller brackets that fasten to the tops of the doors with screws and glide in grooves in the track; and plastic door guides that screw to the floor.

TRIM FOR DOORS & WINDOWS

Doors and windows are treated very similarly when it comes to putting on the finishing touch: the trimwork. The primary difference is that windows have a sill and apron that must be dealt with, while doors have a threshold you've (hopefully) already installed.

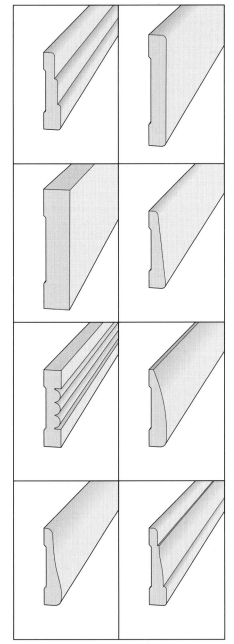

Case molding profiles. If you're looking to dress up your new window or door a bit, you'll find a wealth of case molding styles available by the lineal foot at better lumberyards. See the chart on page 100 for information on estimating how much you'll need.

INTERIOR: CASING

EXTERIOR: BRICKMOLD

Casemolding (also called casing) on the inside and brickmold on the outside is the basic strategy for trimming both doors and windows.

Door Trim Kits

Instead of purchasing lengths of case molding for trimming an interior door, you can buy prepackaged door trim kits that include all the moldings you'll need to complete the job.

Kits are available for casing a door picture-frame style, and the miters are already precut on the head and side casings. You can also find kits for installing butted casings that include corner and plinth blocks. Be sure to buy a kit that matches your door width.

The side casings in the kit are cut long; trim them to length to fit your door.

Window stools, aprons & sills

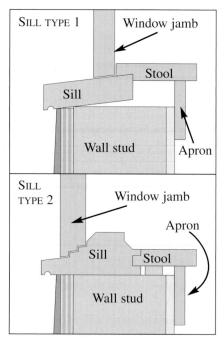

Premilled window stool moldings come in a number of profiles and styles (left photo). Before choosing, inspect the window sill. If it is beveled, you'll want to choose a stool that has a wide, angled rabbet groove on the underside, as with the upper two types pictured to the left.

The rabbet fits over the edge of the sill, following its angle to create a level sill surface. If your sill has a groove in the edge, look for a stool with a premilled tongue to fit into the groove. If the sill is square and level, you can use plain stool molding.

SILL TYPE 1
Window jamb
Stool
Sill
Wall stud
Apron

SILL TYPE 2
Window jamb
Apron
Sill
Stool
Wall stud

The window sill generally comes attached to new window units. But it's up to you to decide how to treat the stool and the apron on the interior side of the house. Choose stool stock that's profiled to fit cleanly over the sill.

Door casing schemes

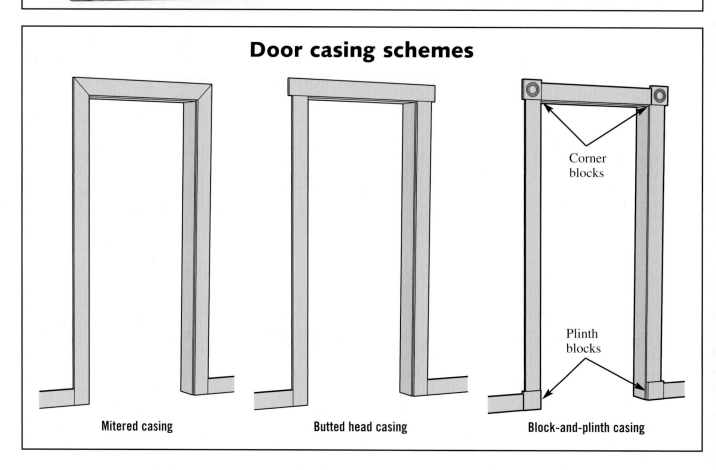

Mitered casing

Butted head casing

Block-and-plinth casing

Corner blocks

Plinth blocks

Window casing schemes

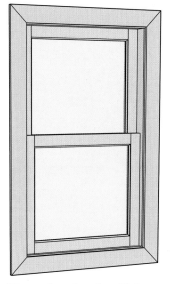

"Picture-frame" casing with four mitered corners.

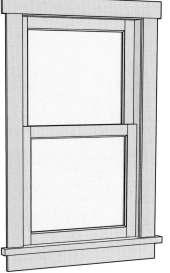

Butted casing with head casing overhang, apron and stool.

Mitered casing with apron and stool.

Calculating mitered casing length

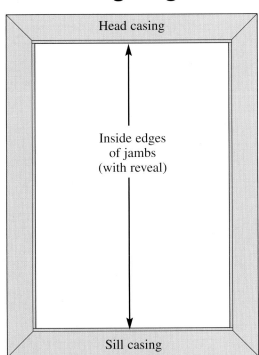

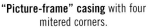
Head casing

Inside edges of jambs (with reveal)

Sill casing

The surest way to get a good fit with mitered case molding is to position each piece on the opening, measure for the reveal from the inside edges of the jambs, then transfer the positions onto the workpiece. But if you need or prefer to measure and mark, simply measure the distance between the inside edges of opposing jambs then add twice the reveal width to get the short measurement on mitered casing.

Brickmold

Brickmold is essentially exterior trim for windows and doors. It is installed between the cut ends of the house siding at the edge of the widow opening and the outside edges of the window jambs. Like casing, you can buy it in kits for doors. Be sure to caulk the joints well after installation.

Door Hardware

Once you've gone through the effort of carefully completing the installation of your new door, the final step is to install the door hardware, including a knobset or lockset, a deadbolt lock for exterior doors, and any miscellaneous types of hardware for specific applications. Installing the hardware carefully and correctly has a direct impact on how successfully the new door fulfills its purpose, as does making good choices when selecting the hardware to be installed.

Just as doors are designed either for interior or exterior purposes, most door hardware is better suited for use with one type or the other.

Interior door hardware. There are two basic types of interior door locksets (the assembly including the doorknobs, the cylinder connecting them inside the door, the latch bolt, and the strike plate for the latch bolt). The most common is the passage lock. This lock has a knob on each side of the door and is used where privacy is not a concern. The second type of interior door lock is the privacy lock. With a locking knob operated by a thumbscrew or push button on the inside knob, the privacy lock is used on bathroom doors and sometimes on bedroom doors. Supplementary locks, like deadbolts, generally aren't used on interior doors.

Because most interior doors have a great enough swing radius to contact the wall when fully opened, a door bumper

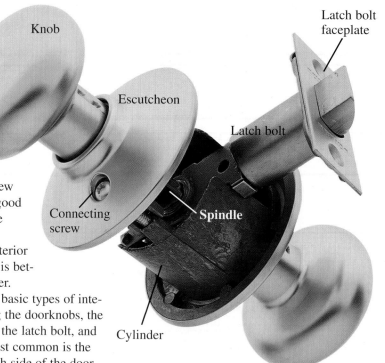

Most door locksets sold today have similar working components. The knobs (which may or may not contain a locking mechanism) are drawn together by a pair of connecting screws that run through the cylinder. Inside the cylinder, a spindle turned by each knob is connected to a latch bolt. The latch bolt extends and retracts according to which direction the knob is turned, causing it to engage or disengage from the recess in the strike plate mounted in the door jamb.

Deadbolt locks

Prehung exterior doors today usually come predrilled to accept a deadbolt lock above the lockset. Deadbolts provide significantly more protection against door kick-ins than the lockset because the lock bolt extends deeper into the door jamb. If any of your exterior doors currently are not fitted with a deadbolt, adding one would be a wise security measure.

Double-keyed deadbolt   Single-keyed deadbolt

Deadbolt locks most commonly have a keyed knob on the exterior side and a thumb-turned lock on the interior knob (called a single-keyed deadbolt). But double-keyed deadbolts are becoming increasingly popular, especially on doors with light panels, to prevent intruders from reaching in and unlocking the deadbolt.

Key coding information lets you buy a lockset and deadbolt that can be operated with the same key. You can also have locks re-keyed to match by a locksmith.

The door hardware sections at most building centers are large, but as you examine the products closely, you'll find that there are really only a handful of choices that will work for your door. This is especially true of doorknobs and plates, the bulk of which come in only two basic shapes and three metal choices: brass, antique brass or brushed steel. If you're looking for something a little fancier or for hardware to match your existing older door hardware, check at a building materials salvage yard or locate a reproduction hardware catalog (you can usually find several of these catalogs, along with toll-free telephone numbers, listed in home renovation magazines).

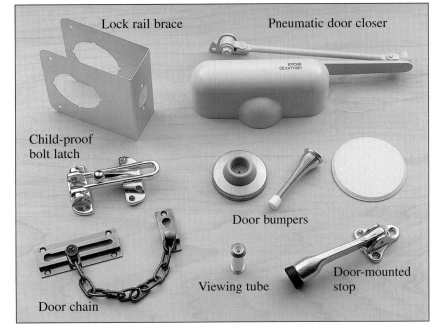

Miscellaneous door hardware is installed on an as-needed basis, usually to address security concerns or to protect the door and the adjoining wall from damage.

Door locksets come in three basic types: passage locksets (sometimes called knobsets) commonly found on hall, closet and bedroom doors; privacy locksets installed on bathroom and bedroom doors; and keyed entry locksets, used mostly on exterior doors.

is normally mounted to the baseboard in the area where the door meets the wall. Hinges are preinstalled on prehung interior doors. When installing a non-prehung door, two 2½- or 3-in. butt hinges with removable hinge pins typically are used.

Exterior door hardware. Locksets for exterior doors generally are somewhat heavier than those for interior doors, and they always include a keyed lock. Deadbolt locks are installed as a standard practice today. Other types of hardware for exterior doors include door chains, door closers, viewing tubes, door stops or bumpers, and various security enhancement devices. Exterior doors generally are hung on three 2½- or 3-in. butt hinges of slightly heavier gauge than interior door hinges. Exterior doors also require a threshold that creates a seal between the sill plate on your house and the bottom of the door. Because they endure so much wear, thresholds require occasional replacement (if not the entire unit, then at least the rubber threshold top strip).

Specialty door hardware. Less common door types, like sliding patio doors and pocket doors, require specialty hardware.

Photo courtesy of Society Brass

Lever-style locksets are a viable alternative to the traditional doorknob. In fact, if you've ever had problems with arthritis or general hand pain, or if you're one of those people who never seems to be entering or leaving the house without an armload of stuff, then a lever would be an excellent option for you.

Weatherstripping & door sweeps (See photos, next page)

1. Tubular gasket

Inexpensive and easily installed with staples, brads or self-adhesive backing strips. Widely adaptable: Can be used to completely seal double-hung and casement windows, or in tandem with other types of window and door weatherstripping. Moderate durability and visible when installed. Type shown (next page) is sponge-filled rubber.

2. Magnetic gasket

Used to seal gaps between jambs and steel doors. A rigid flange is inserted into a groove in the door stop of the jamb. When the door is closed, a magnetic strip in the gasket draws the gasket material flush against the non-hinge edge of the door. Commonly preinstalled at the factory on pre-hung steel exterior doors, can also be installed as a retrofit item. Based on the same principle as refrigerator or freezer door gaskets.

3. Metal-backed vinyl gasket strips

Inexpensive and installed with brads in same locations as tubular gasket. Like tubular gasket, metal-backed strips are also visible when installed, but are a bit more durable and have a neater finished appearance on exposed surfaces. However, they're harder to align and will kink if you overdrive the brads.

4. Adhesive-backed foam compression strip

Inexpensive, easy to install, comes in various widths, usually sold in rolls. Low durability compared to other types. Apply only to tops and bottoms of double-hung sashes or to the insides of casement windows where the sash meets the frame. Adhesive backed foam is self-sticking and water resistant, but is often hard to remove when it wears out. Use foam strips only in places where other weatherstripping won't work—and plan on replacing them every year or two. Product shown is sold in double-wide strips that can be split along the seam for use in tight spots.

5. Metal-backed felt gasket

Another fairly inexpensive product tacked to door and window stops. The felt resists damage from moving windows and doors fairly well, and is strengthened by a reinforcing metal spine that is kerfed to resist kinking. Sold in rolls and attached with brads or tacks. Felt may harden or disintegrate from prolonged exposure to moisture.

6. Spring metal stripping

More expensive and difficult to install than other types, but much more durable and provides an excellent seal. Fits inside window channels or frames, making it invisible when windows are closed. Also suitable for door jambs. Available in brass, bronzed-anodized aluminum or stainless steel. Basic profiles include tension spring metal (shown in photo, next page) and V-strips. Pre-drilled guide holes for brads lessen chance of kinking during installation.

7. Tack-on door sweep

Attached to bottom of interior door face to seal gap between door and threshold. Sweep is made of vinyl (shown in photo, next page) or polyester bristles. Bristles work well with uneven floors.

8. Garage door seal

Wide vinyl strip with profiled edges that fits into tracks on the bottom edge of a garage door.

9. Adjustable door shoe

A two-part door shoe that is composed of two L-shaped members that snap together at the bottom to form a "U" shape. The female "L" is fitted with flexible vinyl strips that seal the door threshold gap. Popular for storm doors because it can be adjusted to fit doors of non-standard thickness.

10. "Automatic" door sweep

A spring-loaded mechanical sweep designed to attach to the exterior side of a door. When the door is opened, the sweep lifts up to clear the threshold. When the door is closed, a pivoting mechanism contacts a strike on the door jamb or stop, causing the sweep to snap down and seal the threshold gap. A good choice for doors with high exposure to rain or snow.

11. Door shoe

A U-shaped accessory that fits over the bottom edge of a door to create a seal between the door and threshold. Most have an integral drip-edge flange on the exterior side.

Common weatherstripping types
(See Chart, previous page)

1. Tubular gasket (sponge-filled rubber)

2. Magnetic gasket (jamb seal for steel doors)

3. Metal-backed vinyl gasket strips

4. Adhesive backed foam compression strip

5. Metal-backed felt gasket

6. Spring metal stripping (brass)

7. Tack-on door sweep (vinyl)

8. Garage door seal

9. Adjustable door shoe (common for storm doors)

10. "Automatic" door sweep (two parts)

11. Door shoe with integral drip edge

ROOFS & ROOF SYSTEMS

The roofing system of a structure is composed of many parts that work together to protect the interior of the structure. The sub-systems that make up the whole are: the roof deck and support structure; the roof covering; the flashing; the cornice and soffit system; the gutter system; and the attic ventilation system (See "Insulation", pages 128 to 143).

Roof Structure. The structure of a roof is composed of the framing lumber, including beams, rafters and sheathing. See appropriate chapters.

Roof Coverings. The first major component of the roof is the covering. It is usually composed of an underlayment of ice guard and building paper (roofing felt) topped off with a durable covering to shed water. Ice and water guard is heavy-duty adhesive-backed membrane. It comes in 3 ft. wide rolls, usually 36 ft. long, and is bonded directly to the roof decking over the

Preparing the roof deck

Illustration courtesy of GAF

Ice guard is a self-adhesive membrane, sometimes with a granular surface, that is installed as the first two courses of underlayment to help prevent ice dam damage. See page 109.

Illustration courtesy of GAF

Building paper, also called roofing felt or tar paper, is installed as an underlayment for most roof coverings. It comes in light-duty 15# thickness and heavier 30# weight. If it is installed carefully, you can use the printed lines for shingle alignment.

Drip edge molding is a metal (usually aluminum) strip that's nailed along the bottom edge (the eave edge) of the roof prior to installing ice guard and building paper. It should also be attached to the rake edges of the roof after the underlayment is in place.

Parts of a Roof System

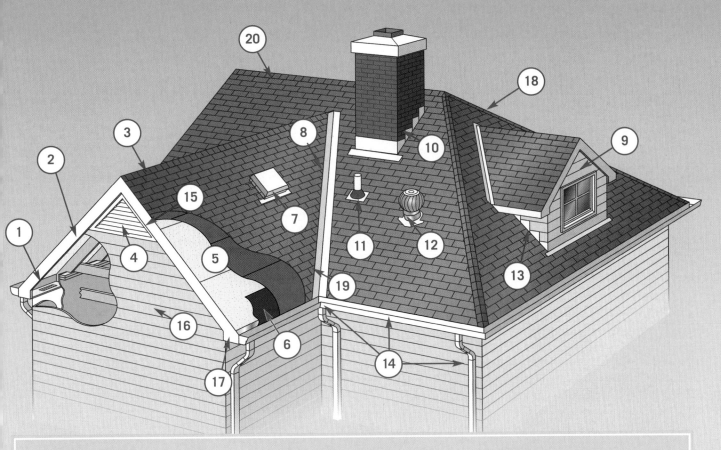

1	**Soffit ventilation system**	7	**Slant-back roof vent**	14	**Gutter/downspout system**
2	**Fascia**	8	**Valley flashing**	15	**Rake**
3	**Ridge cap shingles**	9	**Dormer**	16	**Gable end**
4	**Gable vent**	10	**Counterflashing**	17	**Eave / Cornice**
5	**Roof covering (decking, building paper, shingles)**	11	**DWV stack with boot**	18	**Hip Roof**
6	**Ice guard underlayment (2 courses)**	12	**Turbine style roof vent**	19	**Valley Roof**
		13	**Step flashing**	20	**Ridge**

eave area of the roof (usually two overlapping courses are installed). Because it bonds to the deck, the ice guard forms a barrier that prevents ice from backing up underneath the shingles if ice dames form. It is required in colder climates. It is also installed in potential problem areas, such as around chimneys, valleys and dormers. See page 109.

Most roof coverings require an underlayment of building paper. NOTE: You'll need to install metal drip edge molding at the low edge of the roof deck before you begin installing the underlayment. Drip edge should also be installed along the sloped (rake) edges after the underlayment goes down. Building paper acts as a waterproof barrier between the sheathing and the roofing material. It comes in rolls of 15 lb. and 30 lb. densities and is stapled to the sheathing overlapping by at least two inches from course to course and 4 inches at end seams. It is important that it is applied to clean, dry sheathing. Consult with your local building inspec-

tor about the weight of felt that should be used for the type of covering you chose.

The underlayment is covered with the roof covering layer. Roof-covering options include: fiberglass or asphalt shingles, asphalt roll roofing, metal (corrugated panels, standing seam or metal shingles), clay tiles, wood shingles or shakes, fiber cement and concrete tiles, natural slate, rubber and built-up hot tar.

(Continued on page 110)

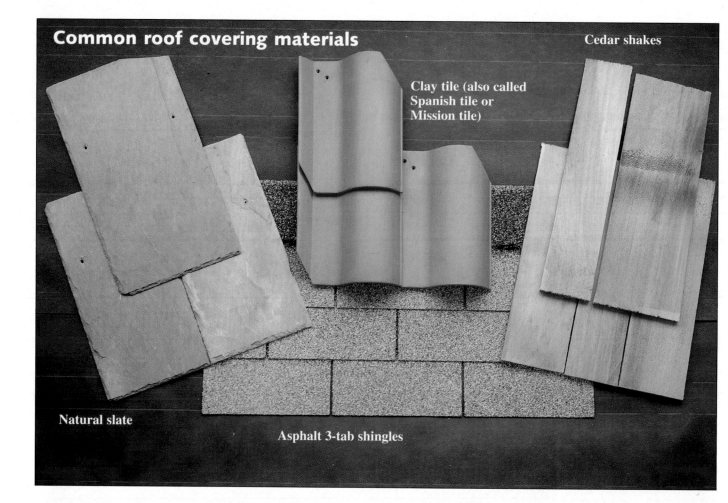

Common roof covering materials

Cedar shakes

Clay tile (also called Spanish tile or Mission tile)

Natural slate

Asphalt 3-tab shingles

Choosing roof covering types

Roofing Type	Minimum slope	Life Expectancy	Cost	Weight (lb./100 ft^2)
Shingles (asphalt/fiberglass)	4:12	15-25 years	Low	approx. 250
Single-coverage roll roofing	2:12	10-15 years	Low	approx. 100
Double-coverage roll roofing	1:12	15 years	Low	approx 150
Wood shake	3:12	50 years	Med./High	approx. 300
Wood shingle	3:12	25-30 years	Med.	approx. 150
Fiber cement	4:12	50 years	Med./High	600 to 1000
Clay tile	4:12	100 years	High	800 to 1200
Slate tile	5:12	100 years	High	750 to 2500
Built-up	0:12	20 years	Med.	approx. 200
Metal panels (corrugated)	3:12	40 years	Low	approx. 50
Standing seam metal	3:12	50 years	Med.	approx. 75
Metal shingles	4:12	50 years	Med./High	30 to 50
Rubber (EPDM)*	0:12	20-30 years	Med.	30 to 50

*Weight does not include rigid insulation panels used in some applications

Roof coverings & underlayment

Ice guard underlayment is installed along the edges of roofs that cover heated areas, as well as in the "trouble areas" indicated above. It is used mostly in colder climates.

Roofing Materials

Roof cement is the glue that holds most roof repairs together. Known by many names in the building trades (including "Blackjack" after a popular brand of roof cement), it is sold in tube cartridges as well as in quart, gallon and 5-gallon cans. While the cans are more economical, they're considerably messier for most jobs. Building paper (15# and 30#) and galvanized roofing nails (with and without rubber gaskets) conclude the list of materials you'll need for many roof repairs.

Aluminum roofing nails (for use with aluminum flashing)

WET-R-DRI
gardner
ASPHALT CORPORATION
WET SURFACE
ROOF CEMENT

SPECIALLY FORMULATED FOR EMERGENCY REPAIRS ON WET OR DRY SURFACES
Meets
ASTM D 4586
ASTM D 3409-81
CAUTION! COMBUSTIBLE
See other cautions on back panel
NET CONTENTS 11 FLUID OZ.

Anatomy of an asphalt or fiberglass shingle roof

Decking

15# building paper

Ice guard membrane

3-tab field shingles

Drip edge molding

Starter strip

Three-tab asphalt or fiberglass shingles are installed at many times the rate of all other residential roofcoverings combined. They are inexpensive, easy for do-it-yourselfers to work with, and offer a good range of styles and colors. Your roof must have a slope of at least 4:12 to be roofed with 3-tabs. The first course (the starter course) is laid upside-down, with the slotted tabs removed or pointing toward the roof ridge. The first full course is overlaid on the starter course, tabs pointing down and overhanging the edge of the drip edge very slightly. Successive courses are laid in a staggered pattern so vertical seams between tabs do not align. At the ridge, individual tabs are cut off the 3-tab shingles and laid in an overlapping pattern (See photo, right).

Estimating shingle quantities

Slope	Mult. Factor
3:12	1.031
4:12	1.054
5:12	1.083
6:12	1.118
7:12	1.158
8:12	1.202
9:12	1.25
10:12	1.302
11:12	1.357
12:12	1.413

Roof type	Waste	Mult. factor
Gable roof	10%	1.1
Gable with valley	15%	1.15
Hip Roof	20%	1.2
Hip with valley	25%	1.25

Since asphalt three-tab and shake-style shingles overlap, estimating their coverage may be difficult. The following information and tables should help you assess the coverage while allowing for slope and waste.

First, find the area to be covered in square feet (length times width). Then, multiply it by the correct slope factor from the table shown to the left. This will give you the sloped roof area. Take that number and multiply that times the waste/starter strip factor for the type of roof structure (See lower left chart). Finally, divide this amount by 100 to get the total number of squares you will need. Shingles are measured in groups called squares. One square is equal to 100 square feet. Normally, three bundles of shingles equals one square. If you're planning to hand-nail the shingles, you'll need approximately two pounds of roofing nails for each square (100 ft.²) of shingled roof.

(Continued from page 107)

ASPHALT & FIBERGLASS ROOFCOVERINGS

Shingles. Asphalt and fiberglass shingles are by far the most popular roof covering materials. Most asphalt shingles sold today are "3-tab" shingles, measuring 12 × 36 in. The bottom half is slotted to create three 12-in. tabs. An adhesive strip on the backside helps to secure the shingle to the building paper layer between the shingles and the roof decking. The mineral granule coatings come in a wide variety of colors, although selections at lumberyards and home improvement centers will be limited and tend to change regularly in accordance with design trends. You'll have better luck with a local roofing supply house.

Fiberglass vs. asphalt. The main difference between asphalt shingles and fiberglass shingles is in fire resistance and cost. Fiberglass is more resistant to fire, but costs more. Asphalt shingles also are more affected by air temperature. Choose a moderately warm day (60 to 75°F) to install or repair asphalt shingles. If it's too cold, the shingles will be brittle and subject to damage; if it's too hot, the shingles will be too soft to work with and the original shingles, as well as vulnerable to scuffing and other forms of damage (plus, you really shouldn't be up on a roof on a hot day anyway).

Asphalt/fiberglass shingles have an average lifespan of 15 to 25 years, which most manufacturers will back up with a warranty. They are sold in bundles that will cover about 1/3 of a square (100 square feet of roof area). They may be installed only on roofs that have a slope of 4:12 (4 inches of vertical drop per 12 inches of horizontal run) or steeper. They are usually installed over an underlayment of 15# building paper.

Re-roofing. It is allowable by most building codes to install a fresh layer of shingles directly over an old shingle roof. As a general rule, however, it's a better idea to remove the old roof covering so you can inspect the roof deck for any damage. A roof-over also can trap a lot of moisture.

Roll roofing. Roll roofing is low cost and is mainly used on low-slope roofs. The reason it can be used on low-slopes is that the seams and laps are sealed with plastic roof cement. Roll roofing has a relatively low lifespan of about 10 years, but it also low in cost and can be installed quickly. Color choices are very limited. It is not recommended that asphalt roll roofing be installed in temperatures lower than 45°F.

There are two rather different methods for installing roll roofing, each using a slightly different roll product:

Single coverage. A single-coverage roll-roofing roof is installed with rolls that have a full granular mineral surface. The courses are overlapped by about two or three inches and bonded together at the seams with cold-set adhesive. The courses can be installed so the roofing nails are exposed or so they are concealed by the course overlapping from above. A single-coverage roof can only be installed on a roof with a slope no shallower than 2:12.

NOTE: If installing a single-coverage roof over a heated room in a colder climate, you're still required to install self-adhesive ice guard membrane at the lower roof area—see page 109.

Double coverage. Double-coverage roll roofing has a 17-in.-wide strip of of mineral surface. The other 19 in. strip (called the selvedge) has no granular surface. Double-coverage roofs can be installed on roofs with a slope as shallow as 1:12. Each course of roofing is fully bonded to the selvedge area of the course below it, and also fully bonded to the roof deck in the nonoverlapping area. Normally, cold-set adhesive is used to bond the roofcovering. Sold in 5-gallon drums, the cold-set is applied with a long-handled, stiff-bristled broom. The starter course of a double-coverage roof is made with the trimmed-off selvedge—reserve the mineral surface you trim off for the last course of the roof.

Single-coverage roll roofing

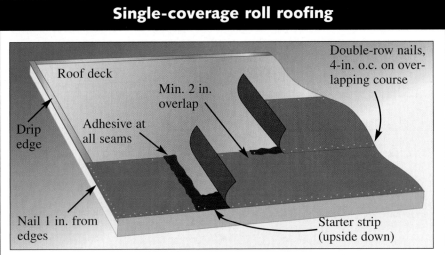

Exposed nail roll roofing installations can be installed quickly, but are slightly more prone to leakage. Use rubber-gasket roofing nails or cover all nailheads with roof cement.

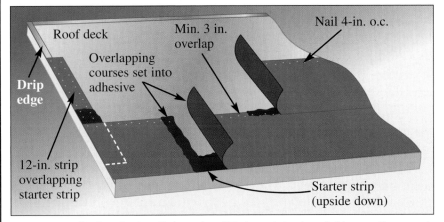

Concealed nail roll roofing installations take a little longer to lay down, but because the exposed roof covering is unbroken by nails, they are less likely to leak.

Double-coverage roll roofing (selvedge)

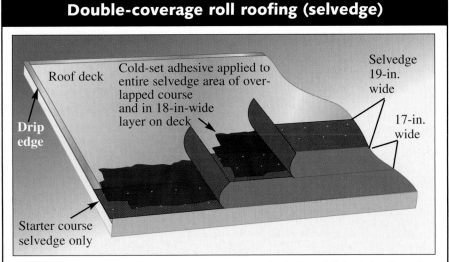

Double-coverage roll roofing installations (also called "selvedge") are fully bonded to the roof deck, so they can be applied on roofs with a slope as shallow as 1:12. Double-coverage roof coverings have a mineral surface on a 17-in-wide section of the roll, with the remaining 19 in. left unsurfaced. As each course is installed, cold-set adhesive is mopped onto the exposed selvedge area and onto an 18-in-wide swath of the roof deck directly above the course to be overlapped.

Anatomy of a wood shake roof

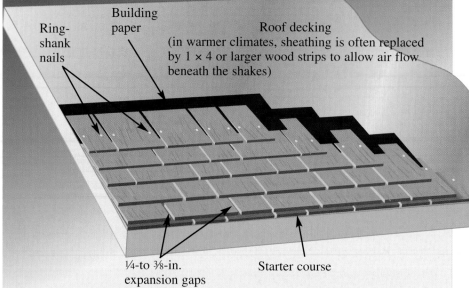

Ring-shank nails

Building paper

Roof decking
(in warmer climates, sheathing is often replaced by 1 × 4 or larger wood strips to allow air flow beneath the shakes)

¼-to ⅜-in. expansion gaps

Starter course

Wood shakes (usually cedar) are attached in straight rows using ring-shank nails. The starter course is a double-thick row of shakes that establishes the bevel (in some climates, metal flashing is required over the front edge of the starter course). Individual shakes should be staggered from row to row with a ¼- to ⅜-in. expansion gap between shakes. A strip of building paper is layered into each course.

Shakes or shingles?

The terms "shakes" and "shingles" are often used interchangeably because the products are quite similar and the techniques used to install and repair them are identical. The difference (which you should be aware of when purchasing replacement materials) is that shingles are sawn to size so they have more uniform dimensions and are generally smaller and smoother on the surfaces and edges. Shakes are split to rough size, making them less regular in appearance. Both can be purchased at most building centers and lumberyards.

Metal Shingles

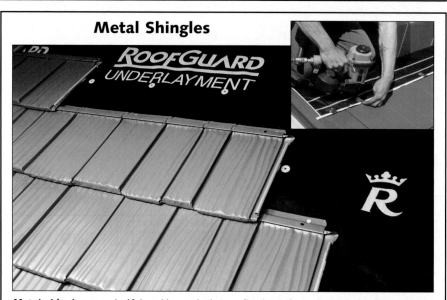

Metal shingles come in 40-in.-wide panels that are fitted together and attached to the roof deck with clips. They require a minimum of a 4:12 slope. Professional installation is recommended.

WOOD SHAKES & SHINGLES

Wood can also be an effective roofing material, typically in the form of cedar shakes and shingles. These terms are commonly interchanged, but there are differences between the two. Cedar shakes do not taper from end to end and are usually more rough and irregular in shape. Cedar shingles taper and are cut to standard lengths of 16, 18 or 24 inches. Shingles are also more common, due to their ease of manufacturing and lower cost. Due to their irregularity, shakes require a layer of roofing felt between each course, whereas shingles have the underlayment applied directly to the entire surface prior to installation.

METAL ROOFS

Metal roofing is a traditional roof-covering that is enjoying revived popularity as new metal products are developed. Historically, a metal roof, often made of copper, has been considered one of the premium materials—and this has always been reflected in the cost. Even today, a fabricated copper roof with standing ridge seams will costs tens of thousands of dollars. But manufactured metal roof products are now available, including corrugated panels and metal shingles, at a much more affordable price. And many products can be installed easily by a do-it-yourselfer. Nevertheless, some metal roofing products (most notably, fabricated, standing seam roofs) should only be installed by professionals.

Corrugated metal roof panels. Used for generations on agricultural buildings, these familiar products can also be used to fashion a long-lasting, attractive, low-cost and lightweight residential roof that's easy to install. The panels are typically about 3 ft. wide and start at 10 ft. in length. They are attached to solid decking or to purlins in the rafters with pole barn screws fitted with rubber gaskets.

CONCRETE & NATURAL SLATE TILES

Roof tiles are also made of concrete or fiber-reinforced cement, and natural stone.

Concrete tiles are precast to form interlocking flanges and are nailed to 1 × 2 battens. Concrete tiles have longevity, due to their composition, but are medium to high in cost and weight, so make sure that your wallet and structure can support them. Installing them is not generally considered a do-it-yourself project, as they can be purchased only through certified installation contractors.

Slate tiles are another roofing product that has been in use for centuries; and can potentially last for centuries as well. They offer a pleasing old-time look at a premium price. They require a minimum slope of 5:12 to avoid wind-driven rain and snow buildup. Slate tiles are installed in much the same way as cedar shingles, but can weigh 3 to 10 times as much per 100 square feet.

Anatomy of a slate tile roof

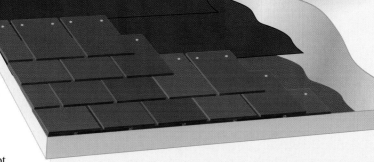

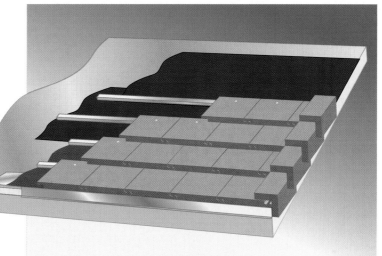

Slate tiles (left). The installation methods for slate tiles are similar to those for wood shake roofs. The main difference is that the tiles are heavy and usually need to be supported by a temporary nailer as they're attached by driving non-corrosive nails through pre-drilled guide holes in the tiles.

Concrete tiles (left) combine the appearance of slate or wood with high durability, fire resistance and the ease of installation that comes with manufactured products. Most are cast with ridged, interlocking flanges so they fit together automatically. They also have a cast lip on the top of the reverse side that fits snugly over 1 × 2 battens, to which the tiles are nailed with non-corrosive nails.

Anatomy of a clay tile roof

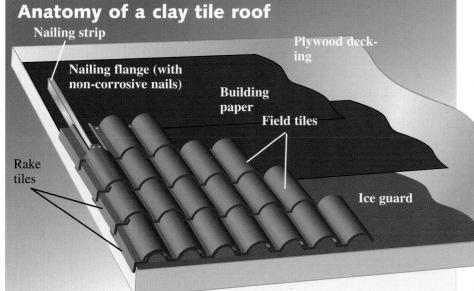

Nailing strip
Nailing flange (with non-corrosive nails)
Plywood decking
Building paper
Field tiles
Ice guard
Rake tiles

Clay roof tiles have a half-round profile attached to a flat nailing flange that is overlapped by the next tile in line. Specially shaped tiles are installed at the rake edge of the roof, as well as on ridges, hips and eaves. Unlike most roof coverings, they are installed in linear rows, normally without staggered joints.

CLAY TILES

Clay tile, also known as Spanish or Mission tile, depending on what style they are, is one of the oldest types of roofing material. It has been around for thousands of years and it is still widely used in many areas of the country and the world. It is not recommended that DIYers install tile themselves, due to the fragility of the units. If they are properly installed by a professional, they could last over 100 years, but the cost will be on the high end. Clay tiles are also one of the heaviest roof coverings ranging between 1-4,000 lbs. per 100 square feet, so make sure that your roof framing can support the weight before selecting them.

FLAT ROOFS

For flat roofs, you have basically two roofing choices: a traditional built-up roof formed from building paper, hot tar and aggregate; or a single membrane roof that is either bonded to the roof deck or held in place over insulation boards with a layer of loose rock. Although you'll find that non-rubber membrane products do exist, the only single membrane product you're likely to run into at a building center is EPDM rubber. Generally sold in precut sheets (10 × 20 ft. is the smallest, in most cases), the do-it-yourself version of the commercial rubber roof is seamed with special tape (as compared to commercial rubber roofs, which are glued together at the seams. The DIY rubber roofs are set into a latex adhesive on top of rigid foam insulation or another smooth surface. The perimeter is fastened with a termination strip and rubber caulk.

Most older flat roofs (or nearly flat roofs) are made of alternating layers of building felt and hot-mopped asphalt or coal tar, topped with gravel or crushed rock. Called "built-up roofs" or a variety of other names, such as "tar-and-gravel", they are relatively "low-tech" roofs that are usually reliable and are easy to maintain. The actual installation of a new built-up roof should be done by a contractor.

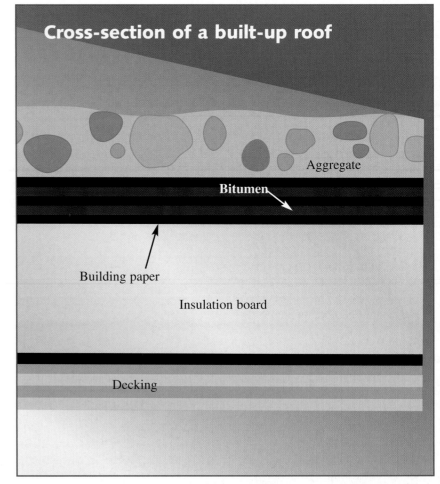

Cross-section of a built-up roof

Aggregate

Bitumen

Building paper

Insulation board

Decking

A built-up roof is a very popular option for flat roofs, but owing to the mess, heavy labor and the irreparable problems that can result from incorrect installation, you're best off leaving the installation to a professional roofing contractor.

Safety tips

✔ Set up shop before you start. Store materials so they're convenient to the worksite, yet out of heavy traffic areas. If you need to store materials outdoors, keep a tarp handy in case it rains. Also, keep a wheelbarrow nearby to remove trash from the site as you work—don't allow nails, old shingles and other debris to accumulate on the ground, as they pose a safety hazard. Set up a work table by laying a half-sheet of plywood over a pair of saw horses. Use the table to store tools and other small items off the ground so they don't get wet and are easy to locate.

✔ Keep an eye on the weather. Do not work during stormy weather or in damp conditions. Stay off the roof if it is wet or if the outdoor temperature is too hot or too cold. Do not take on large jobs if you expect a sudden change in the weather.

✔ Dress for the occasion. Basic safety gear includes heavy work gloves for handling materials, rubber gloves when working with cleaners and solvents, eye protection, a respirator or particle mask, full-length pants and long sleeved shirt. When working on the roof, wear knee pads and soft-soled shoes or sneakers. These provide good traction, flexibility and ankle support when working on slopes. Wear a back brace when lifting heavy materials.

✔ When working on the roof, fasten extension cords to the ladder or at the eaves; the weight of a dangling cord can easily pull it (and the tool it's attached to) off the roof. You can buy a fastening device that permanently attaches to a ladder at most hardware stores. Also, pay special attention to the cord location at all times to avoid tripping over it, especially when working off a ladder. A better option is to use cordless tools in high places.

✔ **Stay clear of power lines, electrical service entrances and electrical masts. Use wood or fiberglass ladders instead of metal whenever possible, and fit all ladders with rubber or plastic insulated handles. Do not pressure-wash or hose down surfaces near electrical cables or fixtures.**

FLASHING

Flashing is installed to create leakproof barriers to water in transition spots of a roof, generally between different building materials.

There are five main types of flashing. They are preformed valley flashing, drip edge, step flashing, roll flashing and vent pipe boot. They are usually made of aluminum or galvanized steel. All flashing should be installed with rubber gasket roofing nails, which help seal out moisture, along with a coat of fiber roof cement or silicone.

Common flashing materials

Valley flashing   **Drip edge**   **Step flashing**   **Roll flashing**

Flashing can be obtained either in prefabricated units, as with step flashing or valley flashing, or in rolls of galvanized steel or aluminum that you fashion into flashing yourself. The most common materials you'll need when flashing a roof are:

Valley flashing: Preformed valley flashing has a ridge bent into the center to help channel the water. See page 116.
Drip edge: A "T-shaped" flashing that is used along the eave to support to the bottom course of the covering and prevent water from backing up underneath it. It also sheds water away from the fascia.
Step flashing: Transitions between shingles and siding or brickwork on a slope. See below.
Roll flashing: Commonly used to customize a part or repair an area, such as a cricket for chimney flashing. By bending and shaping roll flashing, you can meet many of the needs of your roof system.

Step flashing are "L-shaped" pieces of galvanized metal or aluminum that are interwoven and overlapped with shingles to prevent water seepage. They are used wherever a roof plane meets a vertical wall or surface, such as chimneys, dormers and skylights.

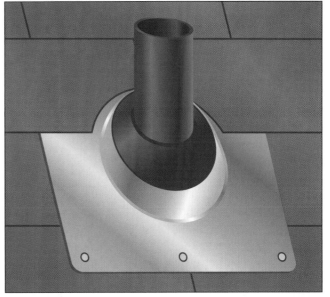

Vent pipe boots are used to seal the area around plumbing and natural gas vent pipes. There are two kinds that can be used for plumbing pipes and they include one with a base and neoprene collar and one with a base and galvanized steel and lead cap. The latter are all but extinct, due to the versatility and ease with which the boot with the neoprene collar installs. The boots that are used with gas heating pipes are all galvanized steel, due to the heat the pipes produce. Once installed, the joint must be sealed with a galvanized water-shed collar, heat-resistant caulk and foil tape.

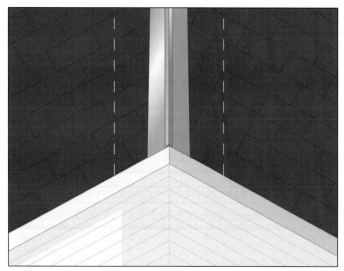

Valley flashing is used on roofs that have a hip-valley combination. Because of the large amount of water they shed, they must be durable. That is why they have a "v-shaped" spine. Valley flashing comes in 10 ft. sections and should be overlapped end to end at lest 4 in. by the covering. You may bend your own valley flashing from roll flashing if you prefer. Some roofcoverings, such as roll roofing, are typically installed with granular roofing strips in the roof valleys.

Lap or base flashing is formed from roll flashing and used to transition between a vertical surface and a roof that are parallel to one another (for example, when flashing the joint between a shed-style roof and an adjoining wall). Bend the roll flashing into an L shape, slip the upper part underneath the siding as far as you can, then attach the bottom to the roof with rubber gasket roofing nails and roof cement.

Bending Flashing

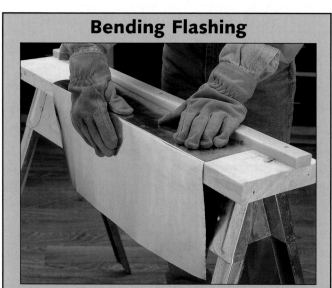

Fabricating roll flashing into usable sizes and shapes is an easy alternative to spending a lot of money on preformed flashings or having flashing custom bent at a metal shop. While there are many "tricks of the trade" offering clever ways to make your own flashing, all you really need to set up an on-site "flashing fabrication center" is a sawhorse with a straightedge attached parallel to one side of the sawhorse top so the distance to the parallel edge of the sawhorse equals the planned width of the flashing. Crease the roll flashing so it follows the edge of the sawhorse top and forms a 90° bend.

The Theory of Flashing

Understanding how flashing works will take you a long way toward working effectively with it. Flashing is all about making transitions between two different types of building materials. To perform this job, it must have the ability to move without leaving the transition area exposed. When temperatures and humidity levels change, building materials expand and contract at different rates. Because of this fact of nature, roof decking that butts up flush to a chimney chase one day can shift away the next, creating a gap that could allow moisture and pests into your home. Even though metal also expands and contracts at its own pace, a good flashing system will continue to cover the transition area whether there is a gap or not. In this example, the flashing works because it is a two-part system. Metal counter flashing embedded in the mortar joints of the chimney is folded down over the top of metal step flashing that is woven into and over the shingles. The two parts are not connected, except by a layer of elastic roof cement, and therefore they can move independently. As you work to install or repair flashing, keep this basic relationship in mind: Each piece of flashing can only be permanently fastened to one of the materials it

How to retrofit continuous ridge vent

1 Use a circular saw to cut through the roof-covering and sheathing 2 in. out from each side of the roof ridge.

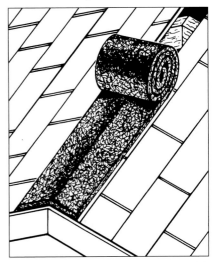

2 Roll fibrous, continuous ridge vent material out over the ridge opening, butting and caulking any joints.

Continuous ridge vents run all the way along the ridge of a roof, allowing for even, effective air outtake. There are several products available on the market for creating a ridge vent, including rigid, covered sections that fit over the open ridge and often do not need to be shingled. One very popular product, shown here, is simply a roll of fibrous material that is loose enough to allow air to pass through it easily. It is rolled out over the open ridge, then covered with ridge shingles, leaving a gap between the shingles and the rest of the roof through which air can escape.

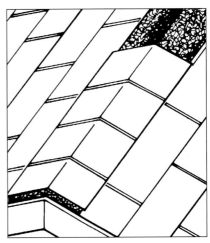

3 Cover the continuous ridge vent material with specially-attached ridge-vent shingles that match the field shingles on your roof.

ROOF VENTILATION

Venting a roof system is very important. It not only reduces heat in the attic area in summer, which increases the load on the air conditioner and could buckle the shingles, but helps prevent other problems like condensation and ice dams which occur in winter. Therefore proper ventilation is needed year-round to improve the efficiency of your home and protect the roof system.

The various types of vents and accessories are found in the chapter on insulation (See pages 128 to 143) as well as how much ventilation you need per square feet of space. An exception is the information on continuous ridge venting found on this page. Although a continuous ridge vent can be installed as a retrofit project, as shown in the sequence on the right of this page, it is generally installed during new construction or re-roofing.

SOFFIT SYSTEM TYPES

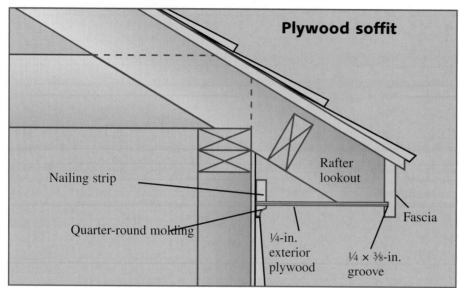

Plywood soffit

Nailing strip

Quarter-round molding

Rafter lookout

Fascia

¼-in. exterior plywood

¼ × ⅜-in. groove

Plywood soffit systems. This very common soffit system type is inexpensive and easy to install. In some cases, the inside faces of the fascia boards are cut with a ¼ × ⅜-in. deep groove near the bottom to accept the outer edges of the plywood soffit panels. The inner edges of the panels are generally attached to nailing strips mounted to the wall and quarter-round molding is attached from below to cover any gaps between the soffit and the wall. In some cases, the front edge of the soffit panel is attached to the rafter lookout, in which case quarter-round molding is usually added in front as well as in back.

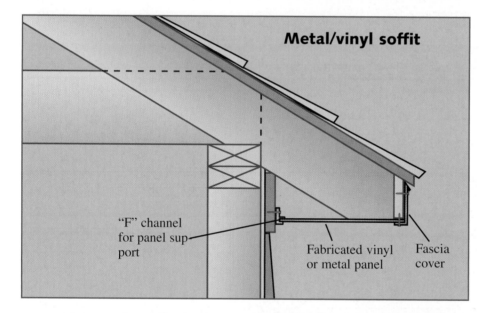

Metal/vinyl soffit

"F" channel for panel support

Fabricated vinyl or metal panel

Fascia cover

Metal or vinyl soffit systems. Installed most often on homes with metal or vinyl siding, this type of soffit system is made up of interlocking fabricated panels that fit into channels in the matching molding and trim pieces (occasionally, metal or vinyl systems are installed on homes with wood or stucco siding as well). A fascia cover with a support channel on the inner face is attached to the fascia board, and an "F" style channel is attached to the wall. The soffit panels are slipped into the two channels. On some styles, each panel has integral venting, but with other types a long, continuous soffit vent is installed along with the soffit panels.

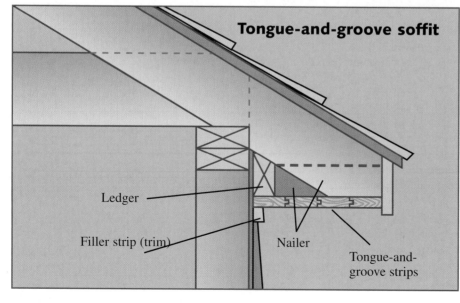

Tongue-and-groove soffit

Ledger

Filler strip (trim)

Nailer

Tongue-and-groove strips

Tongue-and-groove soffit systems. Installed mostly on older (pre-World War II) homes, the tongue-and-groove soffit system is installed using the same basic techniques used to install any tongue-and-groove materials. Unlike other types, these soffit systems feature nailers that run from the ends of the rafter to a ledger on the house to create nailing surfaces for the tongue-and-groove boards at rafter locations. Tongue-and-groove soffit systems are seldom installed today due to cost factors, as well as the fact that they're among the most difficult types to repair and maintain.

Common gutter hanger types

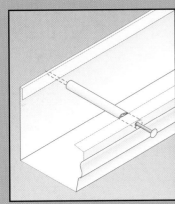

Spike-and-ferrule hangers are driven through the gutter into the fascia at rafter locations. While relatively inexpensive and easy to install, they tend to pull away from the fascia board over time. To remove them, place a short block inside the gutter to support its walls and pull out the spikes with a flat pry bar.

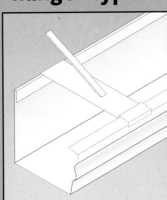

Hidden hangers provide better support than spikes and ferrules and don't show from the outside. They're commonly used on aluminum or steel gutters, although some plastic gutters are hung with similar versions. Screw these into the fascia once the gutter is properly positioned.

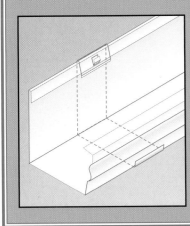

L-brackets and gutter straps provide the strongest support and are often used for heavy-gauge metal gutters. You attach L-brackets to the fascia at rafter locations and strap brackets to the roof sheathing under the shingles, then set the gutter into them. When replacing L-brackets, you'll first need to remove the gutter section(s).

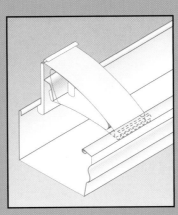

Plastic fascia brackets or snap brackets are commonly used on plastic (PVC) gutters. After screwing these to the fascia, you "snap" the gutter sections into them.

K-metal   **K-vinyl**   **Half-round**

Common gutter profiles, generally available in aluminum or vinyl and 4 or 5 in. size.

GUTTERS

Gutters can be made from plastic (PVC), aluminum, galvanized steel, copper and even wood. Home centers carry PVC and aluminum of various styles, the most popular being, the "K" profile. Some stock beveled, half-round or "U" profiles, although these are becoming scarcer. Since these sections usually come in 10 ft. lengths, they need to be spliced by connectors. Seamless gutters are also available from professional contractors. They are made from rolled steel or vinyl that is formed into the shape of a gutter and made to any length.

Gutters should slope a minimum rate of ¼ in. every 4 ft. They are attached to the roof or fascia. The method of attachment may be determined by the type of roof covering or fascia that is used on your structure. The most common types of hangers are shown above. In order to channel the water from the gutter to the ground and away from the building, downspouts are needed.

The romance of wood shakes and shingles makes them a very appealing siding product. Traditionally made of cedar, they have been a popular product for year, albeit a bit on the spendy side. But newer siding products made from fiber-cement and even hardboard have managed to capture the look and feel of real wood quite successfully, while boasting durability and low-cost that the real stuff has a hard time competing with. The shakes above are fiber-cement.

SIDING

Choosing siding for your construction project can be very simple, but only if you are building an addition and therefore want to match the existing siding. If you have carte blanche to choose a siding type, you have many variables to consider (Incidentally, it's a common practice among design pros to select a different siding type for an attached addition, rather than trying to match what's there and not quite pulling it off).

The world of siding used to be pretty simple: you made a choice based mainly on material type. Wood looked one way, steel or vinyl looked another way, and so on. But in recent years manufacturers have become quite clever at fabricating raw materials to resemble other materials, thereby clouding the picture quite a bit. The siding shown at the top of his page, for example, looks at first glance to be composed of cedar shakes. But, in fact, it is a fiber-cement product manufactured to have the appearance of shakes. So these days, the best place to start when choosing siding is with the question: "What material do I want it to look like?" Together with the shake-style shown above, the photos on the next page give a pretty good cross-section of the range of visual styles you're likely to encounter. In addition to shakes, they include lap siding (also called clapboard in some areas); stucco style; vertical board-and-batten; and brick veneer (brick veneer is still generally made with bricks, but that may change soon too).

Once you've made a selection based on appearance, you'll likely find that you have several material options that can provide that look. It's within the materials arena that sharp contrasts in durability, ease of installation and cost begin to appear. The most popular siding materials today are: wood strips, wood shakes, and other wood products, including hardboard and textured plywood; vinyl and metal strip siding; fiber-cement strips and shakes; stucco and masonry; metal panels; and composite panels.

Siding Appearance Options

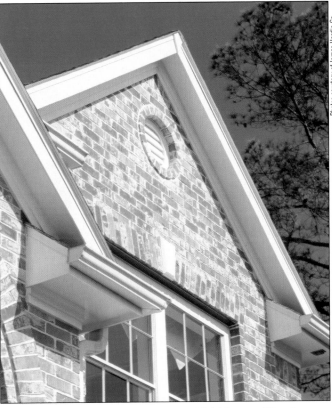

Vertical siding with battens or standing seams is still unconventional enough to command attention, but the look is increasing in usage. It can be achieved the old-fashioned way, with real wood boards, or by using more modern products, such as plywood panels, composite panels, fiber-cement products or fabricated metal.

Brick veneer is the "siding" you see on most brick houses. Although we tend to think of it as a solid brick wall, not siding, it is in fact an applied wall covering just as any other siding is—except a lot thicker and heavier. If you are interested in the charm of brick, there is no substitute for the real thing.

Stucco style is an American classic, but unlike brick veneer, siding products manufacturers have managed to come up with a number of new products that replicate stucco's appeal but can be installed much more easily and cheaply. Prefinished and textured composite panels, for example, can be attached like sheathing, then either seamed or covered with battens.

Lap siding, in most cases, is intended to have the appearance of traditional wood clapboard, regardless of the material it is made of: be it real wood, hardboard, metal, vinyl, or fiber-cement. While the first generation or two of "wood look" siding did not fool too many people, today's products are much more sophisticated and often have a number of benefits over wood.

Traditional horizontal wood siding profiles

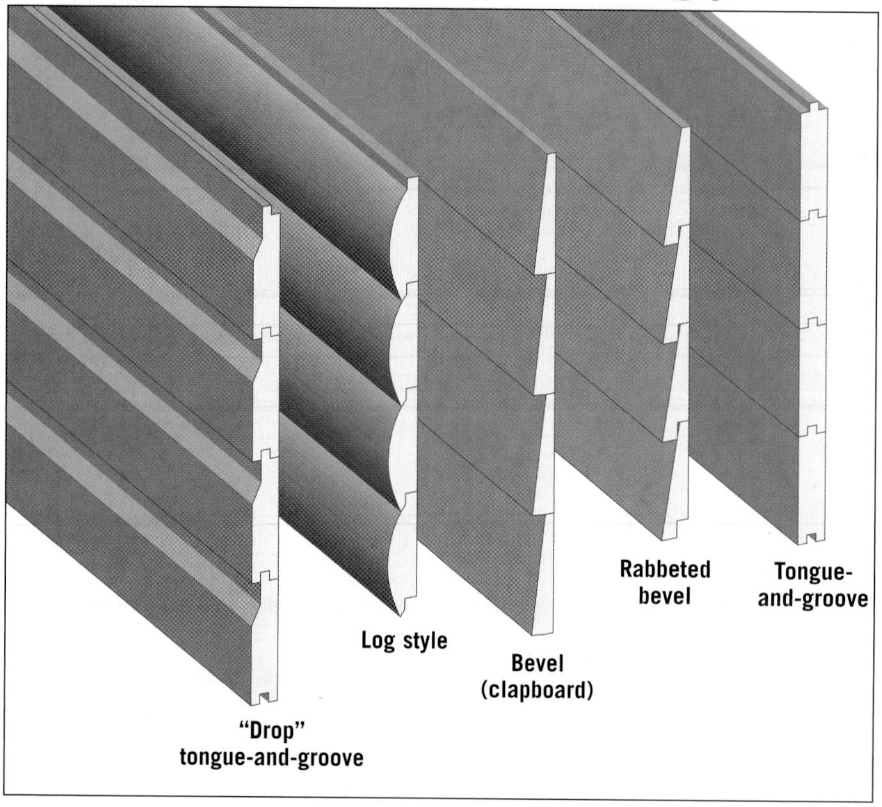

"Drop" tongue-and-groove

Log style

Bevel (clapboard)

Rabbeted bevel

Tongue-and-groove

Siding Coverage

PATTERN	NOMINAL SIZE	AREA FACTOR
Plain bevel (Clapboard)	½ × 4	1.60
	½ × 6	1.33
	¾ × 8	1.28
	¾ × 10	1.21
Rabbeted bevel	¾ × 6	1.20
	1 × 8	1.19
	1 × 10	1.18
	1 × 12	1.12
Tongue & groove	1 × 4	1.28
	1 × 6	1.17
	1 × 8	1.16
	1 × 10	1.13
Drop (T&G or Shiplap)	1 × 6	1.17
	1 × 8	1.16
	1 × 10	1.13
	1 × 12	1.10
Log style	1 × 6	1.22
	1 × 8	1.21
	1 × 10	1.16

Recommended Overlap for Bevel Siding

NOMINAL WIDTH	OVERLAP
4 in.	1 in.
6 in.	1 in.
8 in.	1 to 1⅛ in.
10 in.	1 to 1½ in.
12 in.	1 to 2 in.

Bevel Siding Dimensions (seasoned)

THICKNESS (IN.)	NOMINAL WIDTH (IN.)	FINISHED WIDTH (IN.)
½	4, 6, 8	3½, 5½, 7½
⅝	6, 8	5½, 7½
¾	6, 8, 10	5½, 7½, 9½
⅞	10, 12	9½, 11½
5/4	8, 10, 12	7½, 9½, 11½

Siding Fastening Schedule

SIDING MATERIAL	THICKNESS (IN INCHES)	(Fastener requirement by wall support type)			
		WOOD OR WOOD PANEL	FIBERBOARD SHEATHING	DIRECT TO STUD	SPACING OF FASTENERS
Aluminum lap	.02 in.	1½ in. nail	2 in. nail	Not allowed	Stud spacing
Hardboard-vert.	7/16 in.	2 in. nail	2½ in. nail	1-3/4" nail	6" @edge, 8" @field
Hardboard-horiz.	7/16 in.	2" nail	2½ in. nail	2" nail	2 per stud
Steel lap	29 gauge	1¾ in. staple	2½ in. staple	Not allowed	Stud spacing
Plywood panel	⅜ in.	1⅜ in. staple	2¼ in. staple	1-⅜ in. staple	6" @edge, 12" @field
Vinyl lap	.035"	1¾ in. staple	2½ in. staple	Not allowed	Stud spacing
Wood lap	⅜-19/32 in.	1 in. into stud	1" into stud	2" staple	1/stud<6", 2/stud>8"

Nails and staples should be aluminum, galvanized or rust-preventative

Traditional wood siding types

Horizontal. Traditional horizontal wood siding (lap siding) is heartwood cut, mostly from redwood or western red cedar, making it premium-priced. The boards are cut, routed and planed to form a variety of patterns, such as tongue & groove, shiplap, log cabin and clapboard. Sizes range from 1 × 4 to 1 × 12.

Coverage can be estimated for the following patterns by multiplying the area to be covered (in square feet) by its area factor *(See Chart, upper right, previous page)* and adding 10%. This should yield the amount needed, including waste and trim.

They should be fastened with hot-dipped galvanized or stainless steel nails to the framing. Once installed, they need to be treated with paint or stain to prevent rot and decay. Disadvantages to installing wood siding include moisture and maintenance problems.

Vertical. Vertical wood siding is rustic, usually made of a local, rough-sawn lumber Typical installation patterns include board-and-batten, channel shiplap and reverse board-and-batten.

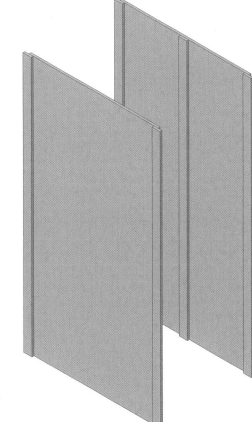

Plywood panels are employed as an inexpensive way to replicate the look of vertical wood strip siding at a fraction of the cost. Battens are placed over the vertical seams for a board-and-batten appearance. They can also be added in the field area to intensify the effect.

Traditional vertical wood siding

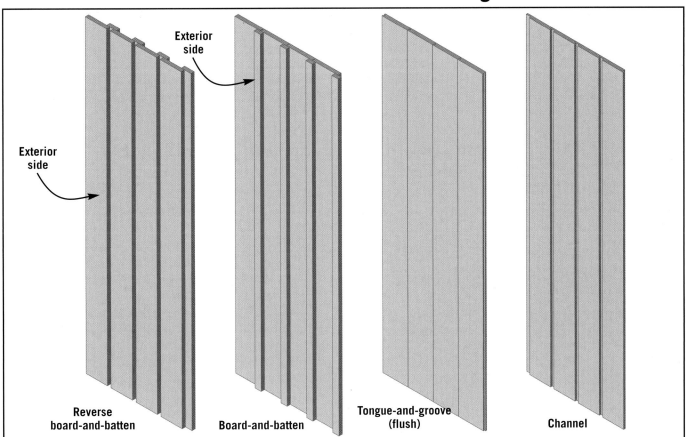

Exterior side

Exterior side

Reverse board-and-batten

Board-and-batten

Tongue-and-groove (flush)

Channel

Siding Types

Hardboard siding. Hardboard is a generic term for a manufactured panel composed of inter-felted ligno-cellulosic fibers which are consolidated under heat and pressure. They come in flat and wood-grain patterns. These panels are then ripped to various widths and sold in most home centers and lumberyards for siding. They are typically 16 ft. long and ⅜ in. thick, making them very flexible and awkward to maneuver. Most panels come pre-primed and need only be painted.

Hardboard siding should be fastened with 8d galvanized nails and backed by 15 lb. building paper or house wrap to protect the sheathing. It should be spaced with a ⅛ in. gap at the ends to allow for expansions. Joints should then be sealed with exterior rated caulk. Hardboard siding is a low cost and easy-to-install product, which makes it a commonly used product. The life span, however is directly related to its price. Hardboard must be well-maintained to prevent swelling and delamination from water damage.

Wood Shakes & Shingles. Cedar siding shingles have been in use for hundreds of years and are still in use today. This premium siding is installed in much the same way as cedar roofing shingles (See page 112), by layering and staggering the individual pieces over a layer of 15 lb. building paper. It is commonly chosen for its good looks and longevity. Unlike other forms of wood siding, it repels water well without being treated. It can, however, be painted or stained. Due to the slow installation process, some manufacturers have pre-mounted them to 1 × 8 ft. and 3 × 8 ft. sheets of plywood that interlock, making a complete, water-repellent siding system.

Metal Siding. Metal siding has become increasingly popular due to its superior weather resistance and low maintenance. Metal siding is made from either steel or aluminum. It comes in horizontal planks, which are fastened with aluminum nails along the top, nailing strip after hooking on to the lower panel. Some contractors install seamless aluminum siding. They cut and form each piece to length. This eliminates unsightly seams and prevents leaks. While aluminum is more susceptible to denting, steel is more durable, yet could rust if scratched.

Cornerboards used to be a surefire sign that a home was clad in real wood, as the metal and vinyl knock-offs usually are installed with small corner caps on each course. But installing perpendicular boards at the corners, then butting the siding material up to the boards, is becoming a common practice with virtually all types of siding.

Vinyl Siding. Because there are no special tools needed to install vinyl siding (you do need a "zip tool" to remove it), it has become a favorite of do-it-yourselfers. It is a low-cost, low-maintenance alternative to other modern types of siding. Vinyl siding comes in both single and double gang units and in various textures. Some contractors install seamless vinyl siding.

Generally speaking, vinyl siding cannot be repainted if damaged, but

Nailable versus non-nailable lap siding installations

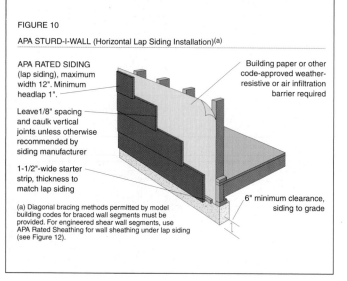

FIGURE 10

APA STURD-I-WALL (Horizontal Lap Siding Installation)(a)

APA RATED SIDING (lap siding), maximum width 12". Minimum headlap 1".

Leave 1/8" spacing and caulk vertical joints unless otherwise recommended by siding manufacturer

1-1/2"-wide starter strip, thickness to match lap siding

Building paper or other code-approved weather-resistive or air infiltration barrier required

6" minimum clearance, siding to grade

(a) Diagonal bracing methods permitted by model building codes for braced wall segments must be provided. For engineered shear wall segments, use APA Rated Sheathing for wall sheathing under lap siding (see Figure 12).

FIGURE 12

APA RATED SIDING (LAP SIDING) OVER NAILABLE SHEATHING

Siding joints, if staggered may occur away from studs with nailable sheathing.

APA RATED SIDING (lap siding), maximum width 12". Minimum headlap 1".

1-1/2"-wide starter strip, thickness to match lap siding

No diagonal wall bracing required with APA RATED SHEATHING

Building paper or other code-approved weather-resistive or air infiltration barrier

Leave 1/8" spacing and caulk vertical joints, unless otherwise recommended by siding manufacturer

6" minimum clearance, siding to grade

check with the manufacturer. Another downfall of vinyl siding is that is can become brittle in colder climates and crack. And although vinyl is "colored" all the way through, it can fade if exposed to sun over time.

Cement Siding. Along with forming a concrete slab or a footing, cement can now be used to side a house. There are three forms that are common throughout the U.S.: fiber-cement planks and panels, stucco and brick.

Fiber-cement is a newer form of siding composed of portland cement, ground sand, cellulose, fiber and water, which is molded into planks and panels in either a flat or wood grain pattern. The planks range from 6 to 12 inches wide and are 12 feet long. Panels come in 4 × 8, 4 × 9 and 4 × 10 sizes. Planks and panels are both $\frac{5}{16}$ in. thick.

There are some definite advantages to fiber-cement siding: It is very durable, since it won't rot, crack or delaminate and it resists moisture. It is also non-combustible and resists termites. Fiber cement siding comes factory primed like hardboard siding and is nailed to the framing, making installation DIY friendly. It can be cut with a circular saw, shear or scored and snapped.

Brick and brick veneer. Brick and brick veneer also very important products in the siding industry. A combination of clay bricks and mortar gives a distinct and sturdy look to any building. While fewer houses are completely sided with brick, more and more houses include brick veneer as a border or transition to other methods of siding, such as vinyl or wood. Brick veneer is simply a kneewall that covers a portion of the exterior wall. It is spaced 1 in. away from the wall sheathing to allow air flow. It also contains weep holes to allow potentially damaging water and moisture to escape. The application of brick veneer is covered more extensively in the Concrete & Masonry, pages 18 to 33.

Metal/vinyl siding cross-section

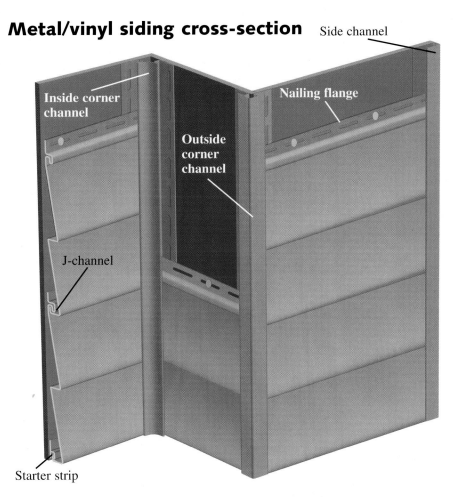

Side channel

Inside corner channel

Nailing flange

Outside corner channel

J-channel

Starter strip

Vinyl, aluminum and steel siding products are installed using similar fittings, fasteners and techniques. Most often, they're attached directly over the exterior wall sheathing. The ends and corners are fitted into trim fittings that contain channels.

Tips for maintaining siding

✔ Caulk all joints and seams between siding and trim, and between board ends with exterior-grade, paintable acrylic latex or siliconized acrylic caulk. These caulks come in a variety of colors that make repairs less conspicuous. Otherwise, touch up caulk lines with matching paint.

✔ Fill small nail holes, dents, cracks and joints (less than $\frac{1}{16}$ in. wide) with exterior wood filler. To fill a dent, rough up the area with sandpaper and apply filler with a wide putty knife. Sand smooth with sandpaper and a sanding block. Paint or stain immediately.

✔ Patch larger holes or rotted areas with exterior wood filler or two-part epoxy wood filler.

✔ To reattach a loose board, carefully pry up the board at nail locations with a flat pry bar. With a caulk gun, apply liberal dabs of construction adhesive at nail locations behind the board. Then, reset the original nails. If the nails won't hold, drive an additional nail or galvanized deck screw about 1 in. above the original ones (use rust-resistant spiral or ring-shank siding nails).

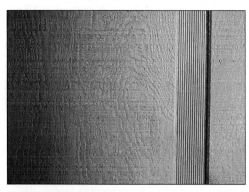

Textured plywood with scored grooves to resemble reverse board-and-batten (See page 123).

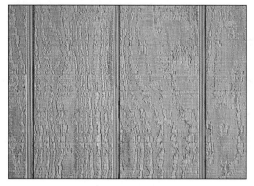

T-1111 textured plywood siding with 4-in. on-center grooves is very popular for outdoor building.

Plain textured plywood can be used in conjunction with a "faux" board-and-batten style, or hung as-is for a truly rustic and simple appearance.

TEXTURED WOOD PANELS

Most plywood siding is rated by the APA (American Plywood Association) for durability, workability and quality. APA-rated sidings are manufactured with waterproof adhesives to help prevent delamination. Typical grades of plywood siding include T-111, a very familiar textured panel with parallel grooves and shiplapped edges. Another type is kerfed, rough-sawn panels, which have a rough-sawn surface and narrow grooves.

Plywood siding should be fastened with galvanized nails to prevent bleeding. It is relatively low cost and easy to install, but could deteriorate from moisture.

Better-quality plywood siding has clean-cut grooves and fewer voids or surface defects than more utility grades, such as T-111 (left).

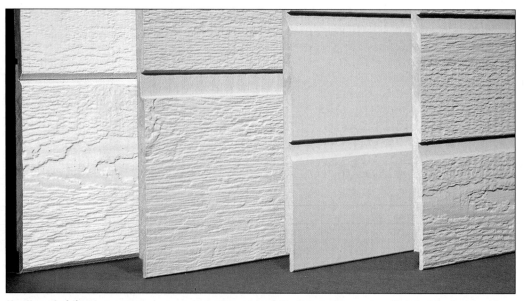

Hardboard siding has a come a long way in design and durability. New designs are less likely to delaminate and feature more convincing wood grain patterns. Hardboard strip siding is also shown above, at the far left.

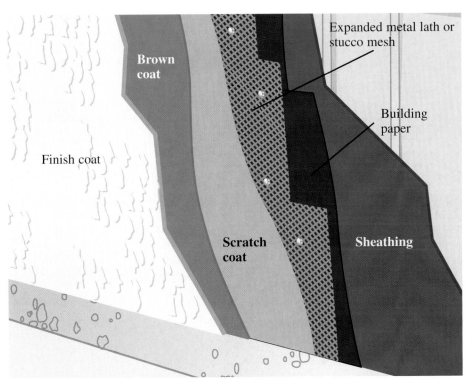

Brown coat

Finish coat

Scratch coat

Expanded metal lath or stucco mesh

Building paper

Sheathing

Stucco is a cementitious siding product applied over wood-framed or masonry walls. It is generally applied in three layers (the scratch coat, the brown coat and the finish coat), with the first layer embedded in expanded metal lath or stucco mesh to hold the siding to the wall.

STUCCO

Stucco is the original low-maintenance siding material. It is composed of three coats of cement product which are applied over metal lath or stucco mesh. The built-up layers adhere to the substrate and make it more durable. Because the consistencies of the mix play a vital role in its effectiveness as a siding material, it is a difficult undertaking for DIYer with no experience in this area.

As with all masonry work, the key is workability. If the coats don't flow properly, it could sag or crack, causing failure. If done correctly, stucco is a durable form of siding, which could last a century or more.

Fiber-cement shingle panels

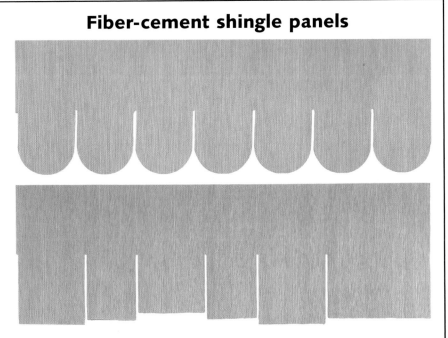

Fabricated fiber-cement panels come in multi-tab sections, just as asphalt 3-tab shingles do. This speeds up installation and ensure a neater job. The two style of panel shown above are intended to replicate the appearance of two popular styles of cedar shakes.

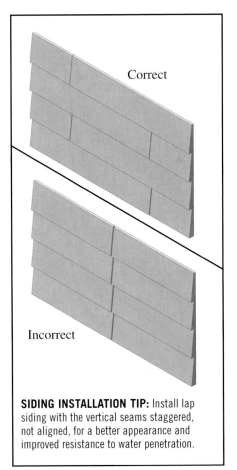

Correct

Incorrect

SIDING INSTALLATION TIP: Install lap siding with the vertical seams staggered, not aligned, for a better appearance and improved resistance to water penetration.

INSULATION

Insulation type recommendations by area

Exterior wall: Fiberglass batts or blankets (rolls).

Unfinished attic: Fiberglass batts or blankets installed in perpendicular layers or loose fiberglass or cellulose blown over a 6 mil polyethylene vapor barrier.

Cathedral ceiling: Faced fiberglass batts or blankets stapled between joist cavities (or rigid foam), allowing for a 1-in.-thick air space on the cold side.

Concrete slab floor: Rigid foam panels laid between 1 × 4 or 2 × 4 sleepers.

Exterior foundation wall (outside): Extruded polystyrene or polyisocyanurate held in place by backfill.

Exterior foundation wall (inside): Expanded polystyrene panels glued between furring strips.

Crawl space/unheated basement: Fiberglass batts or blankets supported in floor joist cavities by tension strips, chicken wire or netting. Or, encapsulated insulation batts if allowed by code. Code may require protective sheathing on unheated side in spaces subject to exposure.

Interior sound control: Fiberglass batts or blankets.

Insulating the walls, ceiling and floor of an addition to your home or a remodeled area with exterior exposure isn't just a good idea—it's required by building codes. Most municipalities enforce very specific requirements for the amount and type of insulation you'll need to install, along with standards for sealing the insulated areas with an adequate vapor retarder.

It's always a good idea to find out the exact insulation requirements for your area while you are still in the planning stages of your project. If your intention is to build a heated addition using 2 × 4 stud walls, for example, you may find that your area requires more wall insulation than 2 × 4s will accommodate, so you'll need to construct the framing with 2 × 6 studs. As you plan, be aware that it's common, especially in colder climates, for the municipality to require a site inspection of the insulation and vapor retarder before you can install the interior wall coverings.

To understand insulation, it helps to know how heat is transferred. Heat

(Continued, page 130)

Where to Install Insulation

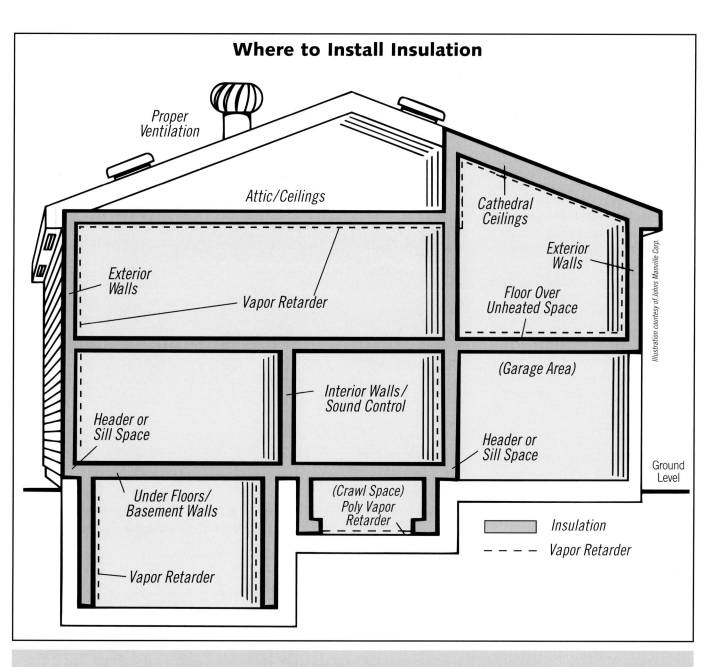

Illustration courtesy of Johns Manville Corp.

Proper Ventilation

Attic/Ceilings

Cathedral Ceilings

Exterior Walls

Exterior Walls

Vapor Retarder

Floor Over Unheated Space

Header or Sill Space

Interior Walls/ Sound Control

(Garage Area)

Header or Sill Space

Under Floors/ Basement Walls

(Crawl Space) Poly Vapor Retarder

Ground Level

Insulation

Vapor Retarder

Vapor Retarder

Characteristics of insulation by material

Insulating Material	R-value/inch Rating	Moisture Resistance	Max. temp.	Fire Resistance
Fiberglass batt or blanket	3.2	Excellent	180°F	Good/Fair
Mineral (rock) wool	3.2	Excellent	500°F	Excellent
Fiberglass loose fill	2.2	Excellent	180°F	Good/Fair
Cellulose loose fill	3.2	Poor	180°F	Good/Fair
Expanded Polystyrene(EPS)	4.0	Good/Fair	165°F	Poor
Extruded Polystyrene (XPS)	5.0	Excellent	165°F	Poor
Polyisocyanurate	6.5	Good/Fair	200°F	Poor
Polyurethane	6.2	Excellent	165°F	Poor

(Continued from page 128)

enters and exits a room in three different and ways: *radiation, conduction* and *convection.* Radiation is the movement of heat through waves, as with sunlight. Conduction is the flow of heat through a medium, from hot toward cold, as the material seeks to establish temperature equilibrium. Convection is the transfer of heat that results from changes in density: colder air is denser that hotter air and will naturally move toward the less dense space. Conduction and convection are the primary types of heat transfer that insulation is designed to impede: conduction occurring through the building materials themselves and convection occurring through any gaps or seams that allow air transfer.

A good insulation material resists the conduction of heat. The extent to which it resists heat flow is measured by its *R-Value:* ("R" stands for resistance). The higher the R-value, the more the material resists heat conduction and the more insulation protection it provides. Technically, R-value is a factor of how long it takes one *BTU* (British

Thermal Unit) of heat to move through a 1-in.-thick, 1-sq.-foot sample of the material and raise the temperature on the unheated side one degree Fahrenheit. All construction materials from 2 × 4s to mortar have an R-value that contributes to the cumulative R-value of the wall, ceiling or floor. If your local codes require that a wall have an R-value of 19, you may add up the R-values of all the wall materials to achieve it (this is important to know, since even if you use R-19 insulation you'll need the added R-value provided by the wall coverings and siding to compensate for the fact that the R-value of R-19 fiberglass is reduced to 17.1 when it is compressed to fit into a 2 × 6 wall cavity—See chart, page 131.

Remember, when working with any

INSULATION TYPES

Kraft-faced fiberglass batt

Unfaced fiberglass batt

Expandable foam

Encapsulated fiberglass insulation

Popular do-it-yourself insulation products include: kraft-faced fiberglass batts for exterior walls; unfaced fiberglass batts for soundproofing and exterior-wall gaps (requires vapor retarder); (C) expandable foam insulation for small gaps; (D) encapsulated fiberglass insulation: the batts or rolls are captured in a sleeve to trap fibers and irritating dust. The encapsulated product shown here also utilizes an innovative fiber binding system that does away with the need for chemical binders that give fiberglass insulation its "scratchy" quality.

Insulation product types

Blankets: Fiberglass batts and rolls are laid in blankets in ceiling and floor cavities or installed in wall cavities.

Loose fill: Cellulose or blown fiberglass is spread in a thick layer, generally in unfinished attic areas.

Rigid boards: Used mainly as wall insulation on the exterior side of the house or between furring strips on an interior basement wall.

Expandable: Injected from a can to fill cracks and crevices, especially around doors and windows.

Estimating insulation coverage & cost

Figuring out how much insulation you'll need for a project can be a little tricky if you're not reading the bags carefully. Most bags of insulation product contain coverage information, generally expressed in square feet of product per bag. Simply by calculating the square footage of the space you're insulating it's not too hard to determine how many bags of insulation you'll need.

The biggest potential for confusion is with batts of fiberglass insulation. Along with the total square footage, bags of insulation batts also feature the dimensions of each batt on the bag (for example, 15 in. by 96 in.), along with the number of batts in the bag. To avoid confusion, ignore this information entirely and focus on the total square footage: you'd be surprised how easy it is to make an error when recalculating the coverage based on the number and size of the batts.

Johns Manville Corp.

Measure the width and height of each wall, ceiling or floor cavity you're planning to insulate. Multiply to find the the square footage, then divide the total square footage by the number of square feet of insulation product in each bag (insulation square footage is generally printed on the bag). Round up to the next whole number to determine how many bags of product you'll need for your project.

kind of insulation, always wear the proper safety devices, including glasses, dust mask, gloves and long sleeve clothing. Another important thing to keep in mind is to pack insulation loosely: compressing it lowers its R-value.

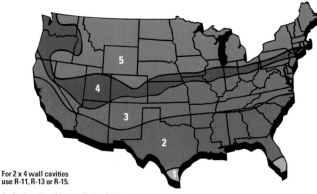

For 2 x 4 wall cavities use R-11, R-13 or R-15.

For 2 x 6 wall cavities use R-19 or R-21. R-19 will actually yield an R-value of R-17.1 because it must be slightly compressed to fit in the 2 x 6 construction.

Safety Equipment

Fiberglass insulation is one of the most notorious building products when it comes to handling. Not only do the loose glass fibers cause irritation and discomfort, they can be hazardous to your health if you breathe them in. In addition to wearing a long-sleeved shirt when working with fiberglass, always wear gloves, goggles (not just safety glasses) and a particle mask or respirator. *Photo above and illustration, right, courtesy of Johns Manville Corp.*

Zone	Attic/ceiling R-value	Ext. Wall R-value	Floor R-value	Basement Wall R-value
1	R-19	R-11	R-11	–
2	R-30	R-13	R-13	R-11
3	R-30	R-13	R-19	R-11
4	R-38	R-15	R-19	R-11
5	R-38	R-21	R-19	R-15

Hawaii = Zone 1   Alaska = Zone 5

R-values of common building materials

Building Material	R-value
Softwood construction lumber	1.25
Softwood plywood	1.25
8 in. concrete block	1.04
Concrete (poured)	0.08
Common brick	0.20
Wallboard (drywall)	0.90
Building paper	0.06
Asphalt roll roofing	0.15
Asphalt / fiberglass shingles	0.44
Cedar shingles	0.94
Stucco	0.20
Aluminum	0.0007
Steel	0.0032
Glass (single pane)	0.88
Glass (½ in. insulating)	1.72
Glass (low-E)	0.00
Plastic sheeting (4 mil)	0.45

Cross-section of an exterior wall (2 × 6)

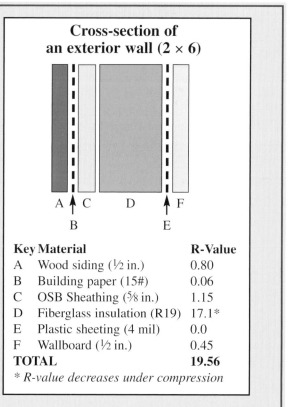

A   C   D   F
   B   E

Key	Material	R-Value
A	Wood siding (½ in.)	0.80
B	Building paper (15#)	0.06
C	OSB Sheathing (⅝ in.)	1.15
D	Fiberglass insulation (R19)	17.1*
E	Plastic sheeting (4 mil)	0.0
F	Wallboard (½ in.)	0.45
TOTAL		**19.56**

* R-value decreases under compression

R-value measures a material's ability to resist heat conduction and thus its value as an insulator. Most building codes stipulate that exterior walls, roofs and unheated floors must meet minimum R-value standards. When planning for insulation, keep in mind that all of the materials in a wall offer some resistance, so the total R-value of the wall is derived by adding up the R-value of each material in the wall.

Fiberglass batts and rolls are by far the most popular type of insulation for do-it-yourself installation. Faced rolls or batts, like kraft-paper backed rolls shown here, are easy to install by simply stapling the unfolded edge flanges to the joists or wall studs. The backing serves as a vapor retarder. *Photo courtesy of Johns Manville Corp.*

Fiberglass insulation thicknesses (standard density)	
R-Value	**Thickness**
R-11	$3\frac{1}{2}$ in.
R-13	$3\frac{5}{8}$ in.
R-19	$6\frac{1}{4}$ in.
R-22	$6\frac{1}{2}$ in.
R-25	8 in.
R-30	10 in.
R-38	12 in.

Standard density fiberglass blankets (as opposed to high-density—see next page) have an average R-value of about R-3.2 per inch.

FIBERGLASS INSULATION

The most common type of insulation used by homeowners is the *fiberglass blanket.* Most do-it-yourselfers find fiberglass blankets easy to work with, plus they come in a wide range of sizes in both *roll* and *batt* form. Continuous rolls are pre-cut to width and are cut to length on-site. Then they are fitted into a wall or joist cavity. Batts are pre-cut to width and length for standard wall sizes. Fiberglass rolls and batts are flexible and easy to handle, which allows them to be maneu-

Batts and rolls of fiberglass insulation come in a wide range of types and sizes. R-13 and R-19 are sized to fit into 2 × 4 and 2 × 6 wall cavities, respectively, making them the most popular thicknesses. *Photo courtesy of Johns Manville Corp.*

vered into place between the framing members. Both come in faced and unfaced units. The faced units have attached kraft paper or foil backers to provide vapor retardation. The backers have a flange on each edge to allow you to staple them to the framing. Unfaced insulation is friction-fit into the cavity. In walls and ceilings, a plastic vapor barrier is generally stapled over the insulation, helping secure it in place. In open floor

joists cavities, where the vapor barrier is installed above the insulation, the batts or rolls are supported from below with wires, braces or netting.

Another form of fiberglass insulation is *loose fiberglass.* Loose fiberglass comes compacted in a large block that is fed into a machine and then blown through a hose to insulate an area. This form of insulation is very common in new construction for attic spaces and can easily be done by the DIYer.

If sound is a problem, there is also a type of fiberglass insulation that is manufactured for the sole purpose of insulating against sound. It is commonly used to insulate bathrooms around the shower or tub and any other area of the home where noise may cause a problem. Sound control insulation is low-density fiberglass that is pre-cut into batts to fit standard wall sizes. Since

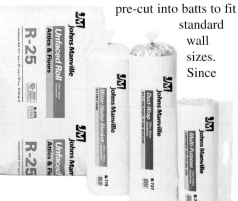

High-density fiberglass

Most fiberglass insulation manufacturers now offer newer "high-density" fiberglass products. High-density fiberglass insulation allows you to pack more "R-value" into a confined space. The tighter matrix of fibers increases R-value from 11 to 13 in a standard 2 × 4 wall cavity,

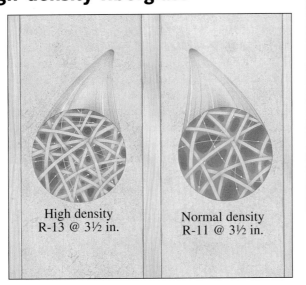

High density
R-13 @ 3½ in.

Normal density
R-11 @ 3½ in.

and from 19 (17.1 when compressed) to 21 in a 2 × 6 wall. The high-density products are especially popular in cathedral ceilings, where space is quite limited, the potential for heat loss is high, and an open gap space must be maintained between the insulation and the roof sheathing. On average, the cost is about 20% higher than standard density products. Despite the advantages of insulation that's manufactured to higher density, note that compressing any insulation product actually reduces its ability to resist heat conduction. *Illustration courtesy of Johns Manville Corp..*

Encapsulated fiberglass

To control the escape of fibers and irritants from their products, most insulation manufacturers now offer encapsulated fiberglass batts, with the insulation contained in a sleeve. *Photo courtesy of Johns Manville Corp.*

they are made for interior walls and floors, they don't have a vapor retarder.

The primary downside to working with fiberglass insulation is the irritation caused by skin contact and the possible health concerns related to breathing the fibers. Recently, manufacturers have introduced new products that minimize these complaints. One of these is *encapsulated insulation* (See photo above) in which the fiberglass batts are encapsulated in a polyethylene (or a similar product) sleeve to trap dust and fibers.

If you are sensitive to dust or airborne particles, encapsulated insulation may be what you need (but it is more expensive). Some manufacturers have also come out with specially formulated fiberglass that can hold together without any added binders—many of which are formaldehyde-based. Often, it is the binders that cause the bulk of the skin irritation issues.

Photo courtesy of Johns Manville Corp.

CERTIFIED
This fiber glass contains a minimum of
25% Recycled Glass
18% post-consumer remelted bottles, 7% pre-consumer
(Johns Manville's North American average)

SCIENTIFIC CERTIFICATION SYSTEMS

Reusing Resources

Fiberglass is manufactured by spinning molten glass so it forms into tiny strands—much like the cotton candy making process. Consequently, fiberglass insulation is well-suited to make use of recycled glass as a raw material. According to the *Johns Manville Corporation,* an average-size house that's fully insulated with fiberglass containing 25% recycled glass fibers (18% post-consumer) will put 6,000 glass beverage containers back into service.

Installation Tips: Fiberglass Insulation

Installing fiberglass insulation can be a messy, unpleasant job. But if you follow a few basic precautions, the work will go quickly, you won't be itching and scratching for days, and you will end up with a more energy efficient home. Here are a few tips for a successful and safe project:

• Always wear a long-sleeve shirt, long pants, full eye protection, work gloves, and a particle mask or respirator. A cap is also a good idea. The point is to avoid any direct contact between your skin and the fiberglass.

• Compress the insulation before cutting. Lay the batt or roll flat on a worksurface and press it down from above with a board. Then, cut through it with a utility knife, long shears or an insulation cutter (See page 136).

• Work from the top down on walls. It seems obvious, but take every opportunity to get gravity working on your side.

• Do not overpack voids, and try to get a smooth, even surface before installing a vapor retarder.

• Do not open packages until you need them—leave the insulation compressed to conserve floor space.

• Clean up and dispose of all waste immediately (although it's a good idea to keep a bag of usable small pieces around for packing into tight corners and voids).

Hanging insulation in open floor joist cavities

Insulation brackets are made of springy metal and sized so they're slightly longer than standard joist cavity widths. Insert them into the bottom of each cavity at 2-ft. intervals to support the insulation. You can pressure-fit lengths of heavy-gauge wire instead, or staple chicken wire or netting under the insulation after it's installed in the cavities.

TIP: Split it down the middle

Cables, pipes and electrical boxes create obstacles to insulating walls. You can makes slices in the insulation so it fits over the obstacles, but this will leave voids. One way around the problem is to split the insulation rolls or batts by tearing them into two pieces of equal thickness. Install one piece before running your cables and pipes, and install the other half after the plumbing or wiring work is completed and approved.

Choose the right size

One of the biggest mistakes first-time insulation installers make is trying to cram overly-large batts or rolls into a cavity. Purchasing product that's precut to the correct width (14½ to 15 in. or 22½ to 23 in., depending on stud spacing) eliminates the need to cut and makes for a neat installation. Buying batts that are precut for length so they fit into a standard 8-ft. wall cavity also decreases cutting time and ensures a tight fit. Use R-11 for 2 × 4 walls and R-19 for 2 × 6 walls.

Pack tricky areas with small pieces of fiberglass before filling the cavity with batts or rolls. For example, stuff insulation behind electrical boxes: the larger batts or rolls will resist fitting in to such a small space. Alternatively, see "Split it down the middle" tip, previous page.

When insulating ceilings, use the vapor retarder to help support the insulation. Pressure-fit the batts or rolls into the cavities first, then simply staple the retarder material (usually 4 or 6-mil plastic) to the ceiling joists. For overhead areas where the vapor retarder is above the insulation, see "Hanging insulation . . ." tip, previous page.

Insulate hot air ductwork, along with water supply pipes and water heaters. Most insulation manufacturers make special products for these purposes.

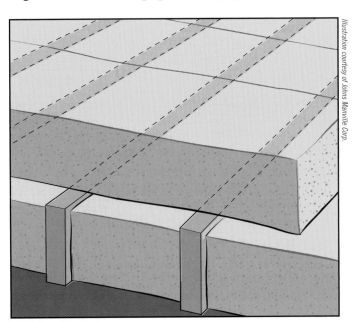

Add an attic blanket. If your home doesn't have enough attic insulation, add unfaced "attic blanket" roll insulation. If the existing insulation is up to or above the ceiling joists, lay the new blanket perpendicular to the joists.

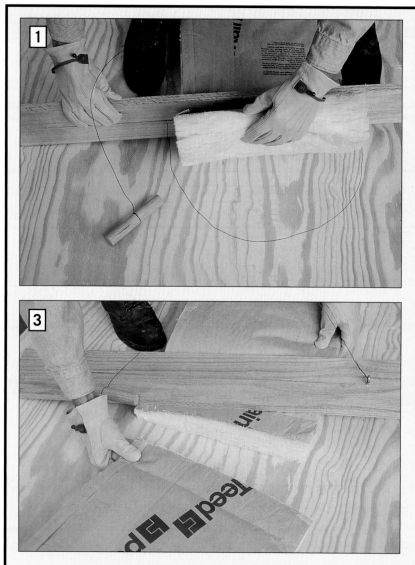

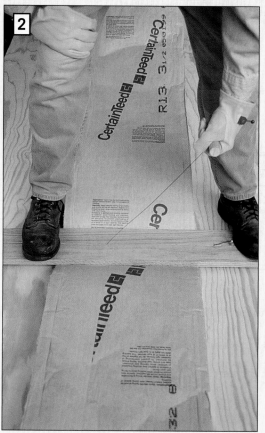

This insulation cutter tool was designed and submitted by a member of the Handyman Club of America. It is one of the best ways we've seen to manage the tricky and messy job of cutting fiberglass insulation to length. And all you need to make it is a few scrap items you probably have lying around your shop. Read the information below for a description of how the insulation cutter is made and used.

A simple tool you can make to cut fiberglass rolls and batts

Handyman Club of America member Tom Brennan of North Babylon, New York, has come up with a very clever and effective way to cut fiberglass insulation to length. The only materials you need to make the tool are a length of baling wire, a screw eye and a board. The board compresses and holds the insulation in place, and the wire, looped around the insulation and drawn through a slot in the board, slices the insulation cleanly. Tom built his insula-

tion cutter from a 3-ft. piece of 1 × 6 with a slot ripped down the center, but stopping about 4 in. from each end of the board. He twisted a screw eye into the board about 1 in. from the slot, making sure that it was in line with the slot. Then he attached a 5-ft. piece of baling wire to the screw eye with a wooden dowel handle on the other end.

To use the insulation cutter, loop the wire through the slot and around the insulation (See photo 1, above). Next, set the board down on the insulation

and use the slot as a reference line for where you want to cut the insulation. Step on the board and pull the wire up through the slot until the wire clears the slot (See photo 2). Pick up the board and repeat for the next cut (See photo 3). This tool is especially helpful if you're insulating an entire house and need to cut many rolls of insulation. Note: Be sure to wear long sleeves and gloves to protect your skin from contact with fiberglass particles.

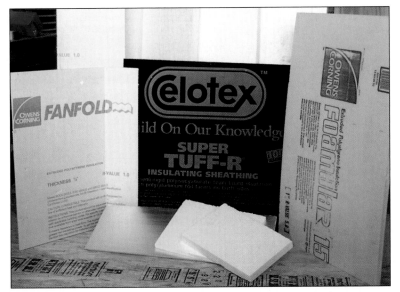

Rigid foam insulation is used in small spaces and in areas of high humidity or potential exposure to the elements. It can be purchased in panel that are sized to fit between standard wall stud spacing, in larger panels (usually 4 × 8 ft.). and even in folded sections that are 50 ft. in length.

RIGID FOAM

Rigid foam insulation costs more than fiberglass, but provides a higher R-value per inch. Its thinness and resistance to air infiltration make it ideal for tight, damp areas, such as basements. There are two general categories of foam insulation: EPS (molded expanded polystyrene) and XPS (extruded expanded polystyrene, polyurethane and polyisocyanurate). EPS is a closed-cell foam commonly known as "beadboard." It has an R-value of about R-4 per inch. Home centers generally stock beadboard in ¾, 1, 1½ and 2 in. thicknesses. It is sold in 4 × 8 sheets or in precut, 14½ in. wide strips that fit between 16-on-center studs for use when furring out a wall with 1 × 2s or 2 × 2s

XPS, also a closed-cell foam, is injected then extruded into panels. XPS panels are generally R-5 per inch of thickness and are more dense and moisture resistant than the EPS panels, which makes them better suited for use on roofs and wall panels. XPS sheets are commonly used as an insulation base for flat roofs topped with built-up or rubber roofing.

Polyurethane and polyisocyanurate are closed-cell foams with R-value of R-7 to R-8 per inch. They come in rigid panels or expandable liquid that's poured by a contractor.

R-values: Rigid Foam Insulation

EPS (Molded Expanded Polystyrene)

¾ ×14½ in. × 4 ft.	R2.9
¾ × 4 in. × 8 ft.	R2.9
1½ × 14½ in. × 8 ft.	R5.9
1½ × 4 in. × 8 ft.	R5.9
2 × 4 in. × 8 ft.	R7.8

XPS (Extruded Expanded Polystyrene)

½ in. × 4 × 8 ft.	R3.0
¾ in. × 4 × 8 ft.	R4.0
1 in. × 4 × 8 ft.	R5.0
1½ in. × 4 × 8 ft.	R7.5
2 in. × 4 × 8 ft.	R10.0

Polyisocyanurate foil faced

½ in. × 4 × 8 ft.	R3.6
¾ in. × 4 × 8 ft.	R5.6
1 in. × 4 × 8 ft.	R7.2

Expandable foam is a handy product for filling hard-to-reach gaps in exterior walls. Most products manufactured today are made to expand in volume at a lower rate than the 3-to-1 expansion rates of first generation foam products. But even these will increase significantly in volume: see photos below.

Expandable foam

Sprayable polyurethane foam is growing in popularity as a convenient, effective product for filling gaps. Common areas of application are between door jambs and studs, around electrical boxes and around cutouts for pipes or cable. Before tapping into a can of expandable foam, fully prepare all the areas you plan to fill with it so you can address them at the same time: generally, the containers cannot be reused after a couple of hours have passed. If you overfill the gap, wait until the foam has cured and slice the overage away, rather than trying to wipe it clean while still liquid. And avoid getting the wet foam on your skin: it's very difficult to clean off.

EXPANSION RATE OF "MINIMAL EXPANDING" FOAM

Expansion rates vary among sprayable foam products. Even "minimal" and "one-to-one" expanding products will increase in volume after the initial application, as seen in the time-lapse photos of "minimal expanding" foam above. As a rule of thumb, fill the gap about half full when applying the product to allow for expansion. If you overfill a gap, the foam may expand with enough pressure to damage or buckle wallcoverings or trim pieces.

Loose fiberglass is a relatively clean blow-in insulation product that, according to its manufacturers, settles less than loose cellulose, retaining nearly all of its original R-value. For best results, use a blower (inset photo) to install loose insulation.

LOOSE INSULATION

Loose insulation (also called *blow-in insulation*) is used almost exclusively in attics. The two primary types of loose insulation are cellulose and fiberglass.

Cellulose is manufactured from recovered wood pulp—typically, newsprint. Loose fiberglass is made from the same basic material as fiberglass blanket insulation, but is less irritating because it does not require scratchy binding agents to hold the strands together. Generally speaking, loose insulation is a very economical product to purchase, although some of the savings versus other types can be lost if you have to rent a pneumatic blower for the installation. Many home centers, however, will let you use a blower for free with a minimum purchase—it's worth asking about.

Because it will settle into small crevices and around obstructions, loose insulation forms an nearly contiguous layer of protection when installed properly (be sure to install scrap-wood dams around any electrical boxes or housings that are not rated IC for insulation contact). It's also easy to install, especially in attics, and you don't have to bother lugging large bags of batts or rolls up into your attic.

Loose insulation can be installed in wall cavities, too. For new construction, you can purchase netting that's attached to the stud walls to contain the blown-in insulation. The netting has holes spaced at regular intervals to accommodate the hose from the blower. For retrofit work, you can drill a hole (usually 2½ in. diameter) in the wallcovering over each stud bay.

Cellulose insulation

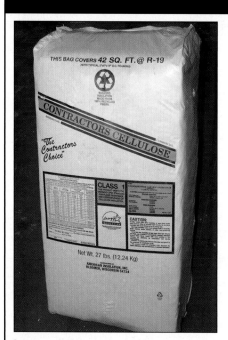

Loose cellulose is simply old newsprint that has been "fiberized" and treated with fire retardant.

Cellulose insulation is heavily compressed. Breaking the blocks apart completely to achieve maximum coverage requires a pneumatic blower.

Allow for some settling when applying cellulose insulation: an extra ½ to 1 in. should be enough.

ESTIMATING GUIDELINES: LOOSE CELLULOSE

R-value desired	Minimum thickness**	Sq. ft. per 27# bag
R-60	17 in.	12.0
R-48	13½ in.	15.0
R-44	12½ in.	16.4
R-38	10¾ in.	18.9
R-24	6¾ in.	30.0
R-19	5½ in.	38.0
R-11	3¼ in.	65.9

* Assumes 2 × 6 framing, 16 in. o.c. Assumes material is installed with pneumatic blower. Amounts listed are for estimating purposes only; see manufacturer's application data for actual guidelines.
** After settling

Other Insulating Products

For most do-it-yourselfers, deciding which type of insulation to use is essentially a matter of deciding between fiberglass, loose cellulose and rigid foam. These are the primary products stocked by building centers and they are made and packaged to be DIY-friendly. But the industry is changing quickly. Many of the recent advances have been improvements to already-popular products, especially fiberglass. But there are also a number of new options that have emerged, along with a few more traditional materials that have been improved and are enjoying a come-back. Here a a few of both:

MINERAL (ROCK) WOOL. If your search for information on insulating has lead you to any home improvement books written before 1970, you probably encountered quite a bit of information on rock wool. Made from stone or blast-furnace slag, mineral wool was a very popular home-insulating product prior to the advent of fiberglass insulation. But today, it's extremely difficult to locate. Because it is heavier and more costly than fiberglass, it has less appeal for most home owners. Its main advantage, and the reason it is still being produced at all, is that it resist heat and fire much better than other insulating products—it has a maximum heat rating of 500°F, compared to less than 200° for most other products. This makes mineral wool a very desirable product in commercial applications where high heat resistance is required.

WET-SPRAY CELLULOSE. The same basic product that's blown into attics can also be sprayed into wall cavities, where it conforms to the shape of the cavity. The difference is that, when sprayed into wall cavities, the cellulose product is mixed with water, and sometimes a chemical binder, then sprayed while wet. As it dries, it becomes rigid enough that excess can be trimmed away. Wet-spray cellulose has the same basic insulating properties as dry-blown, and is equally economical. It is best applied by professional installers, however.

SPRAY-ON POLYISOCYANURATE. Similar to expandable foam insulation, spray-on polyisocyanurate is applied in a thin layer to the back of a wall cavity. Once applied, it expands in thickness, filling the cavity and sealing around outlet boxes, pipes and other obstructions. It has a slightly higher R-value than fiberglass or loose insulation, and can be cost-effective, although it should only be installed by professionals. One drawback (which has been an issue with most blow-in or spray-on insulation but is being corrected by the industry) is that the blowing agents (propellants) can be very harmful to the ozone layer.

COTTON AND WOOL. Those who appreciate "natural" building products might wish to investigate cotton or wool insulation for their home. Fairly new products that can be difficult to find, both materials are now being made into insulation batts. Loose cotton is also available for blowing or pouring. Both are treated with fire retardants, but neither requires the formaldehyde binding agents that are used commonly with fiberglass or cellulose.

INSULATED STRUCTURAL PANELS. Used mostly for roof decking, thick polystyrene insulation is sandwiched between 4 × 8 sheets of OSB sheathing at the factory, then installed as a single unit.

FOAMED-IN PRODUCTS. A number of chemical compounds can be poured into confined cavities, where they form to the shape of the cavity. They generally have a thick liquid or foam consistency when installed. R-values for foamed-in insulation can be as high as R-6. Among the foamed-in types are polyurethane, phenolic foam and magnesium silicate. Of these, magnesium silicate is a popular product because it is free of volatile organic compounds to which some people are extremely sensitive. Professional installation only.

Vapor retarders

Vapor retarders (often called vapor barriers) are required to prevent moisture damage from occurring inside walls. They form an airtight seal between warm and cold air, stopping condensation from forming inside walls when warm and cold air meet. The backing on kraft and foil-faced fiberglass insulation, and sometimes the sleeve of encapsulated insulation (See page 130) serve as vapor retarders, but with unfaced fiberglass and other types of insulation, you'll need to attach a separate barrier, generally created with 4 or 6-mil polyethylene sheet plastic.

The vapor barrier should always be placed on the warm-in-winter side of a room: In climates where the living spaces are heated in the winter, the vapor retarder goes between the insulation and the interior wallcovering; In warmer climates, where air conditioning is the predominant heating/cooling utility, the vapor barrier should between the insulation and exterior wall sheathing. If you live in an inter-

Plastic sheeting (4 or 6-mil poly) is by far the most common material for creating a vapor retardant layer. Do not skimp and buy cheaper sheeting: it doesn't meet codes and will very likely fail because it is so easy to tear. For high-heat areas, such as saunas. you'll need to use a vapor retardant that is heat resistant, such as the reinforced kraft-paper and foil vapor barrier roll shown above (you'll need to contact a specialty insulation supplier or a sauna kit maker to locate foil vapor barrier). Be sure to use tape rated for vapor barrier taping to seal the seams and around obstructions. House wrap tape (the red roll above) can be used seal the seams of either plastic sheeting or foil,, but you can get foil vapor barrier tape for foil if you prefer.

mediate climate that could fall into either category, check with your local building department to find out what they recommend for vapor retarder placement.

Vapor barrier is required because there is always vapor in the air, and the humidity levels tend to be higher inside the house. Everyday household activities such as washing clothes,

House Wrap

House wrap is a building product that has a similar function to vapor retarder, but it not a substitute for it. Unlike vapor retarder material, house wrap does breathe slightly, allowing some water vapor to pass through while still repelling liquid water. House wrap is installed between the wall sheathing and siding. It's primary purposes are to increase energy efficiency by eliminating air flow, and to protect the interior of the wall from water. Historically, roofing felt or building paper has been used for this purpose, and it is still a viable option that many home builders prefer.

One advantage house wrap has over building paper is that it typically comes in 9-ft.wide rolls (usually around 100 ft. in length), so it can be installed faster and with fewer seams. Because of the large size it can also be a bit cumbersome, so it's definitely a good idea to get some help when you staple the house wrap onto your walls.

House wrap should be stapled to the sheathing with one staple per square foot (a hammer stapler is a great tool for this job). Most house wrap products have regular markings you can use as stapling guides. Most products also have front and back faces that are different in the amount of transpiration they allow. Be sure to install house wrap with the printed face out. Also be sure to overlap all seams from above and to seal well around

House wrap creates a barrier against water and air movement, but it does allow some water vapor to pass through so it is not considered a vapor retarder. When installing it, make sure seams overlap from above and that all seams are well sealed with tape (but use special house wrap tape, not duct tape as in the photo above: duct tape can degrade over time, causing the wrap to fail.

windows and doors, as well as tape the seams, with house wrap tape.

showering, doing the dishes, and simply breathing generate as much as 50 quarts of water per day in the form of water vapor.

If vapor barriers are not installed, two bad things can happen. In cold weather, warm inside air containing vapor can get past the wall finish and insulation and condense inside the cooler wall cavity. In hot, humid weather, the same thing can happen from the outside in. If enough water vapor penetrates the wall cavities over time, wood rot and mold, along with a host of other problems could occur. Also, in colder climates that receive snow, problems such as heat loss, ice dams, wet insulation and water damage can also occur, costing a lot of money in remodeling and repairs.

How vapor retarders work

Vapor retarders block the passage of water vapor from warm spaces to colder spaces. Without a suitable and correctly installed vapor retarder, the water vapor will condense out of the warm air when it meets the cold air, causing water damage in the wall.

Illustration courtesy of Johns Manville Corp.

Vapor Barriers

Metallic seaming tape

Foil vapor barrier material creates an impermeable seal while resisting high heat. It is seldom required in residences, but is mandated in many commercial situations. The most common need for foil in the home is when installing a sauna, where plastic vapor barrier is susceptible to melting from the high heat (up to 190° F). Seams are sealed with metallic seaming tape. Normally, you'll need to go to a professional insulation materials supplier to find it. The product shown in the sauna above (also seen in photo, page 140) was purchased in 48-in. wide rolls.

Tape the seams! One of the most common mistakes do-it-yourselfers make when insulating is failing to tape the vapor barrier seams. Even though 4-or-6-mil plastic sheeting comes in 9-foot-wide rolls that make it possible to wrap a room with few or even no seams, you'll still need to seal around cutouts for windows and receptacles, as well as at the tops and bottoms of the walls. If you do end up with seams between vapor barrier sheets, make sure the pieces overlap by 12 inches or so, and be sure to tape them as well. Also tape over staples and any punctures that occur (they're hard to avoid) before installing the wallcovering. Be sure to use vapor-barrier tape, not duct tape or other household products (See photo below).

Air flow is essential to the health of your home, but it's very easy to create problems when you insulate. The most common error is to block air intake vents in the soffits with attic insulation (an error that's easily avoided). If you are building an addition to your home, make sure to check with your local building department to learn the ventilation requirements in your area.

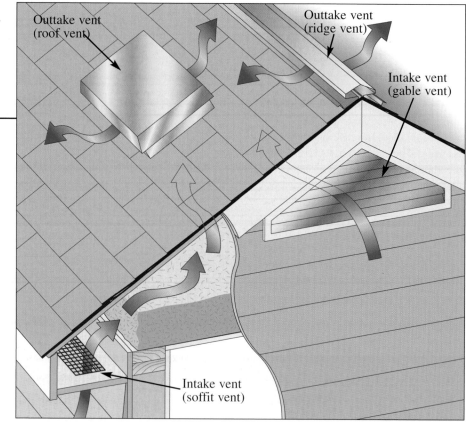

VENTILATION

Creating and maintaining an adequate flow of fresh air through your attic depends on two factors: having a sufficient number of air intake and outtake vents; and making sure the air passages are clear.

Intake vents: *Soffit vents* can be added to increase intake airflow on closed soffit systems. Rectangular, louvered vents are easily added to existing soffits. Continuous soffit vents provide a more even airflow but are designed to be used in conjunction with a prefabricated metal or vinyl soffit system. They can be retrofitted into plywood soffits, but the project is much more complicated than simply adding a few rectangular or round vents. Round soffit vents (also called "round breathers") match common hole saw diameters (2, 3 and 4 in.) and are thus very easy to install in soffits as well as in blocking

between rafters on open-eave homes. *Eave vents* are installed in lieu of blocking between rafters on open-eave roofs, usually during new construction. Eave vents can also be installed in the house siding near the eave area. *Gable*

vents are larger rectangular or triangular vents installed in the siding near the peak of a roof gable.

Outtake vents: *Flat roof vents* are simple nylon, PVC or metal vent covers that fit over holes cut into the roof,

Vent covers prevent pests from entering your home through vent openings. The most common types of vent covers include: (A) turbine-style roof outtake vent; (B) flat roof outtake vent; (C) round soffit vents; (D) louvered (rectangu-lar) soffit intake vent; (E) gable intake vent; (F) continuous metal ridge vent (installed over shingles); (G) plastic ridge vent (shingled over); (H) continuous soffit vent.

usually near the ridge. *Ridge vents* are highly effective, providing even out-take airflow along the entire ridge. Generally, they're installed during initial construction, but they can be added as a retrofit project or when reshingling the roof. *Turbine vents* are installed in much the same way as flat roof vents but provide greater airflow by actively drawing air through the vent area as they spin. Even on a windless day, you'll often see them slowly whirling, due to convection currents from hot air escaping the attic. You can also purchase powered turbine vents driven by an electric motor to establish consistent air flow. Install powered vents only in roofs with a significant air-flow problem.

Understanding baffles

Baffles are rigid plastic or foam panels you install inside your attic in the eave area to prevent insulation from blocking the flow of air up through the eaves. Installing baffles is very simple. Working as far into the eave areas as you can get, pull back the attic insulation and locate the air intake vents in your soffits or in the blocking between rafters. Insert the baffles between your rafters or trusses so the ends extend up to the exterior walls, but leave clear passage from the intakes. Attach them to the roof decking by stapling through the flanges. Replace the insulation up to the baffles.

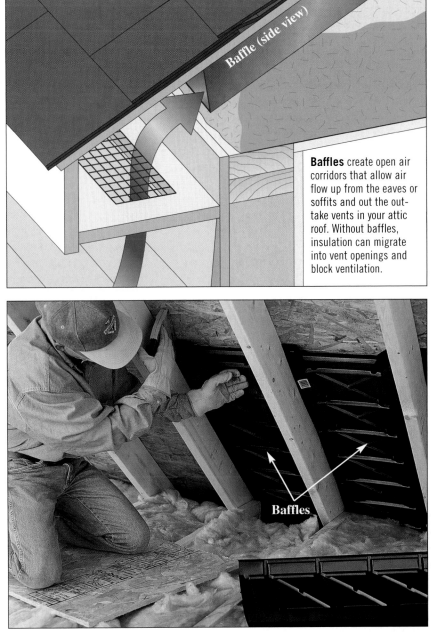

Baffles create open air corridors that allow air flow up from the eaves or soffits and out the out-take vents in your attic roof. Without baffles, insulation can migrate into vent openings and block ventilation.

When installing baffles around attic insulation, wear long pants, a long sleeved shirt and a particle mask. Place a piece of scrap plywood or particle board across the ceiling joists to create a safe work platform.

Photo courtesy of USG Corp.

Wallboard panels are sold in bundles of two, taped together at each end. If you're wallboarding an entire room, think seriously about having the panels delivered. Transporting them yourself is heavy work and damage to the panels is a frequent occurrence. Be sure to inspect deliveries for damage before signing for them.

WALLBOARD

Gypsum wallboard, otherwise known as *sheetrock* or *drywall,* is a low-cost, easy-to-install material for creating walls (and ceilings—See pages 154 to 165). When installed and finished, it provides a flat wall surface that can be painted, textured or used as a substrate. Wallboard is available in different grades and dimensions, from 4 × 8 ft. panels (by far the most common) to 4 × 14 ft. panels. 54-in.-wide panels can be ordered. For most home remodeling projects, ½ in.-thick, *regular core* (R-grade) gypsum drywall is used for walls and ceiling that are 16-on-center. In areas where a firewall is

needed (for example, a wall that separates an attached garage), ⅝-in.-thick *type X* fire-resistant gypsum is used. There are also panels available with a foil backing for areas where a vapor barrier is needed, such as a basement foundation wall that has been furred out for finishing. Water-resistant grade gypsum, typically called *greenboard,* is installed in areas such as bathrooms where moisture levels are high. Greenboard should not be used in areas where it could come into direct contact with water, such as a tub surround. In this situation, *cementboard* is a better choice.

Wallboard is typically fastened to studs or furring strips horizontally. By hanging them in this manner, the number of vertical seams, which are more difficult to mud, is reduced. These vertical seams, however, will be composed of the short edges, which are square-cut, making them difficult to conceal with compound. The longer edges, however, are tapered, allowing the tape and compound to be set in a channel, minimizing ridges. When framing, it is important to keep in mind that inside corners, where two sheets of drywall meet, need proper

(Continued on page 146)

Typical wallboard usage by type

TYPE/THICKNESS	TYPICAL USES (CODES VARY: CONFIRM WITH LOCAL INSPECTOR)
Gypsum Wallboard	
¼ in.	Over existing walls & ceilings
⅜ in.	Over existing walls & ceilings; ceilings with 16 o.c. framing that do not support insulation and are not finished with spray texture
½ in.	Interior walls & ceilings
Type "X" Firecore	
½ in	Interior walls & ceilings where firewall is required by Code
⅝ in.	Interior walls & ceilings where firewall is required by Code or where extra soundproofing is desired
Water-resistant (greenboard) ½ in. or ⅝ in.	Interior walls & ceilings in high humidity areas such as bathrooms, kitchens and utility rooms; as a backer for adhesive-bonded wallcoverings such as ceramic tile, plastic tile or plastic-faced wall panels; ceilings require ⅝ in. thick greenboard unless joist spacing is 12 in. o.c. or closer; not for use in areas with constant moisture (use cementboard); paint with oil-based paints
Cementboard ½ in. and ⅝ in.	Heat shield on walls and floors surrounding solid-fuel heaters and fireplace stoves (check local codes); as a backer for ceramic tile installations in floors, walls and countertops; as a backer for ceramic and other tile types in high-moisture areas, including tub/shower surrounds. Common sizes are 32 in. wide by 48, 60 or 72 in. ⅝-in-thick cementboard may be a special order item.

Other wallboard types

Foil-back gypsum: Coated on back side with kraft-paper backed aluminum; used primarily as a wallsurface on furred wall framing, especially in a basement; foil backing functions as a vapor barrier. Available in ⅜, ½ and ⅝ in. thickness (⅜ in. thick can be used as a base layer in a 2-layer wall only; do not use as a standalone wall covering).

Vinyl-faced gypsum: Standard gypsum wallboard coated on one face with an easy-to-clean vinyl surface in several color options.

Flexible gypsum: Reinforced ¼-in.-thick gypsum panels for bending curves, as in door archways.

Sag-resistant gypsum: Stiffened ½ in. panels used mostly in ceiling to support spray-on, water-based texturing (you need to use ⅝ in. standard wallboard for this purpose).

Exterior gypsum panels: Designed to resist moisture and with anti-sag properties; can be used in eaves and soffits and as wall or ceiling covering in exterior spaces without direct exposure to weather, including carports and porches.

(Continued from page 144)

backing. It is usually worth it to add or position a stud, so both can be fastened securely. If a framing member is not placed there, blocking or drywall clips can be used to provide support. A drywall clip is simply an L-shaped metal clip that is screwed to the framing member, allowing the panel to rest against it and then be secured by the perpendicular panel.

Fasteners. Gypsum panels are hung with either ring-shank drywall nails or "Type W" wallboard screws. Generally, using screws is much faster than nailing, less likely to dimple the wallboard, and the screws are not as likely to "pop" as nails. A bead of panel adhesive on the stud will help secure it to the wall, as well as deaden noise.

Finishing materials. After hanging, wallboard is treated with joint compound (commonly called "mud"), wallboard tape and corner bead. The tape conceals and reinforces seams, while serving as a substrate for the joint compound. The most common and inexpensive tape is made of paper, which is set into a light layer of mud to make it adhere. Other tapes that are used

include self-adhesive fiberglass mesh tape and perforated self-adhesive paper tape. Regardless of the type of tape used, the joints normally are given three coats of compound, the second and third coat being applied after the previous one has dried. With some lightweight joint compound, you can get by with just two layers of mud, according to the manufacturers (See page 148).

At outside and inside corners, and sometimes at transition points between wallcovering types, wallboard bead is installed. Beads come in many shapes, sizes and even materials, such as metal, vinyl or even paper. Corner bead is usually made of metal or vinyl. It is fastened to an outside corner with nails or screws and is used to finish off and protect the corner against bumps and dents. Corner bead can come in either 90° angles or with a bull nose. It can be rigid for a wall or flexible for an archway. Once corner bead is fastened, it is mudded over with compound.

Inside corner bead is less common, but still available. It is typically a metal "L" channel covered with paper that can be mudded in place without being secured.

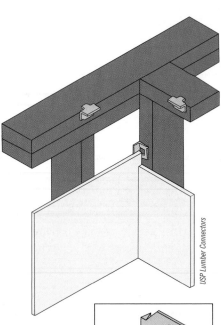

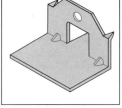

Drywall clips can be mounted to the framing members in corners and along cap plates to provide support for the edges of wallboard panels. They are not designed to receive fasteners—you'll need to install wood blocking for that.

Tools & materials for hanging wallboard

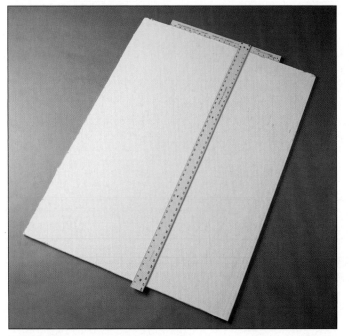

Wallboard T-squares are used to square and measure sheets of wallboard for cutting, and can be used as cutting guides.

Finishing materials for wallboard joints include mesh sanding sheets and a sanding block, a sanding sponge for final sanding and wallboard sealant to apply before painting.

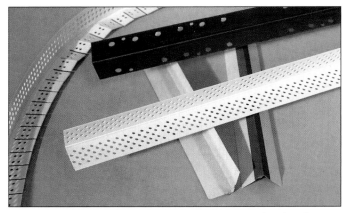

Corner bead reinforces inside and outside corners, protecting them from crushing and giving them a straight edge. Vinyl and metal corner bead offer more protection than paper tape, which may also be used, but they have a tendency to kink when installed and require more joint compound to be concealed. Vinyl corner bead with kerfing can be used on curved edges.

Wallboard tape is applied over seams to reinforce them and to provide tooth for the joint compound. Paper tape (A) is the most common and cheapest. You can also use regular fiberglass mesh tape (B), or self-adhesive tape (C). For repairs, use extra-wide tape (D).

"Mudding tools" include a selection of wallboard knives in a variety of blade widths for spreading joint compound. Wallboard hawks are metal trays equipped with a handle below, making handling smaller quantities of joint compound an easier, neater task.

Wallboard guns and special attachments for your power drill keep you from overdriving wallboard screws. Screwheads should be recessed $\frac{1}{32}$ in. below the paper wallboard surface, without breaking the surface.

Metal furring channel is attached to framed walls to create a larger insulation void. The 1½ in. deep furring channels can support ½ in. or ⅝ in. wallboard when installed 24 in. o.c. Attach them by driving "Type S" wallboard screws through the top and bottom flanges at wall stud locations. Hang the drywall by screwing it directly to the channels with wallboard screws.

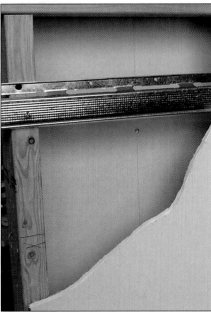

Resilient channels are attached at 24-in.-on-center intervals across wall framing, primarily to provide greater sound control. By isolating the wallboard from the framing members (either wood or steel), the ½-in.-deep resilient channels reduce the transmission of sound through the wall. They are attached perpendicular to the framing members with 1¼ in., "Type S" wallboard screws. When hanging the wallboard, drive wallboard screws into studs, through the resilient channels.

All joint compound is not alike. Setting times, hardness, ease of sanding, resistance to shrinkage, and general workability all vary from product to product. In some cases, specific properties of the compound are advantges, while in others they work against it.

Premixed vs. powder. When choosing the joint compound to use in your wallboard project, the first decision you'll need to make is whether you prefer buckets of pre-mixed compound or dry powder that you mix yourself. Even professional "mudders" debate this decision hotly. The information to the right to can help you decide which type is better for you, but the best way to find out is simply to try working with both and see which one you prefer.

Special-purpose vs. all-purpose. Another choice you'll need to make is whether to use two or more specially formulated compounds for different stages of your project, or a single all-purpose product. Most do-it-yourselfers choose the all-purpose option. See tip box, next page.

Setting-type vs. drying-type. Most joint compound sold today is drying type, which is generally easier to work with at all stages: it trowels on smoother and sands more easily than setting type. But setting type is hard, less like to crack, and more resistant to moisture (see next page).

Lightweight compound. Available in both powder and premixed form, lightweight joint compounds are less dense than conventional joint compound and weigh about 35% less. If you're doing a big taping and mudding project, you'll feel the difference in the weight of the hawk over the course of a day. The lighter weight has little or no impact on the durability of the dried mixture, and has the added benefit of being very easy to sand smooth. It can be smoothed using only 150-grit sandpaper or 220-grit sanding mesh.

Premixed vs. dry-powder joint compound

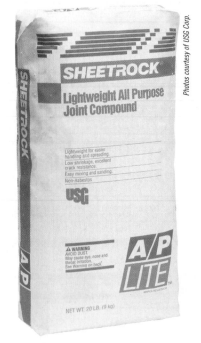

Photos courtesy of USG Corp.

PREMIXED: At first glance, premixed product seems to have more plusses in its favor.

PLUSSES:
• Faster to use (simply because you don't have to stop your work to mix more).
• Consistent thickness.
• Has an almost unlimited *open time* (the time before it hardens or clumps up, making it unusable) as long as you close the container tightly.
• There is no clean-up involved, other than rinsing out the bucket it came in if you want to save it.
• Can be thinned with water for application of final coat.

MINUSES:
• More expensive.
• Tends to shrink more when drying.
• Limited shelf life once container is opened.

DRY POWDER: Dry powder has several advantages that work in its favor.

PLUSSES:
• Can easily adjust the consistency of the compound to meet your preferences.
• Generally, dries harder than pre-mix, with less shrinkage.
• Bags are lighter in weight for easy transportation.
• More options of type and setting/open times.
• Costs less than premixed.

MINUSES:
• Mixing with water takes time and makes a mess.
• Difficult to get uniform consistency from batch to batch.
• Empty paper bags are not as handy to keep around the shop as empty 5-gallon buckets of pre-mixed compound.

Topping & Taping Compounds: a reliable dry-mix combo

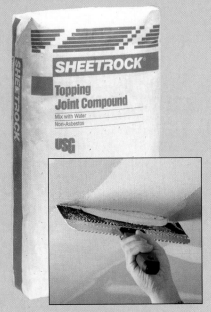

Topping joint compound is designed for smooth feathering and smooth sanding, making it the product to use for your final coat or two of compound.

Taping joint compound is designed for excellent bonding and minimal shrinkage, making it the product to use for embedding tape, coating over wallboard bead, and thicker coats in general.

OR, Choose an all-purpose product

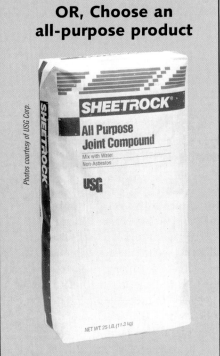

Photos courtesy of USG Corp.

All-purpose joint compound does an adequate job of both taping and topping functions, although the special-purpose compounds will each outperform it for their specific function.

Setting-type vs. drying type

Joint compound comes in two fundamental formulations: drying-type and setting-type. Most of the all-purpose, pre-mixed compound used today is drying type: the water in it evaporates, leaving the sus-pended product behind to harden and dry. Setting-type joint compound hardens as a chemical reaction occurs, which creates a harder surface that shrinks less and is less affected by humidity than dry-ing compound. Setting compounds are made with a range of setting times (20, 45, 90, 210 and 300 min-utes). Product with longer setting times can be reworked and you can mix them in bigger batches. Product with shorter setting times may be recoated or finished sooner.

Photo courtesy of USG Corp.

Use a mixing paddle attachment for an electric drill to blend batches of dry-mix joint compound or spray texture with water. The paddle mixes the product many times faster and much more evenly than stirring by hand.

Working with wallboard

Before installing wallboard, make certain inspections for plumbing, electrical and insulation have been completed. If your project includes insulation and the insulation is unfaced, install a proper vapor barrier before attaching the wallboard. Make certain a metal protector plate covers any spot where wiring or pipes are closer than 1½ in. to the edge of the joist.

Estimating wallboard materials:
• Divide the square footage of the ceiling (length times width) by 32 (the square footage of one 4 × 8-ft. sheet)
• Add 10% for waste, then round up to the next full sheet (a multiple of 32). You usually can return unused sheets.
• For every 1000 square feet of wallboard, purchase 370 ft. of paper tape, 140 pounds of premixed joint compound and 700 screws.

Cutting wallboard

Step 1: Prop the wallboard sheet in a vertical position and score the finish surface along the cutting lines with a sharp utility knife. Use a wallboard T-square to ensure straight cuts. Anchor both ends of the straightedge when scoring to keep the straightedge from wandering during the cut.

Step 2: With the scored face of the wallboard facing away from you, snap the wallboard to break the gypsum along the cutting line. For full pieces, hold the wallboard on both sides of the cutting line and snap the piece in against your knee.

Step 3: Slice through the paper on the unfinished side of the wallboard, following the cutting line.

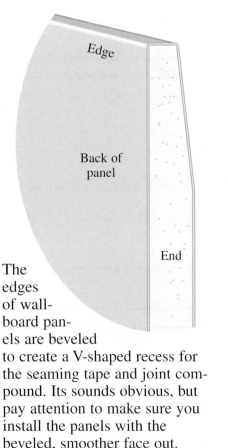

The edges of wallboard panels are beveled to create a V-shaped recess for the seaming tape and joint compound. Its sounds obvious, but pay attention to make sure you install the panels with the beveled, smoother face out.

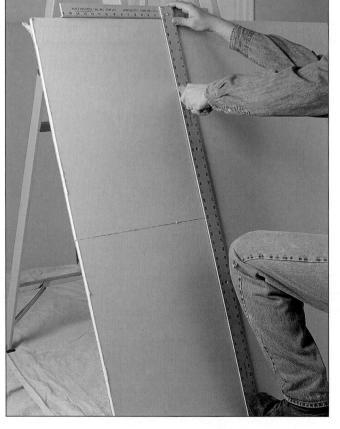

Making cutouts

The goal, when cutting wallboard, is to create workpieces that are as large as possible, reducing your taping and mudding time. To make square cutouts, where neither leg runs all the way across the panel, first use a wallboard saw to cut the shorter leg of the corner. Then, score and snap the remaining leg of the cutout.

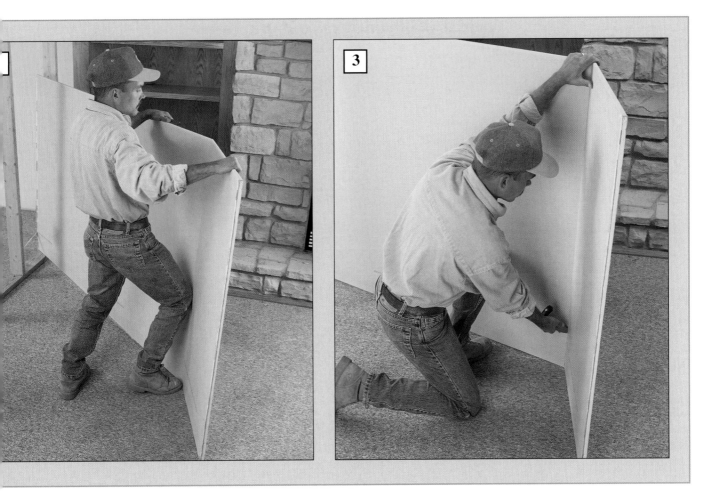

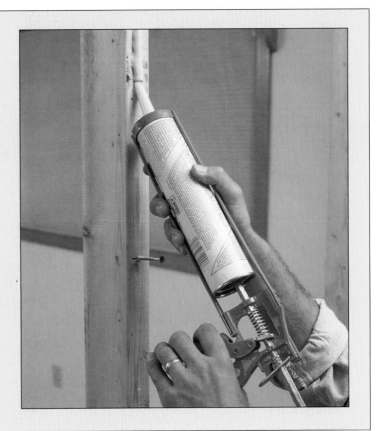

Panel adhesives & sound control

Apply a bead of wallboard adhesive to the wall framing members before installing each piece of wallboard. Wallboard adhesive (you can get by with ordinary construction adhesive) strengthens the wall and helps deaden sound transfer through the wall. Most wallboard product manufacturers do make special acoustical sealant, which is sold in caulk-gun cartridges. It is intended primarily for use with sound-rated partition walls and ceiling systems. It can also be used to seal around exterior walls to reduce sound transmission.

Photo courtesy of USG Corp.

Typical wallboard layout patterns

OPTION 1
HORIZONTAL
(ALSO DESCRIBED AS
"PERPENDICULAR")

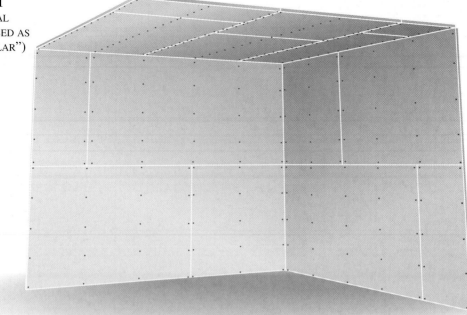

TIPS FOR HANGING WALLBOARD

• Cover ceilings first, then walls.
• After positioning the panel, begin attaching it by driving screws or nails in the field area, not at the edges.
• Use a foot-activated wallboard lifter to raise panels off the floor slightly before attaching. Be sure to leave a gap (1/16 in. or so) between panels to allow for slight movement and let the joint compound get a good grip.

• Always store wallboard flat to reduce risk of damaging edges and injury if panels tip.
• In new construction, allow wood framing members to rest for at least a few days before installing wallboard. This will give the wood a chance to acclimate.

OPTION 2:
VERTICAL
(ALSO DESCRIBED
AS "PARALLEL")

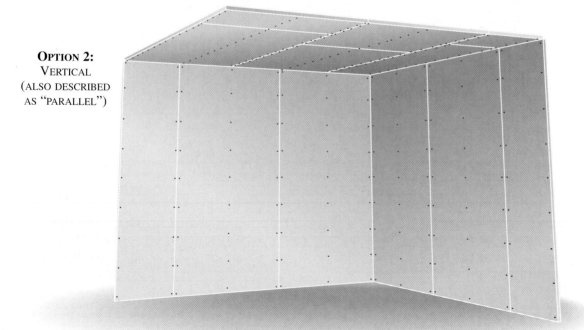

TIP: Hang wallboard on the horizontal

Minimize vertical seams by hanging wallboard horizontally whenever possible. Vertical seams are tougher to reach for taping and finishing, and you'll have more of them. One drawback to hanging wallboard horizontally is that end joints where wallboard sheets meet will not have a "channel" for joint compound. In these cases, feather successive layers of compound carefully so as not to mound the joints, which will require more sanding to mask them.

Tips for driving fasteners: Keep fasteners at least ⅜ in. from the ends and edges of the panel. If nailing, use ring-shank wallboard nails spaced no more than 7 in. apart on-center in ceilings, and no more than 8 in. on walls. If using screws, use 1¼-in., Type "W" wallboard screws spaced no more than 16 in, apart on-center for walls and no more than 12 in. apart on ceilings.

Countersink screwheads 1/32-in. deep

Seaming: Start by spreading a thin layer (1/16 in. or so) of setting-type joint compound into the "V" created by the beveled edges of the panels, using a 5-or-6 in. taping knife. Press the paper or fiberglass tape into the compound, embedding it. Immediately cover with a thin layer of joint compound. After the compound dries, apply a second coat over the tape, using the seam knife. Feather the second coat so it expends about 2 in. past the edge of the tape on each side. When dry, sand down any ridges or bumps, then apply a final coat of joint compound with a 10-in. taping knife. Feather the final layer so it extends 2 in. past each edge of the second coat. Sand smooth when dry.

CEILING MATERIALS

There is a wealth of materials and methods available for turning a plain ceiling into a striking feature of a room's decor.

The choice between a smooth or textured ceiling finish will determine the kind of work done to the ceiling surface. Smooth finishes are created with paint or wallpaper over a wallboard surface. Textured finishes can be created with wallpaper, texturing prod-ucts sprayed onto the ceiling surface or by adding a new surface of pressed metal panels. If ongoing access to elec-trical, plumbing or heating and cooling systems above the ceiling is necessary, then a suspended ceiling with remov-able panels is a good choice.

A smooth-finished ceiling requires a flat ceiling without noticeable blem-ishes. If you're painting or updating an existing ceiling, minor repairs of cracks, small holes or water stains may be all that's needed to make the ceiling surface ready. But unevenness caused by joists that are not level or major repairs will show through. This means the old ceiling should be replaced. New wallboard should be installed with smooth joints for a blemish-free surface.

Prepare for a ceiling-finishing proj-ect like you would for any remodeling project. Wear appropriate eye, ear and respiratory protection. Cover doorways and duct work openings with plastic. Check with the local building inspector for any code regulations affecting your project, and make certain inspections for electrical and plumbing work, if necessary, are completed before installing new wallboard. Remember that electrical boxes that contain live cables can't be covered with wallboard or other materials (a solid box coverplate is necessary so the wires can be accessed). Empty or disconnected electrical boxes may be covered.

Removing old ceiling materials. Many remodeling projects include upgrades to wiring or plumbing systems. To access the old wires or pipes and work on them, you'll very likely need to cut into your existing ceiling. If you do enough cutting, you'll probably decide it's easier to replace the old ceiling materials completely than to try to patch all the holes. Here are a few tips on how to remove an old ceiling:

Plaster and lath. Protect flooring before you start by laying down a layer of thick cardboard covered with a tarp. Wearing safety glasses and a dust mask, begin by carefully pulling down any loose areas. Use a maul or the flat side of a hammer against the plaster surface between joists to break it loose from the keys holding it to the lath. Then slip a pry bar behind the plaster to finish pulling it off the ceiling. Work carefully around electrical boxes, since they may be attached to the plaster. Make certain the power is off to the boxes. Work in small sections and not directly overhead, as plaster is surprisingly heavy.

Wallboard. Protect the floor and don your safety gear as noted above. Snap chalklines between joist locations and cut along the lines. Make certain you know the location of any electrical and plumbing in the ceiling and that the power is off to fixture boxes. Cut just deeply enough to sever the wallboard. Break and pull the wallboard away from the joists. A pry bar will be helpful. If screws attach the wallboard, use a drill/driver to remove them.

Options for ceiling coverings

Photo courtesy of Armstrong World Industries, Inc.

Ceiling tiles can be suspended from a gridwork of support rails or adhered directly to the ceiling.

Metal ceiling panels are a high-end option that's growing in popularity.

Wallboard with an applied textured surface is one of the most popular ceiling options today.

See "Wallboard," pages 144 to 153, for more information on wallboard and wallboard materials

Wallboard is a very popular ceiling material because it is inexpensive and adaptable to a number of finishes, including paint, spray texture and wallpaper. For most ceilings with 16-on-center joists, ½ in.-thick wallboard is suitable.

WALLBOARD CEILINGS

Installing wallboard on a ceiling is one of those projects that's legendary for being a pain in the neck, so to speak. That reputation is due largely to the suffering endured by the many who have tried to accomplish the task without the help of lifts or jacks to support the heavy panels while they're positioned. Even with a lift or jacks, there's no way of getting around the neck and back stress that comes from driving screws, taping and mudding overhead. Nevertheless, wallboard is by far the most common ceiling material used today. Once its seamed and taped, it can be primed and painted for a smooth finish, or finished with ceiling texture.

Install a new wallboard ceiling in additions and other new construction building projects. Wallboard installation techniques also are used when making ceiling repairs.

In most cases, you can install ½-in.-thick wallboard on ceiling joists that are spaced 16 in. on-center. Some building codes do require ⅝-in.-thick wallboard on all ceilings; check with your local building inspector for requirements concerning your project. Trusses or joists spaced 24 in. on-center require ⅝-in.-thick wallboard.

If you are covering over an existing ceiling surface (of cracked plaster, for example) ½-in. or even ⅜-in. material is fine, but make certain you use screws long enough to penetrate into the ceiling joists at least 1 in. When installing wallboard in a bathroom ceiling above a shower or another wet area, use water-resistant wallboard (which usually has a green paper surface and is often called "greenboard").

Prepare for your wallboard project by sealing the project area from the rest of your house: wallboard dust is very fine and penetrates nearby areas easily. Cover doorways, heating/cooling vents and other large openings with plastic sheeting. Tarps laid over a layer of cardboard will protect flooring. Spread a tarp outside the room entrance to prevent tracking wallboard dust into other rooms. Remember to wear eye and respiratory protection when working with wallboard, as the dust is an irritant.

Before you start installing the wallboard, make sure the ceiling joists are straight and spaced properly. Use cross blocking between joists to straighten curved joists and add 2 × 4 nailers when joists are spaced too far apart. Also, make certain there are adequate nailing surfaces for attaching the wallboard. No edge of a sheet should be unsupported for more than 2 ft. Extra nailing surfaces often are needed at non-load-bearing walls and on vaulted ceilings.

Wallboard lifts

A wallboard lift is a rental tool used to raise sheets of wallboard up to the ceiling for positioning and to hold them in place while you screw them to the ceilings joists. Set the sheet on the wallboard lift with the back side facing the ceiling joists and raise it into position. Make certain the sheet is properly aligned with both walls in the corner, or to the perpendicular line, and the end is centered on the joist.

Tool Tips

Installing wallboard on a ceiling is never as easy task, but any of the tools shown here will be a big help.

Stilts (Left photo): Wallboard installers use special stilts, available at rental centers, when taping and applying joint compound on a ceiling. Using the stilts is much quicker than constantly moving a ladder or scaffolding. The working height on the stilts is adjustable and they are surprisingly stable.

STILTS   DUSTLESS SANDER   WALLBOARD JACK

Dustless sanders (Middle photo) remove most of the sanding dust and make the job less messy. The unit attaches to any shop vacuum and extension handle. The dust is extracted through small holes in the sanding block and caught in the water chamber, which prevents the dust from passing through the vacuum and back into the air. You should still wear a dust mask, and also ear protection for the vacuum noise.

A wallboard jack (right photo) is a handy, home-made lifting device made of 2 × 4s. The jack should be an inch or two taller than the distance from the wall to the bottoms of the joists.

Before installing wallboard on the ceiling, make certain inspections for plumbing, electrical and insulation have been completed. If your project includes insulation and the insulation is unfaced, install a proper vapor barrier before attaching the wallboard. A metal protector plate should cover any spot where wiring or pipes are closer than 1½ in. to the edge of the joist.

Install wallboard sheets perpendicular to the ceiling joists, and stagger the end seams. This provides the greatest ceiling strength and will help prevent cracks or sagging seams. Determine a layout that uses the fewest pieces, for economy and ease of installation. Use the method to the right to estimate the number of sheets needed.

Always cut wallboard through the finish surface and install the wallboard so the finish surface faces the room. The finish surface is smoother and a lighter color than the back (usually a darker gray). Change blades frequently in your utility knife. Sharp blades make accurate cuts much more easily, but the dense wallboard material quickly dulls the blades.

Use wallboard screws long enough to penetrate at least 1 in. into the ceiling joists when attaching the wallboard to the ceiling joists. Screws make a more stable ceiling and there is much less risk of "pops" than with nails. Use nails to tack a sheet into position when it's awkward to use a screw gun, but finish attaching the sheet with screws.

How to estimate wallboard materials:

1 Divide the square footage of the ceiling (length times width) by 32 (the square footage of one 4 × 8-ft. sheet)

2 Add 10% for waste, then round up to the next full sheet (a multiple of 32). You usually can return unused sheets.

3 For every 1000 square feet of wallboard, purchase 370 ft. of paper tape, 140 pounds of premixed joint compound and 700 screws.

SPRAY TEXTURE

Spraying a texture compound onto a ceiling is a quick and inexpensive technique for finishing a ceiling. A sprayed texture covers any irregularity less than ⅛ in. in dimension. It allows for a quicker installation of wallboard since it subtracts one round of joint compound application and lessens sanding time. It disguises an uneven ceiling, too, because the textured surface minimizes the shadows and reflections that light makes across a smooth ceiling.

There are two basic types of sprayed texture compounds for ceilings. Pebbled texture is a mixture of joint compound, white latex paint and small-aggregate particles. When sprayed on the ceiling, it creates a surface covered with tiny "pebbles." Application of this ceiling texture is the quickest because all you have to do is spray it on the ceiling. But it can't be painted later because the pebble-like particles will be knocked off. Knockdown texture is a compound resembling thinned joint compound (many professionals make it from just that). It sprays on the ceiling, leaving many different levels of compound. After this sets up for a few minutes, the high points of the texture are flattened with a broad taping knife. This process takes longer and you have to be careful not to leave edges with the taping knife. Knockdown texture can be painted easily after it is dry.

A less common method for texturing a ceiling, used mostly by do-it-yourselfers, is to paint the ceiling with roll-on texture compound or a paint containing texture additive. With some practice and care, rolled-on texture has the potential to look appealing, but it is unlikely to ever look as uniform and neat as sprayed texture.

Roll texturing compound, available at home centers, looks like soft-serve ice cream. It is applied with a special roller that fits on a standard roller frame. Texture beads made from perlite can also give a raised look. Sold in a box, they are simply stirred into the paint. It is then mixed and applied with a special roller cover. The look is similar to spray texture, but can be uneven.

Mixing the spray mixture by hand can be a lot of work—simplify the process by using a mixing paddle attachment for an electric drill. For pebble texture (non-paintable) blend dry spray texture mix with water and (if the texture manufacturer suggests) latex-based paint. If you're using knockdown texture, see next page.

Load the hopper of the sprayer with well-mixed texture material. Fill it only about three-quarters full at a time. In case of spills, set the hopper and spray mechanism into a bucket before filling. Wear disposable coveralls along with face and eye protection. Hold the spray gun at about a 45° angle to the ceiling, 2 to 4 ft. away, and spray on the texture. Keep the hopper moving at all times and take care not to apply a layer that's too heavy.

Ceiling Texture

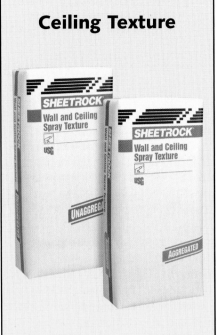

When choosing a texturing product for your ceiling, you'll first need to decide if you want it to contain any aggregates at all (aggregated or unaggregated, above). If so, you'll need to select the best size aggregate for your needs (fine, medium or coarse, below).

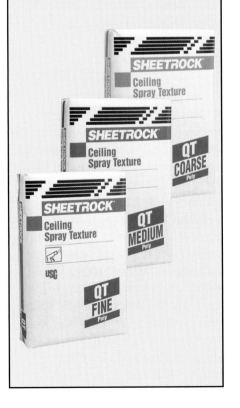

Texture paint

If you'd rather not trouble yourself with the mess and fuss of a applying spray-on texture, look for premixed texture paint instead. Applied with a paint roller (usually with a ¾ in. nap), texture paint is sold in several formulations for a variety of applications. The main difference between types is with the aggregate (or lack of aggregate—see below). Some texture paint is suitable for ceilings only, so read the label carefully. All texture paint is white: if you want a different color, the best solution is simply to paint over it with the color you prefer.

Knockdown texture

Combine dry, unaggregated ceiling texture with water in a clean bucket, following the manufacturer's directions. For even blending (and minimal back strain) use a mixing paddle attachment installed in an electric drill to blend the material. Apply the texture with the power sprayer then let it set up for a few minutes. Use a 12-in. taping knife to flatten the top edges of the sprayed texture. Work quickly and move the knife in random directions, being careful not to gouge the texture with the edge of the knife.

Ceiling panels are manufactured in a growing array of styles that give homeowners plenty of design options. Acoustical tile, which is generally attached directly to the ceiling, also deadens sound in the room. *Photo courtesy of USG Corp.*

CEILING TILES

Ceiling tiles may be affixed directly to the existing ceiling surface, or suspended in a metal gridwork that's attached to or hung from the ceiling or ceiling joists. A suspended ceiling is useful when permanent access to the ceiling area behind it is needed; for example, if you're remodeling a basement and the plumbing, electrical or ductwork must remain accessible. The most common installation is a grid framework made of lightweight metal brackets hung beneath the existing ceiling surface or joists. Pieces of ceiling panel are placed on the flanges of the brackets, filling the open spaces in the grid between the brackets. The panels are easily removed when access is needed, and then quickly replaced when work is finished. A suspended ceiling also is a simple and relatively inexpensive way to convert a room with a high ceiling to a standard 8-ft. ceiling height or cover over a damaged ceiling surface.

A minimum space of 4 in. must be left behind the suspended ceiling framework so the panel pieces can be placed in or taken out of the brackets. Keep this in mind when deciding if a suspended ceiling is right for your project, as this significant change in ceiling height can affect the function of doors, lighting fixtures, wall cabinets and shelving. Plus, many building codes have minimum ceiling height regulations that could apply to a suspended ceiling installation. Check with your local building inspector about any restrictions for your project.

Suspended ceiling panels are available in 2 × 2 or 2 × 4-ft. sections. Fluorescent light fixtures designed to fit within the grid framework also are available. Or you can use standard incandescent and recessed light fixtures in the suspended ceiling, though their installation will require some adaptation to fit the suspended ceiling height. Hire a pro if you aren't confident about your ability to make these electrical installations.

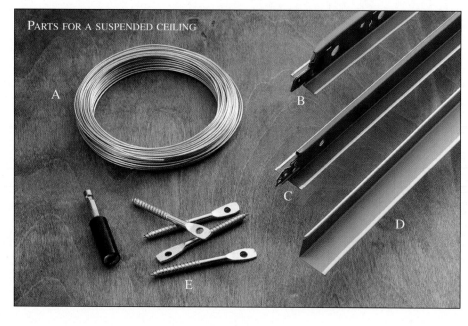

PARTS FOR A SUSPENDED CEILING

A common suspended ceiling system includes: Wall angle pieces (D) that are attached to the walls around the room's perimeter; Runners (B) rest on the wall angles at the ends of the room and are supported by wires attached to the ceiling joists; Cross-tees (C) attach between the runners (or between runners and wall angles at the sides of the room) and complete the grid sections for the ceiling panels; Screw eyes (E) are attached to the ceiling joists to hang support wires (A) that are cut to length and hold up the grid framework.

Ceiling panel styles

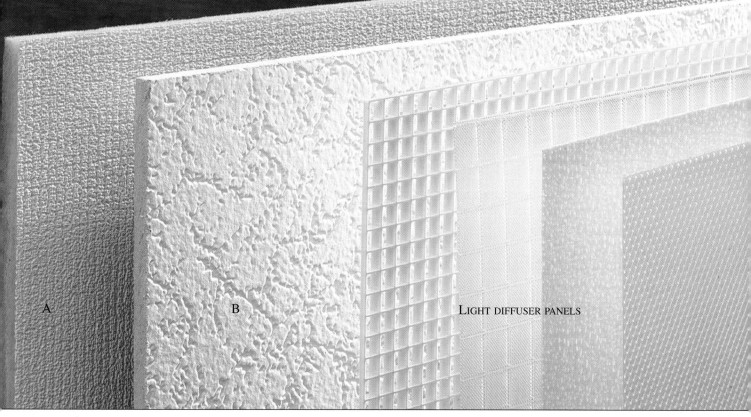

A B LIGHT DIFFUSER PANELS

Common ceiling and diffuser panels include: Insulated panels (A); Acoustical tiles (B) that dampen the sound in a room. Light diffuser panels come in a wide range of styles and opacities. They are designed to fit into a grid with 2 × 4-ft. openings, in conjunction with a 4-ft.-long fluorescent light fixture.

You will need to determine joist locations if installing a suspended ceiling in a room with an existing ceiling surface. Runners should be installed perpendicular to the ceiling joists and the support wires for the metal framework must be attached to the joists. If the ceiling joists are visible, remember that a minimum of 4 in. of space must be available beneath the lowest structural members, pipes or cables in the ceiling area.

Purchasing Tips: Choose a suspended ceiling system with lightweight metal brackets. Some systems use plastic hardware that is not as durable. Also choose a system where a level ceiling is established during installation. Systems that attach directly to the existing ceiling or joists (designed to save ceiling height) may look uneven, depending on the irregularity of the existing surfaces, plus they may not allow enough access space for the mechanical systems in the ceiling area.

Ceiling Tiles

Photo courtesy of Armstrong World Industries, Inc.

Ceiling tiles (also called acoustical tiles) are a similar product to ceiling panels, but usually come in 12 × 12-in. pieces. They are glued or stapled to the ceiling surface or to furring strips attached to joists, or they can be clipped into metal tracks attached to the ceiling. Because they are permanently attached, ceiling tiles can't be used where ceiling access is necessary. But they will cover a damaged ceiling surface, provide sound dampening in noisy rooms and offer decorative possibilities.

Ceiling panel installation systems

Suspended ceiling gridwork

Gridwork attached to ceiling

Gridwork attached to ceiling joists

Suspended Ceiling: A gridwork of metal runners and cross-tees is hung from the ceiling or the floor joists above the room. Ceiling panels are inserted into the frames. A good choice for basements and other areas where access to the space above the ceiling is needed.

USG Corp.

(Above) Wall angles for a suspended ceiling are attached (level) around the perimeter of the room, then the runners and cross-tees are tied into the wall angles and hung from the ceiling.

Ceiling Tiles:
The simplest way to install ceiling tiles is to staple or bond them directly to the ceiling or ceiling joist, with no need for a support framework. gridwork of frames, as seen in the illustration below. The biggest drawback to this type of installation is that any unevenness or instability in the ceiling can throw off the installation. You're more likely to get a nice, flat ceiling by using a gridwork of mounting strips that are attached to either the ceiling surface or the ceiling joists. The installation is similar to a suspended ceiling, but you gain more headroom at the expense of space for pipes.

USG Corp.

(Above) Some types of ceiling tiles can be stapled directly to ceiling joists or purlins (furring strips that are spaced so their nailing surfaces align with the edges of the tiles.

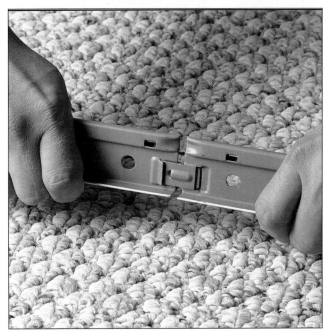

Install light fixtures before installing the ceiling panels. Mounting clips are used to attach the 4-ft. fluorescent fixture shown above to the cross-tees at the ends of the panel opening. Wires attached to the joists or ceiling can be used for additional support.

Make splices in the runners by forming a mechanical joint with the tabs and slots that are formed into the ends of the pieces.

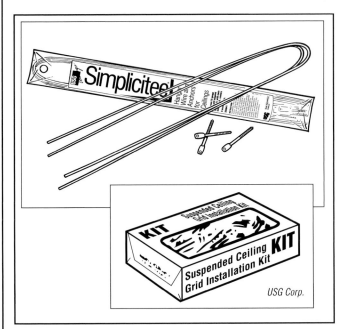

USG Corp.

Photo courtesy of Armstrong World Industries, Inc.

Hanger kits provide all the accessories you'll need to hang the gridwork. Look for kits made by the same manufacturer as the ceiling panels.

Hanger hardware differs from manufacturer to manufacturer. The clips shown above are fitted into a track that's attached directly to the ceiling. The clips will only work with panels made for this installation system.

Pressed metal ceiling panels give any room turn-of-the-century charm, especially when coupled with matching metal crown moldings.

METAL CEILINGS

Pressed metal ceiling panels (also known as embossed metal panels) give character and individuality to a room. Patterned after the tin ceilings of the late 1800s, this product is available at some home centers or by mail order from companies found in home building and remodeling magazines, as well as over the Internet.

The original tin ceilings were a cheaper and more practical substitute for ornate plaster or woodwork. The modern version offers a wide variety of design possibilities. Depending on the manufacturer, you can find dozens of patterns, with metal cornices and molding to mix or match. Filler panels also are available as an option for filling the area between full panel pieces and the ceiling perimeter. You can paint these pressed metal ceiling pieces to resemble elaborate plasterwork at a fraction of the cost. Pressed metal panels can be used for wainscoting or wall panels. You also can combine metal panels with wood cove moldings or other trim.

Standard sizes for metal ceiling panels are 2 × 2, 2 × 4 or 2 × 8 ft. The panels have round catches, called *beads,* that fit into one another to properly align the pieces where they overlap. These beads also serve as nailing points for attaching the panels to the ceiling surface. Most manufacturers provide 1-in. conehead nails for attaching the panels to the nailing surface, but you can use flathead nails instead.

Common layouts for metal ceiling panels include:

• Completely covering the ceiling with metal panels and installing a metal cornice or wood crown or cove moldings. Begin installation with full panel pieces in the corner of the room farthest from the entrance, so that partial panels fall on the two least noticeable sides of the room.

• Creating a centered section of full panels bordered with molding pieces. The ceiling surface between the molding and the cornice can be completed with filler pieces, painted or covered with wallpaper.

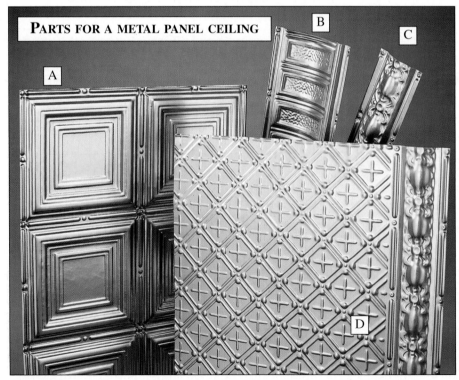

PARTS FOR A METAL PANEL CEILING

A   B   C   D

A typical metal ceiling installation requires a few different panel and trim types. Field panels (A) are used for the field area; Cornice trim (B) is installed like crown molding to transition from ceiling to wall; Molding strips (C) are used to create a decorative border between the field panels and the cornice; Filler strips (D) are also installed between the field panels and the cornice. Some, like the one shown here, have a molding strip pressed into the edge.

Tips for installing metal ceiling panels

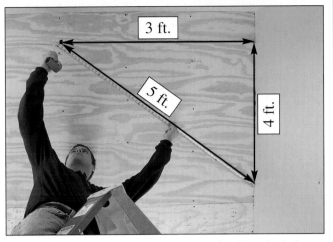

Wear work gloves when handling metal panels and trim. Their edges are sharp, plus skin oils from touching the raw metal can cause stains that will blemish the surface, even under a coat of polyurethane. After handling, clean the metal with denatured alcohol. Seal the backsides of each piece with a coat of clear polyurethane or primer, depending on which finish you will use for the finished side. Coat all the exposed surfaces of the metal parts with polyurethane if you want to retain the finish.

To make panel layout lines, use the 3-4-5 right triangle principle. Mark the intersection of the ceiling and wall where you want the line to begin. Make a mark 3 ft. from this corner along the wall/ceiling intersection. Make another mark 4 ft. from the corner along the ceiling in the direction the line will take. The distance on the diagonal between these last two marks should be 5 ft. If it isn't, adjust the mark on the ceiling until it is. Snap a chalkline through this ceiling mark to create a perpendicular layout line.

Attach a plywood "subbase" onto the ceiling before for the metal ceiling panels. The metal panels are attached with nails that can only be driven through the edges of the panels, where they will be concealed by the adjacent panels and by the cornice trim. Plywood creates an all-over nailing surface.

At cornice corners, snip the mitered edge of one piece with ⅛-in.-deep cuts, ⅛ in. apart. After installing, tap the head of a nail against these small tabs to seal the joint.

FLOORING

Few remodeling projects can provide a greater return for a minimal investment of time and money than floor remodeling projects. Depending on the type of floorcovering you choose, you can give any room a fresh new look in a single weekend: a new surface of self-adhesive vinyl tiles or foam-back carpet are just two examples of quick-and-easy floor remodeling projects that won't break your back or your bank account. But if your tastes run a little more toward the high end, there are plenty of top-of-the-line floorcovering projects that will add character, richness and individuality to your home. Installing ceramic or natural stone tile or wood flooring generally takes more time and money, but these projects remain among the most popular floor remodeling approaches.

If you are remodeling an existing kitchen or bathroom, remove base cabinets and vanities if possible. Installation of the underlayment will be easier and you won't 'lock in' the cabinets (which can cause problems if you want to replace cabinets at a future date). Also remove any floor-mounted fixtures, like toilets or floor-standing appliances. If you are replacing the tub or shower in the bathroom, this should be done before installing underlayment. You will also need to remove the trim molding around the floor. Flooring is a key aspect in designing any building. The type of flooring used helps set the mood and determine what the room will be used for. When it comes to flooring there's no shortage of options, whatever your main concern may be: color, type, style, size or simply cost. The main types of residential flooring include: ceramic and stone tile, wood, resilient and carpet.

Ceramic and stone tile. Tile, whether ceramic or stone, is one of the most beautiful and durable floor coverings. It is commonly used in kitchens and bathrooms because of its resistance to moisture. You'll find many options in style, color, texture and size among the primary types, which are glazed ceramic, porcelain and natural stone. See pages 172 to 174.

Wood and engineered wood. Wood flooring today comes in two main forms: solid wood and engineered wood. Solid wood, cut from a variety of species like pine, oak and maple, are cut into narrow boards, which are usually ¾ in. thick. Engineered wood flooring has become extremely popular because it is pre-finished, maintenance-free and easy to install. Engineered flooring is made of a plywood or particleboard substrate, with a real-wood veneer or synthetic surface. Synthetic surfaces are photo-reproduced to imitate wood or other materials, such as tile or stone. Although they can cost as much or more than solid wood, they are usually easier to install and most are prefinished, saving a lot of time. See pages 176 to 181.

Resilient Flooring. Resilient flooring is a versatile flooring option made essentially of vinyl. Although it comes in a multitude of colors and styles, resembling anything from ceramic tile to wood, there are three main types: adhesive-backed vinyl, dry-back vinyl and sheet vinyl. These types are relatively inexpensive, easy to install and durable, making them popular choices for do-it-yourselfers. See pages 182 to 184.

Carpeting. Carpeting can bring warmth and texture to a room, making it more comfortable. While carpeting is a great choice for some areas, such as bedrooms and family rooms, it isn't a wise choice for areas where moisture may be a problem, such as kitchens and baths. Carpet is a flooring material that can be very inexpensive or very costly, depending upon the type you choose. See page 185.

1: Install underlayment (resin paper is being stapled to the subfloor here)

3: Apply the finish (red oak stain with low-gloss polyurethane topcoat was applied to the floor shown in these photos)

2: Install the floor covering (natural fir strip flooring is awaiting installation here)

The basic steps to installing flooring project are: Install and level the underlayment, which can be ¼ in. plywood, cementboard, resin paper or building paper, or carpet pad; Install the floorcovering, which typically will be wood, tile, sheet vinyl or carpet; then finish or topcoat if needed.

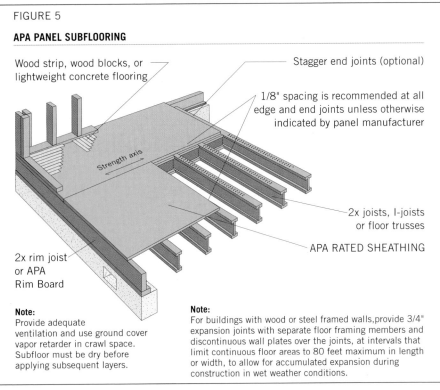

FIGURE 5

APA PANEL SUBFLOORING

Wood strip, wood blocks, or lightweight concrete flooring

Stagger end joints (optional)

1/8" spacing is recommended at all edge and end joints unless otherwise indicated by panel manufacturer

Strength axis

2x joists, I-joists or floor trusses

APA RATED SHEATHING

2x rim joist or APA Rim Board

Note:
Provide adequate ventilation and use ground cover vapor retarder in crawl space. Subfloor must be dry before applying subsequent layers.

Note:
For buildings with wood or steel framed walls, provide 3/4" expansion joints with separate floor framing members and discontinuous wall plates over the joints, at intervals that limit continuous floor areas to 80 feet maximum in length or width, to allow for accumulated expansion during construction in wet weather conditions.

Make certain the subfloor is solid. For new construction, choose full ¾-in.-thick, tongue-and-groove plywood floor decking. Install it as shown above. See "Framing Materials" (pages 34 to 51) and "Sheet Goods" (pages 52 to 65) for more information on floor supports and subfloor decks.

Flooring Options

Natural stone tile (marble shown above)

Carpeting

Adhesive-backed vinyl tile

Ceramic or porcelain tile

Finish Flooring Materials

CHARACTERISTIC	CARPET	RESILIENT	WOOD	CERAMIC TILE
Durability	fair	good	good	excellent
Ease of Cleaning	fair	excellent	excellent	good
Moisture Resistance	poor	good	fair	excellent
Stain Resistance	poor	good	fair	good
Dent/Chip Resistance	excellent	excellent	poor	fair
Resilience	excellent	fair	fair	poor
Traction	excellent	fair	poor	fair
Ability to refinish	no	no	yes	no
Cost	low/med.	med.	med.	high

Flooring Options

Solid wood strip flooring (oak shown here)

Resilient sheet vinyl

Parquet wood floor tiles

Dry-back vinyl composite tiles

Engineered wood floor system

UNDERLAYMENT

Without a sturdy, level subfloor and underlayment materials that are flat, stable and in good condition, your flooring projects are at risk—despite the high quality of materials or installation techniques you use.

Subfloor. A solid, level subfloor is the beginning of all successful flooring projects. Subflooring is usually made of ¾-in.-thick plywood, although many homes built before the 1950s have subfloors made of pine boards installed on the diagonal across the floor joists. This material must be in good condition; any damaged or low areas must be repaired before underlayment or flooring materials are installed.

Underlayment. Underlayment that is smooth and stable is vital for the durability and attractiveness of most flooring materials. A flat underlayment without seams, gaps or ridges is a must for vinyl floors. Underlayment for tile and stone floors can have small gaps or seams and be rougher in texture, but must be level and without ridges. This underlayment must also be rigid—any give to the floor will result in cracking or loosened tiles. Typical underlayment materials include ¼ in., sanded plywood; cementboard; ¼ in. lauan plywood; and ¼ in. oriented strand board (See photo, above right).

Exceptions: Wood flooring and carpet are usually installed directly over the subfloor, but with underlayment of building paper or resin paper and carpet pad, respectively).

A concrete slab that is smooth and stable provides adequate support for ceramic tile and other glued-down flooring materials. Dips and minor unevenness can be filled with floor leveler compound. Cracks should be covered with isolation membrane (See photo, right). It is best to float an engineered-wood floor over concrete so a moisture barrier can be installed. A nailed-down wood floor generally is not practical over concrete.

Some new flooring materials can be installed over existing flooring (check product recommendations), but the existing flooring must be tightly bonded to the underlayment.

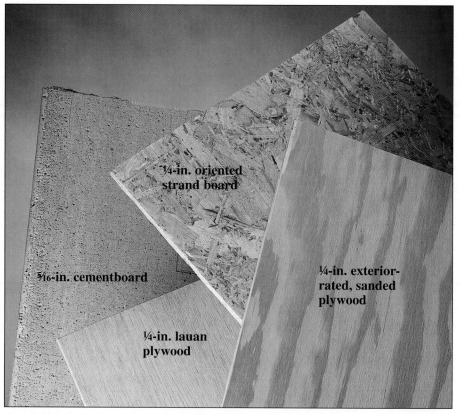

Choose floor underlayment material based on the type of floor covering and the general exposure to moisture. For bathroom installations, use exterior-rated plywood (BC) as an underlayment, except when laying ceramic floor tile, which requires a cementboard underlayment. In drier areas, you can save a little money by using oriented strand board or lauan plywood, but only with certain types of sheet flooring. Generally, exterior-rated, BC plywood is preferred over lauan.

Isolation membrane

Isolation membrane protects tile flooring from the independent movement between areas of a cracked concrete subfloor. If there are only a few cracks, cut strips of membrane wide enough to cover the crack by several inches on either side. Spread the adhesive recommended by the manufacturer (often thin-set mortar) over the crack area, then press and flatten the membrane into the adhesive. Install isolation membrane over the entire floor when there are many cracks. Cut sheets of membrane several inches longer than the room width. Spread adhesive for one sheet at a time, then embed the membrane in the adhesive. Use a flooring roller to flatten the membrane, then trim it flush with the walls using a straightedge and utility knife. You may need to roll and trim a few times to remove all ridges from the membrane. Make certain to butt the seams of adjoining sheets without any overlap.

Underlayment Installation Tips

Quarter-inch plywood: Remove base moldings, vent covers and other obstacles that can be taken off the floor area, such as toilets. Installing new underlayment is easiest without base cabinets in place, which is why a flooring project is a great time to plan on replacing cabinets. Check the condition of the subfloor and make repairs as needed. Clean the subfloor thoroughly. Any dirt or other debris caught between subflooring and underlayment can cause noise or flooring failure in the future. Cut and install each piece of the underlayment using screws long enough to penetrate into the joists. Drive screws every 6 in. at the edges of the underlayment pieces, and every 12 in. in the field, but keep screws at least ½ in. from the edge of the plywood. Drive screw heads just below the surface of the underlayment. Leave a ⅛-in. gap between pieces and a ½-in. gap along walls to allow for expansion.

Cementboard: Spread a layer of thin-set mortar on the subfloor before attaching cementboard sheets, using a ¼-in. notched trowel. Drive deck screws (long enough to penetrate the joists) every 8 in. at the edges, keeping screws at least ½ in. from edges. Drill pilot holes to make this easier. Leave a ⅛-in. gap between sheets and a ½-in. gap along walls. Drive shorter deck screws at 8 in. intervals in the field.

Using Floor Leveler Products

Floor leveler products are used to fill small irregularities in concrete, subfloor or underlayment surfaces. Some, called embossing levelers, are spread over existing flooring such as tile or vinyl, allowing installation of new flooring without removal of the old (left photo). Floor levelers usually come as a dry mixture that is combined with a latex or acrylic additive, but premixed products are available. Spread floor leveler compound to fill low spots or

feather out uneven areas, and also to cover nail or screw heads. Apply several thin layers of leveler rather than one thick one (right photo). When dry, check with a straightedge to make certain the floor leveler compound is flat and level with the surrounding subfloor. Apply more leveler if necessary. Let dry and sand smooth.

TILE TYPES

Glazed ceramic tile is the most common and inexpensive hard tile type. It's sold in sizes ranging from mosaic sheets to 20 × 20 in. tiles. The glazing option allows for an almost unlimited variety of colors and designs.

Porcelain tile is more durable (and generally more expensive) than ceramic tile. The color is integral: it runs all the way through the tile, making it less prone to scratching. Porcelain is also relatively difficult to cut and the range of colors and designs is more limited.

Natural stone tiles can get expensive, but for durability and appearance they are tough to beat. Granite, marble, slate, limestone and terra cotta are common varieties.

Pattern options

Diagonal: In a perfectly square room, diagonal lines marked from corner to corner are usable reference lines (just make certain they are perpendicular). Otherwise, mark perpendicular reference lines in the most visible floor area. Mark another reference line at a 45° angle to these lines, through their intersection. You

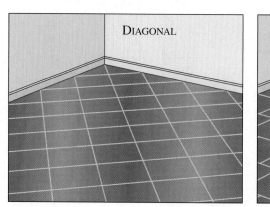

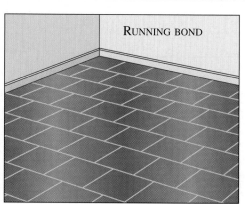

can use the 3-4-5 right triangle method for marking perpendicular lines for this, too—both angles opposite the right 90° angle are 45° angles. After making this diagonal reference line, mark a line perpendicular to it, again through the intersection of the first set of lines. Dry-fit tiles and adjust their layout as with the standard tile layout. It is best to have full tiles and half tiles in the most

visible areas. Make sure your tile cutter is large enough to make diagonal trim cuts on the tile you are installing.

Running bond: Determine the final layout reference lines as in a standard tile layout. When balancing the tile layout, use two rows of tiles, since one row offsets the other by half a tile length. Additional grid lines are very helpful with these narrower tiles. Make certain to allow for proper spac-

CERAMIC TILE

Tiles come in a variety of sizes and shapes. Most tiles are glazed ceramic; a layer of colored glaze is baked onto the clay tile material. Mosaic tiles can be made of either glazed ceramic or porcelain, a harder tile material that is a uniform color throughout. Quarry tiles also are the same color throughout. They are softer, porous, unglazed clay tiles that are usually thicker than glazed ceramic tiles. Natural stone tiles are usually made from marble, slate, limestone or granite. They are much more expensive than ceramic tiles—but ceramic tiles that closely resemble natural stone are available at a fraction of their cost.

Tips for choosing tile:
• Large tiles make a room look larger; small tiles make it look smaller.
• Square tiles are the easiest to install.
• Larger tiles have fewer grout lines, requiring less installation time and maintenance.
• Small tiles, like mosaics, are usually joined together in fiber-backed sheets to make them easier to install. Unlike larger tiles, they can be installed on a floor that isn't perfectly level.

Tiling supplies

Tools and materials for installing tile include: tile cutter (A); notched trowel (B); grout sealer (C); grout float (D); grout (E); latex grout additive (F); thinset mortar (G); grout sponge (H); cementboard (I); fiberglass seam tape (J); tile spacers (K); rod saw for cutting tiles (L); and tile nippers (M).

• Tiles with irregular shapes, like hexagons, take the most installation time. Some require that smaller square or round tiles be installed in the spaces between the field tiles.
• Border, accent and base-trim tiles help create showpiece floors but require extra work.
• Glazed tiles have different finishes that affect how easily they scratch and how slippery they are.

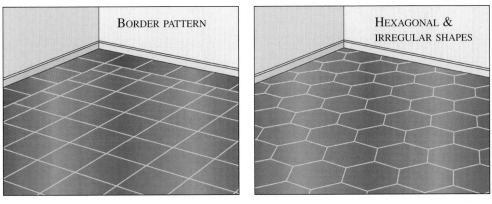

BORDER PATTERN

HEXAGONAL & IRREGULAR SHAPES

ing between tiles and the offset distance when marking grid lines. Spread mortar on the backs of tiles that overlap reference lines due to the offset.

Border pattern: Mark initial reference lines as for a standard floor-tile layout. Dry-fit main floor tiles and border tiles along the reference lines to create a balanced layout requiring minimal cutting of main tiles—border tiles should

remain full-size. After adjusting the layout, snap perpendicular lines for the main tiles and also for the border tiles. You can combine several design elements, using border tiles between different patterns or shaped tiles. Simply follow the layout instructions from the appropriate pattern.

Hexagonal & irregular shapes: Determine the final layout reference lines as in a standard tile layout. When balancing the tile layout, dry-fit enough tiles to be certain a properly aligned pattern is tested. Additional grid lines may be very helpful for keeping irregular tile shapes aligned during installation. Make certain to allow for proper spacing between tiles. Spread mortar on the backs of tiles that overlap reference lines.

Installing cementboard tile underlayment

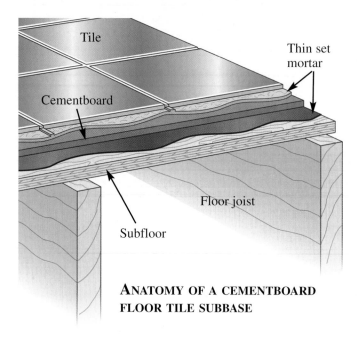

Tile

Thin set mortar

Cementboard

Floor joist

Subfloor

ANATOMY OF A CEMENTBOARD FLOOR TILE SUBBASE

The most stable underlayment for ceramic tile flooring is cementboard (also known as concrete backerboard). Cementboard underlayment for floor tile installations is bonded to a sturdy subfloor with thin-set mortar. The seams and screw heads should be taped and filled with thin-set. Then, the tile can be set into a mortar bed applied over the cementboard.

Fill the gaps between sheets with thin-set mortar, then embed fiberglass joint tape into the thin-set. Spread more mortar over the tape and smooth it out in as thin a layer as possible. After the mortar has dried thoroughly, strike off any rough ridges with a putty knife.

Optional ceramic tile underlayment: Poured mortar bed

1 A sloping subfloor is difficult to correct with floor leveler prior to installing cementboard underlayment. One alternative is to pour a level mortar bed to use as a base for the tile. First, install a layer of 15-lb. roofing felt over the subfloor. Then, staple self-furring metal lath to the floor. Tip: set the heights of the nails to level as reference guides when leveling the mud base.

2 Fill the work area with a stiff mixture of mortar, preferably containing a latex or acrylic fortifier. Use a screed to strike off the mortar so it is level with the tops of the reference nails. Float the surface with a wood float, then a magnesium float.

3 Square the edge of the mud for a threshold, if needed. Let the mortar bed cure for at least a couple of days before installing the tile.

How to Use a Tile Cutter

Push scoring tool forward

Scoring tool

Sizing gauge

1 (Above) Set the tile on the bed of the tile cutter so the cutting line is aligned with the point of the scoring tool. Some tile cutters, like the one above, are equipped with a sizing gauge so you can set the tool to make multiple cuts that are the same width. Lighter duty cutters often cut on the pull stroke, but the rented, heavy-duty model shown here cuts on the push stroke. Press down on the lever that lowers the scoring tool and push forward, scoring the cutting line.

2 (Right) Retract the scoring tool clear of the tile, then lower the lever that controls the breaking bars. These bars exert downward pressure toward the trough in the center of the bed, causing the tile to snap along the scored line.

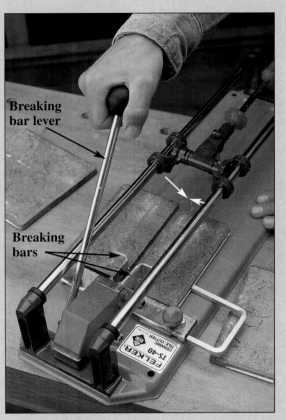

Breaking bar lever

Breaking bars

Tips for doorways & thresholds

Cut the jamb, not the tile. It usually is easier to cut off the bottom of jamb molding than it is to mark and cut the tile to fit around it. Use a jamb saw, which is designed to cut while resting on a flat surface. Determine the height of a tile set in thinset mortar (usually the thickness of the tile plus 1/8 in.). Add a spacer to a piece of tile so their combined thickness is about 1/16 in. more than this height, and place them next to the jamb molding (protect the tile surface by placing the spacer piece on top of the tile). Rest the jamb saw on the spacer and cut the jamb molding.

Reducer
(Tile to vinyl)

Flush transition
(Tile to tile or wood)

Square nose
(Tile to carpet)

T-molding
(Tile to tile or wood)

Transition strips are needed whenever you move from one floor covering material to another. This is especially true of tile floor, since they're frequently higher than other floor coverings in the home. If the tile floor and the adjoining surface are at the same height, choose a flat tile or solid-surface transition strip that is set directly into thinset. If one floor surface is higher than the other, you may be able to find a tile transition strip that's beveled to create a small ramp between the surfaces, but more likely you'll need to look for a beveled wood transition strip.

Southern Yellow Pine: One of the most affordable solid wood flooring options, pine is generally available through flooring dealers and lumberyards.

Red Oak: A very common wood flooring material, red oak is inexpensively priced when plainsawn and moderately priced when quartersawn.

Maple: Well known for its excellent durability characteristics, maple is often the material used to make bowling alleys and athletic surfaces. A very traditional hardwood floor material.

Ash: Slightly less common due to its restricted availability, ash is a durable yet unique floor hardwood. If boards are plainsawn, the potential for strong grain contrast is high.

Brazilian Cherry: This exotic import carries a higher price tag because it is almost twice as hard as its North American cousin. It is still one of the few exotics available in solid (non-engineered) form.

Choosing wood flooring

There are two basic types of wood flooring boards available: solid wood (left photos) and engineered wood (next page). Both types of boards are available in either strips or planks—less than 3 in. wide is considered strip flooring, wider boards are labeled "planks."

Solid wood flooring: Solid wood flooring is made from lumber (usually ¾ in. thick) of varying species, the most common being oak, maple, cherry, ash and pine. Solid wood flooring will last for the lifetime of a house, especially since it can be refinished several times. It also offers the richest color and greatest variety of grain patterns. This flooring comes in several grades, from select and clear (premium, knot free boards that are the most expensive) to common and #2 (less expensive but containing knots and other blemishes).

Solid wood boards must be nailed down. When installing solid wood as a remodeling project, the thickness of the boards will require trimming of doors and casings and transitions between flooring levels in bordering rooms.

Solid wood flooring is susceptible to warping, so boards must be stored in a dry, well-ventilated area. The boards should be stacked in the installation area for 2 to 3 days to acclimate prior to beginning the project. If the boards are delivered bundled, unbind them and loosely stack them so they can "breathe." This susceptibility to moisture makes solid wood a poor choice for damp areas, such as bathrooms and basements. Some manufacturers provide prefinished solid wood flooring, though only in a small choice of species and colors. While care must be taken not to scratch the surface during installation, this can speed up a project considerably.

Engineered flooring: Engineered wood flooring is essentially plywood or particleboard, with the top veneer layer made from hardwood of a wide variety of species and colors. Another type of engineered flooring, called laminate flooring, has a synthetic veneer bonded to the plywood or particleboard backing. This synthetic surface is made to resemble many materials, including varieties of stone as well as wood.

While the cost of engineered flooring can be as

expensive, if not more expensive, than that of lower-cost solid wood boards, its ease of installation and factory-applied finish make installing it a very manageable home improvement project. Since it is basically plywood, it is more dimensionally stable, allowing installation anywhere, including basements and bathrooms. The hardwood surface veneer on quality engineered flooring is at least ⅛ in. thick, allowing for one refinishing, but this should be done by a professional. Engineered flooring is significantly thinner than solid wood flooring (generally ⅜ to ½ in. thick) making it a good choice when floor height is an issue. Thicker engineered boards are nailed down, and some can be either glued down to the subfloor or installed as a floating floor over a foam pad (wood glue is applied only to the tongue-and-grooved board edges). Some newer products are manufactured with a peel-off, self-adhesive backing, and others have a modified tongue-and-groove edge joining system that allows them to simply be snapped together. Check with the flooring dealer or manufacturer concerning requirements for specific flooring products.

Laminate flooring is usually the thinnest engineered wood flooring type and is most frequently installed as a floating floor over a foam pad. This makes it an excellent surface over concrete (though a vapor barrier is necessary underneath the pad). Its durable acrylic protective topcoat also makes it a good choice for kitchens and other high-traffic areas.

Manufacturers of engineered flooring usually offer flooring with either a flat or eased edge treatment on the boards. An eased edge (with either a small bevel or roundover) can help hide any unevenness between boards, but dirt will collect in the tiny groove it creates.

Buying wood flooring: Once you've made a flooring choice, take your room measurements to the flooring dealer. Determining the amount of flooring needed depends on the width of the boards, available board lengths and other factors that the dealer will be able to calculate for you. This is particularly true if your installation includes a border or other decorative treatment.

Engineered wood flooring with a real wood veneer layer (red oak is shown here) offers the natural beauty of wood combined with economy and ease of installation. It can be installed as a floating floor system or glued to the subfloor.

Similar to the wood-veneer flooring shown above it, this engineered wood product has a peel-and-stick adhesive backing for an extremely clean installation process.

Wood-veneer pattern plastic laminate: For an exotic look at an affordable price, wood-veneer pattern laminate is an excellent choice. In addition to variety, laminate flooring provides a durable surface highly resistant to scratches, indentations, burns and moisture. Impervious to dust and dirt, it allows easy cleanup in high-traffic areas like kitchens and dining rooms.

Non-wood pattern laminate: Most laminate flooring manufacturers also offer several non-wood patterned faces in their product lines. Typical options include checkerboard layouts and stone re-creations. As only the look is different, these designs maintain the same dependability as more traditional laminate products.

Common solid wood flooring types: by species (photos on pages 176 to 177)

WOOD	WIDTHS	STRENGTHS	WEAKNESSES	COST
Red Oak	1½, 2¼ in. (also parquet)	Stiff and dense, good wear and shock resistance, widely available in several types and styles	Large pores can produce strong stain contrasts when finishing.	Inexpensive
White Oak	1½, 2¼ in., (also parquet)	Highly durable, well-protected against insects and rot due to high tannic concentration	Tannins can react with certain finishes turning the wood green or brown	Moderate
Maple	1½, 2¼ in. (also parquet)	Extremely dense and strong, highly resistant to the most abrasive wear	High durability characteristics make it difficult to machine, light color can easily expose sanding marks	Moderate
Ash	1½, 2¼ in.	Hard but elastic make-up remains smooth under friction	Frequent grain variations can cause sporadic patterning	Moderate
Brazilian Cherry (Exotic)	1½, 2¼ in. (also parquet)	Extremely strong and durable, sands well, finishes to warm russet hue	High density makes it difficult to machine, darkens upon exposure to sunlight	Expensive
Pine (Southern Yellow)	3, 5 in.	Ease in finishing allows for a durable topcoat to help compensate for lack of hardness	Softness makes it vulnerable to scuffs dents and abrasions	Inexpensive

*Source: National Wood Flooring Association

Wood floor underlayment & other materials

In addition to the flooring boards themselves, you'll need a few other materials for wood flooring projects. Purchase them from building centers or flooring stores.

• An underlayment layer protects the floorboards by absorbing shock. It also reduces squeaking and reverberation that can cause the flooring nails to loosen prematurely. Traditionally, 15-pound, asphalt-impregnated building paper (tar paper) has been used for the underlayment layer, but a newer, resin-based underlayment paper provides the same protection without the mess and smell of building paper (See photo, right).

• A reducing strip or threshold covers the transition from wood flooring to other flooring materials (See page 180).

• Wood putty, either stainable or tinted to match floor color, fills nail holes and minor damage in flooring.

• Nails are used to attach solid wood floors to the subfloor. Near walls you'll need to hand-nail using 8d finish nails or, for a little extra holding power, spiral or ring shank nails. Nail coils for flooring nailers are available wherever the tools are rented.

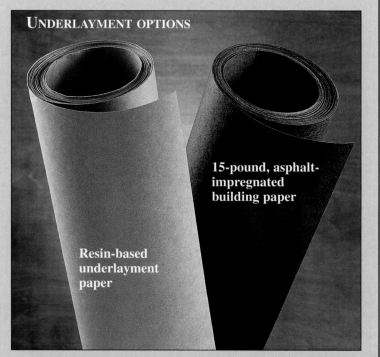

UNDERLAYMENT OPTIONS

15-pound, asphalt-impregnated building paper

Resin-based underlayment paper

• Polyurethane varnish, either oil- or water-based, is the standard topcoating product these days for solid wood floors. Products specially formulated for floors (usually indicated on the label) typically have a harder, glossier surface. Some solid wood flooring is available prefinished, but these are best for new-home installations.

ENGINEERED WOOD FLOOR SYSTEMS

Engineered wood flooring systems have made a huge impact in the do-it-yourself home flooring market in recent years. Advances in quality, appearance and ease of installation are the primary reasons behind their explosion in popularity. More manufacturers now are entering this product market and, as a result, the relative cost has decreased to the point that these systems can be cheaper to install than traditional oak, maple or pine solid wood flooring.

Engineered wood flooring products are man-made formulations created by applying veneer or wood-grain plastic laminate to a wood-based substrate. Where standard tongue-and-groove flooring is ¾ in. thick, most engineered wood floor panels are only ⅜ in. thick, making them easier to handle and more economical to produce. The most common engineered wood floors frequently are referred to as "floating floors" because they are not nailed down or otherwise attached to the subfloor. Instead, they "float" on an underlayment pad and are bonded to one another with glued tongue-and-groove joints. In most cases, they can be installed with simple shop tools just about every handyman or weekender already owns.

The main differences between engineered wood flooring products are in the material used for the pattern layer and the body of the product. The more expensive products usually have a layer of real wood veneer on top, laminated to a body composed of three ⅛-in.-thick plywood plies. Typically, they are prefinished with a hard, polymerized topcoat or a laminated wear layer. The more common products these days, however, feature a pattern layer of plastic laminate with a printed pattern, generally a wood grain. The "topcoat" is usually a wear layer of high-tech material such as clear melamine. The body of most mass-market engineered flooring products is made of particleboard or medium-density fiberboard (MDF). Some products also feature a laminate backing to discourage moisture pene-

Laminate flooring enables you to mix wood, tile and stone patterns in the same floor. Shown above (clockwise) are striped, complex designs using Bruce brand flooring and island and check patterns using Wilsonart flooring. **The laminated flooring samples** shown below are from Formica.

tration from below.

Most manufacturers offer a selection of underlayment pads, typically made of various grades of foam. Sheets of plastic moisture barrier also are available for installations over concrete.

Glues, trim pieces and some specialty installation tools also are offered by the flooring system manufacturer.

~Michael Morris

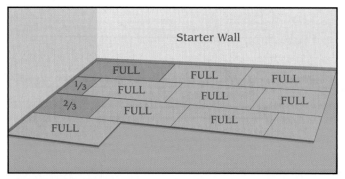

LAYOUT SEQUENCE: Although the visible surfaces of most engineered wood floor panels are composed of multiple "boards" of varying length, you'll generally get the best visual results if you stagger the panels at one end of the room. Make the first panel in the first row a full panel; then, cut the first panel in the second row to one-third length; use the cut-off two-thirds of this panel to begin the third row.

Engineered wood flooring is composed of a tongue-and-groove body formed from plywood or particleboard, covered with a pattern layer of printed plastic laminate or real wood veneer. A wear layer is laminated on top of the pattern layer. On some types, a thin cushion material is laminated between the pattern layer and the body of the panel.

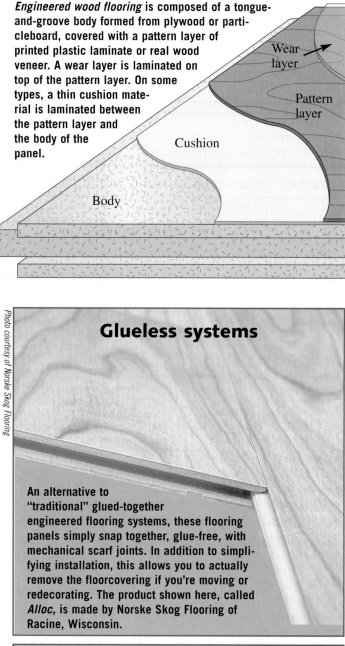

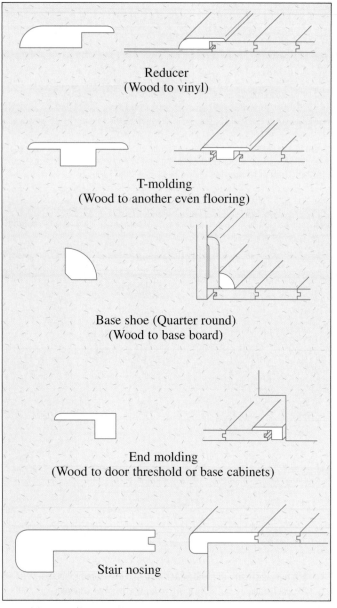

Reducer
(Wood to vinyl)

T-molding
(Wood to another even flooring)

Base shoe (Quarter round)
(Wood to base board)

End molding
(Wood to door threshold or base cabinets)

Stair nosing

Transition moldings for floating floors are used to bridge gaps between adjoining floor surfaces and between the floors and walls or base cabinets. Specific products vary by manufacturer.

Photo courtesy of Norske Skog Flooring

Glueless systems

An alternative to "traditional" glued-together engineered flooring systems, these flooring panels simply snap together, glue-free, with mechanical scarf joints. In addition to simplifying installation, this allows you to actually remove the floorcovering if you're moving or redecorating. The product shown here, called *Alloc,* is made by Norske Skog Flooring of Racine, Wisconsin.

Installing & maintaining engineered wood floors

• Let the flooring panels acclimate in the project room for two or three days before installing them.

• When ordering floorboards, add 10 to 15% to the total square footage of the room to allow for waste.

• Install a vapor barrier before beneath the underlayment pad if the subfloor is concrete—even if you're installing the flooring over another floorcovering.

• Clean surfaces with a vacuum cleaner (non-beater) then damp-mop with warm water. Avoid strong detergents and any abrasive cleaners.

• Always use protective pads on the bottoms of furniture legs to prevent scratching.

Installation Tips for Engineered Wood Floor Systems

Roll out the foam-pad underlayment so the seams are butted together and perpendicular to the direction of the flooring panels. Tape the seams together to keep the underlayment from shifting.

Begin by installing a complete row of panels along the starting wall. To reinforce the tongue-and-groove joints, squirt a healthy dab of glue into the groove then slip the grooved panel over the mating tongue. Press the boards together tightly.

After you've glued together enough panels to fill out around 4 ft. in width, draw the panels together at several points along the rows to tighten the tongue-and-groove joints. Make sure to do this before the glue has set up (a typical "open time" for glue is around 20 to 30 minutes). The specialty strap clamp shown above is produced by the Pergo flooring manufacturing company for use with their product.

It's been our experience that the better-made floor system products fit together well enough that they can be held together with adequate pressure using masking tape instead of clamps. But if you choose to use this method, be aware that it may not conform to the manufacturer's suggested installation techniques and using it may have implications on your product warranty.

Adhesive-backed vinyl tiles are peel-and-stick products offering great economy and easy installation.

Dry-back vinyl tiles are set into a bed of flooring adhesive. Generally, they are more durable than self-adhesive types.

Sheet vinyl is a preferred floor covering for wet areas because it is a seamless product in many installations, making it impervious to moisture.

RESILIENT FLOORING

Resilient flooring is a versatile flooring type offering a wide variety of colors, patterns and styles in a range of relatively inexpensive products made essentially from vinyl. It can resemble ceramic tile, natural stone or wood floors, provide a bold geometric design or bring striking color into a room. The combination of ease of installation, durability and low cost make it a popular home improvement material.

Resilient vinyl flooring is available in two basic product types, sheet vinyl and vinyl tiles. Sheet vinyl is purchased by the lineal foot off of 6- or 12-ft.-wide rolls and is either full-spread-bonded or perimeter-bonded to the floor underlayment. Full-spread means adhesive is spread over the entire underlayment surface. This takes longer to do but creates a more durable installation. In a perimeter-bond installation, adhesive is spread only around the edges of the room and underneath seams. Perimeter-bond is installed very quickly but is more likely to come loose. The lack of seams in a sheet vinyl installation makes it attractive in rooms where moisture is common, such as bathrooms, kitchens and laundry rooms.

Vinyl tiles, usually available in 12 × 12-in. squares, are either dry-back or self-adhesive. Dry-back tiles require

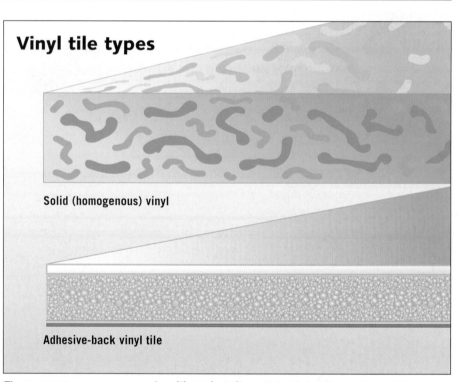

Vinyl tile types

Solid (homogenous) vinyl

Adhesive-back vinyl tile

The two most common types of resilient vinyl tile you'll find in building centers are thinner, 12 × 12 in. adhesive back tiles with traditional printed patterns (often called "Stickybacks")and 12 × 12 in. homogenous vinyl tile (also known as vinyl composite tile). The two types cost about the same amount per square foot, and are very inexpensive.

spreading of adhesive underneath them. Generally, these tiles form an extremely durable and inexpensive floorcovering. A paper backing protects the adhesive on self-adhesive tiles and is removed just prior to positioning and setting on the underlayment. This is the easiest type of all flooring products to install, but the adhesive on self-

adhesive tiles does not form as durable a bond as spread adhesive.

The thickness of vinyl flooring is a good gauge of quality since thicker vinyl flooring contains more vinyl. Solid vinyl is the most expensive type. The color and pattern run throughout the flooring. Vinyl composition floor-

(Continued on page184)

Tips for working with resilient tile

The importance of smooth, clean floor underlayment

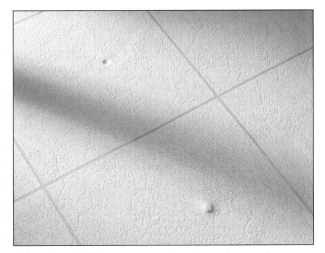

Minor irregularities may seem harmless when you're inspecting your floor underlayment, but with some types of floorcoverings (especially thinner resilient vinyl products), they will show up as glaring errors after the floorcoverings have been installed. Seams that are not taped, screw counterbores that are not filled, screw or nailheads that are not recessed and general debris can all show through your new floor, as seen in the example above.

Prepare the underlayment by filling all seams and screw head holes with floor leveler compound. Roll on a coat of underlayment primer to improve adhesion with the tiles.

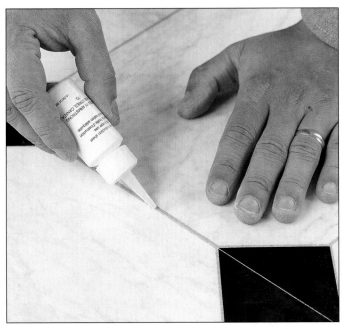

Seaming sheet vinyl: Weld the two sheets together. Nearly all sheet vinyl flooring installed in homes today is composed mostly of PVC, and can be solvent-welded in much the same way that PVC pipes are solvent-welded for plumbing. Some commercial tile can be heat-welded to close off the seam. The distributor that sold the sheet vinyl to you should also be able to provide a solvent-welding kit for seaming the flooring. The kit being used above (manufactured by Armstrong World Industries) consists of four separate chemical application steps. Follow the instructions and safety recommendations on your kit carefully.

Make a cutting pattern for sheet vinyl using paper, building paper (shown above) or a special patternmaking kit some sheet vinyl manufacturers sell. On a clean, dry, flat surface, lay the sheet vinyl pattern-side up, then fit the template on top of the sheet. Tape the template down to the sheet to prevent slippage. Take measurements to make sure the template is not distorted and check to make sure all of the cutout areas are the correct distance from the edges of the template. Transfer the pattern.

(Continued from page182)

ing has less vinyl, which is combined with non-vinyl fillers to create the design. The color and pattern on printed vinyl flooring is printed on a very thin non-vinyl layer that is bonded to a layer of urethane and vinyl to provide durability. Check with a flooring dealer for advice on the best vinyl-flooring product for your project.

Always use the adhesive recommended by the manufacturer under vinyl flooring. Besides risking flooring failure, using the wrong adhesive usually voids the product warranty. Don't attempt to use additional adhesive on self-adhesive tiles to strengthen the bond because chemicals in the two types of adhesive may react to ruin the flooring. Keep the project area well ventilated when spreading adhesives because many adhesives produce harmful vapors.

How to cut a hole in vinyl tile

1 Measure from the edges of adjacent installed tiles to locate the center of a hole for a pipe. Mark this position on a tile, support the tile with a scrap wood backer, then use a drill and hole saw slightly larger than the pipe diameter to cut the opening.

2 Use a straightedge as a guide to cut the tile in half, through the center of the hole. Remove the protective paper and install each half around the pipe.

Tips for Installing Vinyl Tile

Roll it. When you're finished, make a final inspection of the seams to make sure there are no ridges between tiles. Then, roll the entire floor surface with a floor roller (a rental item). Let the tile dry undisturbed as long as required by the adhesive manufacturer.

Clean & buff. Clean up any adhesive residue with a rag lightly dampened in mineral spirits, or another solvent if directed by the adhesive manufacturer. Install base trim (we used vinyl cove base adhesive). Because the commercial tile we installed does not have a glossy wear layer, we rented a floor buffer and applied three coats of floor wax for a high, protective gloss.

CARPETING

Carpet can be a relatively inexpensive floor covering in large rooms and over old flooring materials or subfloors with minor irregularities. It is softer, more comfortable flooring, particularly in bedrooms and family rooms. In cooler climate zones it provides warmer flooring than hard-surfaced materials such as tile and vinyl.

There are two basic types of carpet. *Foam-backed carpet* (also known as cushion-backed) has a polyurethane foam backing. It is generally less expensive and of lower quality than carpet installed over a separate pad. Foam-backed carpet is attached directly to the subfloor or old floorcovering with carpet adhesive or double-sided tape and is a simple do-it-yourself installation.

Conventional carpet is stretched over a separate underlayment pad and secured on tack strips. This requires special tools and techniques that are best left to professional installers, especially when carpeting large rooms. This type of carpet is usually a higher-quality product and offers a greater range of colors, textures and styles than foam-backed.

Fibers. Carpet is generally available in five different kinds of fibers. Nylon is the most popular because it is very durable and cleans easily, but it is the most expensive of the synthetic fibers. Olefin (also known as polypropylene) is less expensive than nylon, and while not quite as durable, is very resistant to stains and fading. Polyester is the softest synthetic fiber but isn't very durable on its own and is often combined with nylon. Acrylic provides the feel and look of wool, but because it isn't very durable it is usually blended with other fibers. Wool, the only natural fiber used in carpet, is soft and wears well but usually costs more than synthetic.

Cross-section of a carpet installation

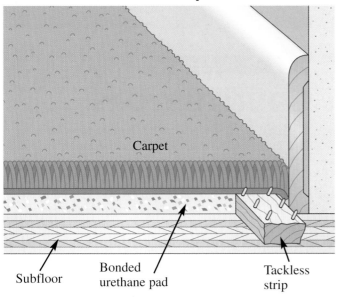

A typical carpet installation is accomplished by tacking strips of wood with sharp metal points, called "tackless strips," around the perimeter of a room, then laying a pad on the floor, stretching carpeting over the pad and pressing the edges of the carpet between the tackless strips and the wall. The points in the tackless strip secure the carpeting.

Carpet & pad types

Foam-back carpet (also called *cushion-back* or *kanga-back*) does not require a separate carpet pad and no stretching is needed for installation.

Conventional carpet doesn't have an attached pad backing. It is laid over a separate pad and stretched tightly onto the floor. It's the most common type.

Indoor/outdoor carpet is an unpadded, synthetic fiber material designed to be stapled or bonded directly to floors in wet areas.

Bonded urethane pad is often called "foam" pad and is the most common type of carpet pad.

Closed-cell foam pad resists deterioration and has a hard, slick surface coating for extra protection. It is more costly than other carpet pads.

Carpet Materials		
FIBER	**ADVANTAGES**	**DISADVANTAGES**
Acrylic	Resembles wool	Low durability
Nylon	Very tough Resists dirt Resembles wool Low static buildup	None
Polyester	Soft, luxurious	Low durability Attracts oily dirt
Polypropylene	Waterproof Resists fading Resists stains Easy to clean	Crushes easily
Wool	Durable Easy to clean Feels good Easily dyed	Expensive

Photo courtesy of Whirlpool Corporation

Chapter Contents:

CABINETS & COUNTERTOPS

Cabinets and countertops may seem to be better classified as home furnishings than as building materials. But because they're generally built in to the room and therefore impact the room design, it's best to make your cabinetry plan as part of your general project planning.

Most large home centers will carry a variety of in-stock and special-order cabinets, along with both preformed countertops and materials for building custom countertops.

If you're looking for cabinets that are a bit unusual in design, material or construction technique, specialty kitchen and bath supply stores, mail-order cabinetry catalogs or custom cabinetry shops will offer an almost infinite number of choices.

As a percentage of the total cost of a major remodeling project or addition, cabinetry is often the greatest expense. This is especially true with kitchens. But perhaps more than any other feature, the cabinets have a major influ-

(Continued, page 188)

Choose Cabinets & Countertops Carefully

Even in the simplest kitchen or bathroom, the style, color and layout of your cabinetry has a major impact on the overall appearance and functionality of the room. The four photos below provide a good example of how much difference cabinetry can make.

(ABOVE) Inexpensive or even second-hand cabinets can be given a refreshing facelift with a couple coats of paint. Be sure to use good quality, enamel paint for durability and washability. You can paint the cabinets and doors in place with a brush or paint them prior to installation, ideally with a paint sprayer. The simulated wood-grain, postform countertop shown is economical but not too exciting from a design standpoint.

(ABOVE) Real wood and genuine veneer provide warmth and richness to a room, and don't always cost as much as you'd think. Generally, a clear finish or only a very light wood stain will create a more open, fresher feeling that most people prefer in a kitchen. Darker stains and dark woods, however, have a certain Old World charm that is appropriate and effective in certain situations **(BELOW RIGHT).**

(LEFT) Ready-to-assemble cabinets are manufactured in a huge array of styles, colors and finishes. The Shaker-inspired cabinets to the left offer a modern, updated appearance that is reflective of current design trends. The addition of the crown molding on the upper cabinets demonstrates how just about any style of cabinet can be dressed up with a bit of trimwork. The countertop shown is also postform, but with a travertine pattern that is also more in keeping with current kitchen designs.

(Continued, from page 186)
ence on the appearance and the functionality of the room. So it's worth taking some time to investigate your options. It's also worth investing a fair amount of your budget in the cabinet and countertop materials.

The most frequently purchased cabinets installed by DIYers are packaged in flat cartons containing the ready-to-assemble cabinet components. The cabinets doors generally are sold separately (this is important to keep in mind when you're estimating cost). Additional items you'll need include filler strips that are fastened between the cabinets to conceal gaps; end panels for cabinets that terminate a run of cabinetry and are not against a wall or major appliance; toe kicks to conceal the space between the bottom of a base cabinets and the floor; and in some cases, door and drawer pulls. Matching crown molding is available to finish the tops of the upper cabinets in some styles.

Most larger building centers also carry a smaller selection of stock cabinets that are preassembled and ready to install. Generally, these are unfinished units at the lower end of the quality range. Very often, they are made of red

(Continued, page 190)

Common Cabinet Types & Sizes

CABINET	WIDTH	TYPICAL FEATURES
Base	9 in.	No drawers or shelves; may have a vertical partition
Base	12-24 in.	Single door with or without a drawer; ½ or full depth shelf
Base	27-48 in.	Double doors; single or double drawers
Drawer base	12-24 in.	Three or four stacked drawers; may include a cutting board
Sink base	24 in.	Single door; no drawer or shelf
Sink base	27-48 in.	Double doors; false drawer front or fronts; no shelving
Peninsula base	24/27 in.	Doors, doors and toe kicks on both sides; cabinet width can be adjusted from 24 to 27 in.
Lazy Susan base	36 in.	Fits in corner of cabinet run; two swiveling shelves; door forms a 90° angle
Blind corner base	36-51 in.	Fits in corner of a cabinet run; available with doors and drawers offset on either end of the cabinet
Pantry base	18, 24, 30 in.	Typically 59 or 72 in. tall with single or double doors; interior may be outfitted with adjustable or swiveling shelves and door storage
Oven base	27 or 33 in.	Houses an oven or microwave separate from the cooktop
Vanity sink base	24, 30, 36 in. *	Single or double doors, with or without drawers; false drawer front above doors and drawers; no shelves
Vanity sink base (mini)	18 in. *	Narrowest available sink base; one door, no drawers
Vanity drawer base	12, 15, 18 in. *	Three or four stacked drawers; installed next to the sink base for added drawer storage

* At 30½ or 32½ in, vanity cabinets are usually 4 to 6 in. shorter than kitchen base cabinets

CABINET	WIDTH/HEIGHT	TYPICAL FEATURES
Wall	9-24 in./30 in.	Single door; two shelves
Wall	27-48 in./30 in.	Double doors; two shelves
Wall	30,33,36 in./15 in.	Double doors, no shelves; used above cooktops or refrigerators
Lazy Susan wall	24 in./30 in.	Fits in corner of cabinet run; door is flat; two swivelling shelves
Diagonal wall	24 in./30 in.	Same shape as Lazy Susan wall but with fixed or adjustable shelves
Blind corner wall	24-39 in./30 in.	Available with a door offset on either end of the cabinet; two shelves
Blind corner wall	42-51 in./30 in.	Same as narrower blind corner wall cabinet but with double doors

Wall (upper) cabinet examples

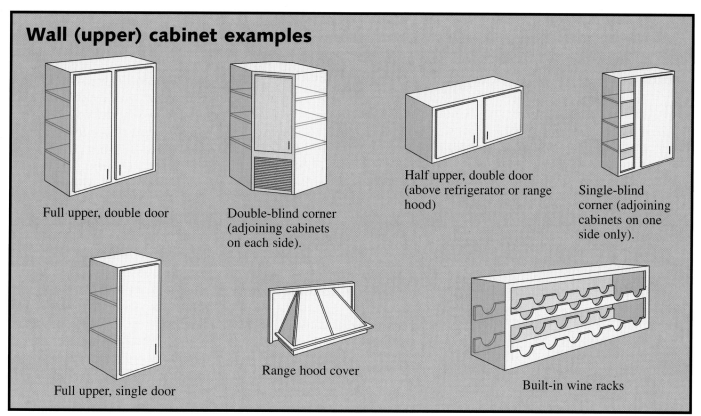

Full upper, double door

Double-blind corner (adjoining cabinets on each side).

Half upper, double door (above refrigerator or range hood)

Single-blind corner (adjoining cabinets on one side only).

Full upper, single door

Range hood cover

Built-in wine racks

Wall-hung (upper) cabinet types come in standard heights ranging from 12 to 48 in., with 30 in. being the most common height (typically stopping short of the ceiling). Width depends greatly on the style. Single-door cabinets generally come as narrow as 9 in., and double-door cabinets start at 24 in. in width. They are seldom wider than 36 in., but can be ordered as wide as 48 in.

Base cabinet examples

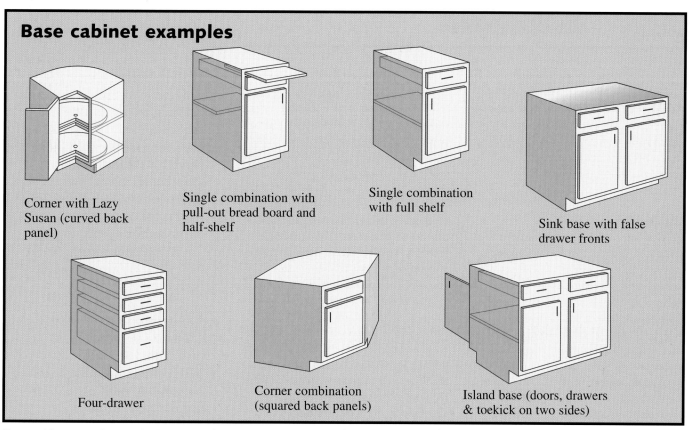

Corner with Lazy Susan (curved back panel)

Single combination with pull-out bread board and half-shelf

Single combination with full shelf

Sink base with false drawer fronts

Four-drawer

Corner combination (squared back panels)

Island base (doors, drawers & toekick on two sides)

Base cabinets come in a standard height of 34½ in. When combined with a 1½ in. thick countertop or countertop with build-up, this creates a base with a surface that's 36 in. above the floor. Configurations vary, with width generally echoing upper cabinet widths.

Ready-to-assemble modular cabinets

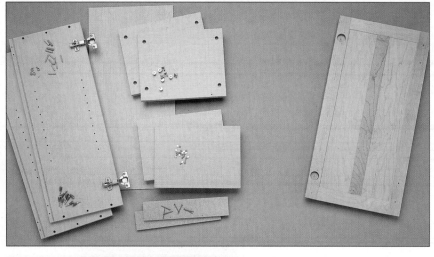

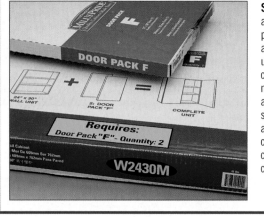

Stock cabinets. A typical ready-to-assemble cabinet includes the cabinet panels, shelves, nailing strips, doors and/or drawer fronts and the hardware used to assemble the cabinet. In many cases, assembling all your boxed cabinets can take longer than installing the assembled units. Cabinet doors on in-stock cabinets are normally sold in separate cartons coded to match the cabinet. Keep this in mind when purchasing cabinets and when estimating costs.

(Continued, from page 188)
oak and red-oak veneered particle board, with raised panel doors. They're suitable for staining or painting. If you don't want to spend a lot of time assembling cabinet components they might be the right product for your project.

Cabinet Types & Styles

Kitchen cabinets and bathroom vanities are the most common cabinets in our homes, and they're the ones you're most likely to repair or replace over time. The emphasis of this chapter will be on these two cabinet types, although a wide variety of other storage units and display furniture are also called cabinets.

The cabinet industry divides kitchen cabinets into two broad categories: *wall cabinets* and *base cabinets*. Most kitchen cabinets use walls as attachment surfaces, but the ones called wall cabinets don't touch the floor. Base cabinets are always floorstanding and covered with either a countertop work-surface or a sink. Bathroom vanities are constructed the same way as kitchen sink base cabinets, but vanities are generally a few inches shallower and shorter.

Base, wall and vanity cabinets are designed in two primary styles: *face frame* and *frameless*. The difference involves whether or not the cabinet has a wood frame that covers the front edges of the cabinet box. Face frame cabinets originated before frameless cabinets, when cabinets were built entirely of solid-wood frames and panels. They continue to be the more traditional cabinet variety, but sheet goods are now used instead of solid wood for the door panels and the cabinet box. The face frame serves primarily as an attachment surface for door hinges. It also helps to stiffen and square the cab-

Buying by the numbers

Modular cabinets are sold in a range of sizes to suit different installation situations. Manufacturers use a naming convention of letters and numbers to identify the type and size of each cabinet.

Base cabinets. Base cabinets are always 34½ in. tall to keep countertop work heights consistent. They're generally 24½ in. deep. Since heights and widths are standardized, a base cabinet will be labeled with a letter designation for its type, usually "B" for base, accompanied by a number that represents width. For example, "B18" identifies an 18-in.-wide base cabinet. Sometimes multiple letters are used in the name to identify special attributes, such as "SB" for sink base.

Wall cabinets. Generally wall cabinets are 12 in. deep, but heights and widths will vary. Wall cabinets usually have four numbers in their name plus a letter or letters to indicate cabinet type. The first two numbers represent width, followed by two numbers for height. So, a "W1530" stands for a wall cabinet 15 in. wide and 30 in. tall.

Vanity cabinets. Vanity cabinets are typically 21 in. deep and 30 in. tall. Like base cabinets, vanities are named by width. A "VB15" represents a 15-in.-wide vanity base.

inet to some degree. Doors and drawers on a face frame cabinet are surrounded by the face frame, so they don't have to be situated immediately next to one another to cover the cabinet front.

Frameless cabinets, also called European or "Euro-style" cabinets, were developed as a result of lumber shortages in Europe following World War II. Limited lumber reserves stimulated a need for more plentiful building materials like plywood and particleboard. These products made it possible to build cabinet components from single pieces of sheet stock instead of frames and panels of solid wood. Cabinet builders discovered that the face frame could be omitted without compromising strength. Along with a frameless design came new concealed hinges and metal drawer slide hardware, which enabled doors and drawers to be hung from the cabinet sides rather than the face frame.

Unlike face frame cabinetry of the time, which was usually built in place in long units, frameless cabinets were were constructed in individual, standard-sized modules. This way, cabinets could be assembled and installed efficiently in a variety of configurations to meet the needs of different room spaces. Fixed cabinets also became removable and reusable.

Modular construction methods have revolutionized cabinet-building in America. Today, nearly all face frame and frameless cabinets are modular, whether they're custom-built or fabricated in a factory. Modular cabinets are easier to jockey in and out of truck beds, doorways and into place at the job site. The cabinet industry has also largely adopted European hinge and drawer slide hardware because of it's durability, low cost and ease of installation. Over time numerous derivatives of European-style cup hinges and metal drawer slide hardware have been developed for use with traditional face frame cabinets as well.

Build or Buy?

Whichever cabinet style you choose, building cabinets yourself can be a satisfying woodworking project. It allows you the freedom to custom-design cabi-

Cabinets options & accessories

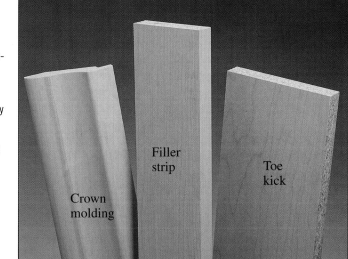

Accessories that should be ordered at the same time as your prefinished cabinets include filler strips, toe-kicks and crown molding for upper cabinets. If you purchase unfinished cabinets, you may find it easier and cheaper to make these parts yourself from raw lumber of the same species.

Crown molding

Filler strip

Toe kick

End panels. Many prefabricated cabinets manufactured today are not made with finished end panels on the sides (the assumption is that they will be stacked next to other cabinets so the end panels won't be visible anyway). Some cabinetry manufacturers offer prefinished end panels that match the cabinets perfectly. Other wise, create your own by attaching a piece of ¼ in. plywood of matching wood species and finish to the cabinet ends on each side of the opening. Use construction adhesive and small wire nails to attach the end panels. Generally, base cabinets have finished ends.

nets that suit your specific needs, as well as choose whatever building materials you see fit. Be aware, however, that building your own cabinets may not save you money over buying them already made. You should also have at least moderate woodworking skills and access to a table saw, jointer, planer and router table.

If you'd rather buy than build, mass production and wholesale pricing make replacing cabinets more affordable than it used to be. Prefabricated cabinets are available in a wide assortment of shapes and sizes, hardware and wood options and door and drawer designs. But manufactured cabinets can still be

quite expensive, even if you install them yourself.

Whether you choose to build or buy cabinets for your next remodeling project, be sure to educate yourself about your options. This is especially important if you are renovating a kitchen, where cabinet function and layout are critical to kitchen performance. Many sources of cabinet plans and kitchen design help are available, including magazines, books, videos and design software for your home computer. Most large home centers will have a kitchen design consultant on staff that can offer advice.

CABINET DOORS

Doors probably contribute more to cabinet styling than any other part. For one thing, they're the largest visible components. Since doors are closed far more than they're open, we notice them continually, so it's important that they be attractive. Doors also suffer their share of abuse—frequent opening and closing, slamming, scuffs, spills—so they need to be durable as well as beautiful.

If you buy manufactured cabinets, you'll probably have a range of door style options and at least a few different woods from which to choose for the doors. Another option is to build the cabinet boxes yourself and purchase, rather than build, the doors. Doors tend to be more complex to build and require more specialized tools than general cabinet construction. Cabinet doors can be ordered in dozens of styles and sizes, and there are often discounts for ordering in bulk. Sources for door distributors can be found on the Internet, in the classified sections of woodworking and home improvement magazines or in the Yellow Pages under the heading "Cabinets."

Mass-marketed cabinets, such as those for sale at home centers, will offer doors in two principal styles: *slab* and *frame-and-panel.* Slab-style doors are made of a single panel of wood or sheet stock. Slab doors originated in the days when a single wide board could make a door. These days slab doors are made of sheet good materials like MDF, particleboard or plywood. The door panels are covered with a layer of high-pressure laminate, melamine or wood veneer to make them more attractive. The outer layer also protects the brittle edges of particleboard and hides the edge laminations of plywood. Slab doors are often standard issue on lower grade cabinetry intended for utility purposes.

Slab doors aren't as popular as they were a few decades ago. Cabinetry trends in the 1970s and 80s favored the use of plastic laminate as a covering for most cabinet surfaces, including the doors. Slab doors provided a smooth flat surface for applying the laminate. At the time, this look was considered to be a clean, modern approach, especially in kitchen design. Plastic laminate has since fallen out of favor for covering exterior cabinet surfaces, especially doors. A more contemporary approach is to cover them with an attractive wood veneer instead of laminate.

Cabinet door styles

Slab doors are solid wood or solid wood panels, without a frame. The slab doors above are flush-mounted (set into the opening): this requires some skill to get the gaps even.

Glass-lite doors have a glass panel held into the door frame. They're usually made with a single piece of glass. Often, decorative "muntins" are overlaid to create the look of a multi-lite panel.

Frame-and-panel doors are constructed with an insert panel (usually ¼ in. plywood stock) set into a solid wood frame. More elaborate versions feature a raised-panel insert with coped or chamfered edges.

Woods species for cabinet doors

Cabinet doors can be ordered in numerous different wood species. Most doors intended for clear finishes are manufactured from hardwood, although pine is also relatively common. Paint-grade or melamine-covered doors are usually made of medium-density fiberboard, particleboard, lauan plywood or lower grades of lumber. Better doors are made of the following woods:

Oak (both red and white)
Poplar
Cherry
Birch
Maple
Hickory
Honduras Mahogany
African Mahogany
Pine
Walnut
Ash
Red Alder

In contrast to slab doors, frame-and-panel doors are used widely on both custom-built and mass-produced cabinets. In this design, doors consist of a central panel framed by two horizontal rails and two vertical stiles. Frame-and-panel doors have been around for hundreds of years, and they are the best design for solid-wood doors which must have some allowance provided for wood movement. When the door panel is made of solid wood, it "floats" without glue in shallow grooves milled around the inside edges of the frame. This way, the panel can expand and contract in the frame without damaging itself or the frame, and the fluctuation in panel size doesn't change the dimensions of the door frame.

Frame-and-panel doors offer a wider range of styling options than slab doors. The center panel can be made of solid wood, painted or veneer-covered sheet goods, strips of wainscot, a piece of glass or even sheet metal. The outside face of the center panel can be flat, but more commonly the panel is milled around the four face edges to appear "raised" in the frame. The inside edges of the frame may also be milled in a decorative profile.

Manufacturers also offer frame-and-panel doors with arched top and bottom rails. When the upper rail is arched, doors are often called "cathedral" or "crown" style. The panel on arched doors is also cut and shaped to match the rail profiles. Expect to pay slightly more for doors with this extra arch detailing.

Door edge treatments

Cabinet manufacturers install doors in several different ways. One option is to outfit cabinets with doors that are slightly larger than the cabinet openings so the doors overlap the openings. When doors overlap the cabinet by their full thickness, the edge treatment is called *overlay*. The overlap helps to hide any misalignments between the doors and their fit over the cabinet openings.

Both slab and frame-and-panel doors can be installed overlay style. On cabinets with face frames, the edge treatment is known as *flush overlay*.

Cabinet door types

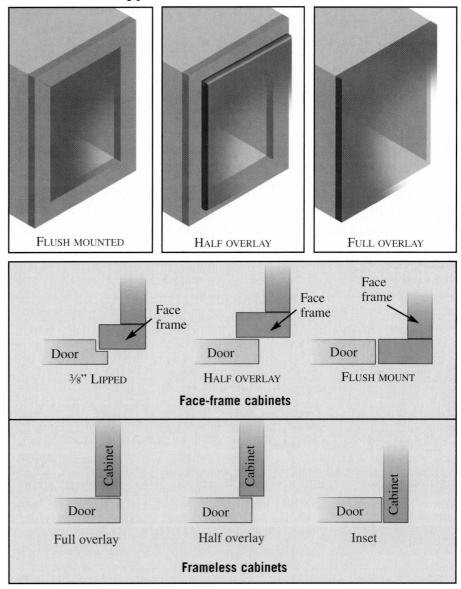

FLUSH MOUNTED   HALF OVERLAY   FULL OVERLAY

3/8" LIPPED   HALF OVERLAY   FLUSH MOUNT

Face-frame cabinets

Full overlay   Half overlay   Inset

Frameless cabinets

The three main types of cabinet doors are *flush-mounted,* also called *inset,* which fit inside the inner perimeter of a face frame or outer cabinet edges; *half-overlay,* which close against the outer face of the face frame (or the outer edges of a frameless cabinet); and *full overlay,* which are sized so all edges are flush with the outer edges of the cabinet or cabinet face frame. Overlay doors often are rabbeted on all inner edges. Called *lipped* cabinet doors, they fit partially into the door opening while overlapping the face frame.

The amount of actual overlap can vary depending on door sizing and the type of hinge hardware used, but typically it is 3/8 in. all around the door.

Frameless cabinets can be outfitted with either *half-* or *full-overlay* doors. The difference concerns whether the doors cover the cabinet front edges fully or by only half their thickness. Full overlay doors are more common than half overlay doors.

A second door edge treatment is to set doors partially into their cabinet openings while still overlapping the edges. The convention for accomplishing this is to mill 3/8-in. rabbets around the back faces of the doors so they recess into the cabinet opening by half their thickness. Doors modified this way are called *lipped,* and they are reserved for face frame applications. Lipped doors have the same benefits as overlay: they don't have to fit perfectly into the face frame openings because the lips hide any alignment problems. Lipped edges give doors and drawers a more subtle, fitted appearance on cabinets than overlay doors.

A third edge treatment involves sizing the doors slightly smaller than their cabinet openings so they fit flush with the cabinet front. Manufacturers call this treatment *inset* or *flush mount.* Inset doors are sometimes used on frameless cabinets, but this leaves the cabinet front edges completely exposed when the doors are closed. Inset doors are far more common on face frame cabinets.

Setting doors into cabinet openings without the benefit of an overlap requires carefully engineered doors and a higher level of installation precision. The cabinets or face frame openings and the doors must be square to keep gaps around the doors consistent. When inset doors are an option on manufactured cabinetry, it's an indication of high quality (usually accompanied by an equally high price tag).

CABINET HARDWARE

Cabinet hardware manufacturers produce countless variations of every type of hardware you'll need for your cabinet project. Hinges are a prime example. Primarily, there are four different kinds of hinges: *concealed, butt, formed* and *pivot/knife.* Each hinge type is offered in an assortment of different styles, metals and finishes. Whether you choose period reproduction or modern hinges, brass or plated steel, hammered or antiqued finish is purely a matter of personal choice. The more important issue is to select hinges that will withstand the rigors of countless

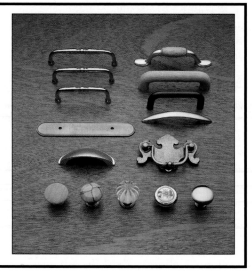

Knobs & pulls

Door and drawer knobs and pulls serve an important operating function on cabinet doors, but they can also be a significant design detail. Cabinet hardware catalogs offer a wide assortment of knobs and pulls made of materials like brass, nickel, steel, aluminum, glass, plastic, wood, ceramic and even marble.

Knobs and pulls are detailed and finished in various ways to match every architectural style, from period to modern. Be sure to factor the cost of this hardware into your project budget. Door hardware can be quite expensive, especially if it's hand-forged or made of solid metal.

openings and closings over the lifetime of the cabinet. They'll need to be able to bear the weight of the doors without sagging or binding. When and if the hinges do fall out of alignment, it helps if they can be adjusted. Not all types are adjustable.

Concealed hinges: Also called Euro-style hinges, these hinges are the type originally developed by European hardware designers for use on frameless Euro-style cabinets. Concealed hinges are so named because the case and door hardware is completely hidden when the door is closed. Unlike other hinges that consist of a pair of hinge leaves connected by a pin, concealed hinges are made of two independent parts that lock together: a mounting plate that fastens to the cabinet case and a cup-shaped component that fits into a flat-bottomed mortise drilled into the back of the cabinet door. The door connects to the cabinet carcase by engaging a pivot arm on the cup with the mounting plate.

Concealed hinges have become the

preferred hinge within the cabinet industry. The hinges are stoutly engineered for years of reliable service. The cup-style door mount can support more door weight than any hinge connected with screws alone. The hinges are easy to install with the proper Forstner-style drill bit and guide template, and the hinges allow for six directions of door adjustment: up, down, left, right, in and out by simply turning adjustment screws. Concealed hinges are available for both frameless and face frame-style cabinets in models that fit either overlay or inset doors. They allow for up to 170° of door swing and are self-closing.

Butt hinges: Butt hinges are small versions of the flat leaved variety found on all passage doors. The hinge leaves are held together with a pin that is either removable or fixed, and they allow for a full 180° of cabinet door swing. Butt hinges only work on inset cabinet doors. A shallow hinge mortise needs to be routed or chiseled into both the door edge and the cabinet face frame, then the hinge fastens into the mortises with screws. When the doors are closed, just the hinge knuckle is visible. Butt hinges are not self closing, so door catches are necessary (See bottom photo, this page).

Wraparound hinges: Sometimes called "formed" hinges, one or both leaves are bent in various ways to fit around the edges and backs of doors and face frames. Bends in the hinge leaves make formed hinges more versa-

Match hinge choice to cabinet door type	
TYPE OF DOOR	**SUITABLE HINGE TYPES**
Full overlay	*Concealed (Euro-style), knife*
Half overlay	*Concealed (Euro-style), wraparound, knife*
Lipped	*Wraparound, knife*
Inset (no face frame)	*Concealed, butt*
Flush mount (in face frame)	*Concealed, butt*

Cabinet Hinge Types

Butt hinges are popular with do-it-yourselfers because they're inexpensive and everyone's used them before. In cabinetmaking, however, they're seldom used these days, in favor of hinges that are faster to install and easier to adjust.

Concealed hinges are quick to install (with a special 35 mm drill bit), self-closing, concealed from the exterior and easy to adjust. They're also known as "European" or "Euro-style," or by popular brand names (*Grass* and *Blum,* for example).

Wraparound hinges are extremely common in cabinetmaking. They are inexpensive, only the barrel is visible when the door is closed, and most are self-closing when doors are opened less than 28°.

tile than other hinge types. You'll find different models to fit full overlay, half-overlay and lipped doors, on either frameless or face-frame carcases. The amount of possible adjustment in these hinges depends on whether or not the screw holes are elongated. Most styles allow for some vertical adjustment on the cabinet-side leaf and horizontal tweaking on the door-side leaf. These hinges are self-closing and provide 180° of door swing.

Knife (pivot) hinges mount to the top and bottom ends of cabinet doors near the corners. You'll find them sold for installation on both inset and overlay doors. A small pin pivots the hinge leaves 180° on one end, like a pocket knife, rather than along the edge, like a butt hinge. Some types have only one hinge leaf that mounts to the cabinet. A pin on this leaf fits into a metal socket sunk into a hole in the door end. Knife hinges are a sleek, nearly concealed alternative to hinges with long visible knuckles, but they offer little or no adjustability. Depending on the leaf thickness, knife hinges may also need to be mortised into the cabinet parts. Generally, these hinges are not self-closing.

Cabinet Door Latches & Catches

Mechanical touch latch

Magnetic touch latch

Safety latch

Spring roller catch

Bullet catch

Magnetic catch

Mechanical touch latch releases and opens cabinet doors when the door is pressed lightly.
Magnetic touch latch has spring-loaded magnets to release the door with only a light touch.
Safety latch is a plastic, mechanical latch that withstands jarring and bouncing without releasing its hold.
Spring roller catch is inexpensive and sturdy, although prone to falling out of alignment.
Bullet catch is probably the smallest door latch, but holds well as long as the door and frame remain aligned.
Magnetic catch holds cabinet door shut securely, placing very little stress on door.

Drawer "false fronts"

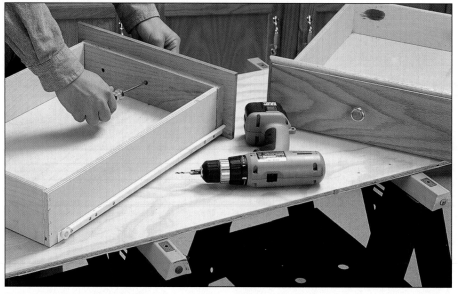

Drawer fronts can be made with either a single panel that forms both the front of the drawer box and the drawer face or with a separate "false front" that attaches to the front of the drawer box. Durability is unaffected by style, but a two-piece drawer front (above) makes the drawer face easier to adjust for an even fit in its opening.

Drawer slides

Heavy-duty slides. This heavy-duty version of side-mounted drawer slide features parts that roll on lubricated ball bearings. The slide consists of three telescoping components that nest together when the drawer closes.

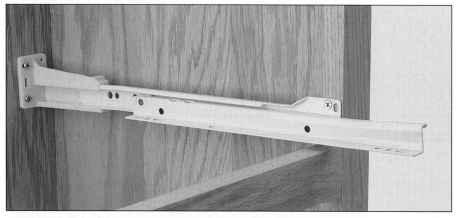

Light-duty slides. For lighter-duty applications, this slide hardware wraps around the bottom edges of the drawer sides and attaches from beneath. There are two sliding components that roll on a pair of nylon wheels, one in front and one in back.

Drawers provide indispensible shallow storage in almost every room of our homes. Cabinets are outfitted with drawers in two ways: Drawers are either installed in the space above the doors, or the cabinet may be made up entirely of drawers stacked on top of one another.

Drawers take their share of daily abuse, and they tend to be the first components on a cabinet to fail. Whether you build or buy cabinets for your next remodeling project, the drawers should be constructed for years of hard use. A number of factors contribute to a well-built drawer, but pay particular attention to the corner joints and the method used for sliding drawers in and out.

Drawer joinery

An assortment of different woodworking joints are used for assembling the front, back and sides of a drawer box. For light-duty cabinetry or on economy grades of manufactured cabinets, drawers may be constructed with simple butt or rabbet joints reinforced with glue and nails. These joints are quick and easy to build, but their strength is determined to a large extent by the glue that holds them together. Eventually glue joints fail, and when they do, so does the drawer.

Drawers in higher quality cabinets should be assembled with interlocking corner joints. The most common among these are dovetail joints, which are designed to hold parts together even without the added benefit of glue. Manufactured cabinets will employ dovetails almost exclusively over other forms of interlocking joints. If you are building cabinet drawers, dovetail joints are rather complicated to make without a dedicated dovetail jig and a router. Other interlocking joints to consider are finger, double-dado or tongue and groove. All of these can be made easily with a table saw and dado blade.

Slide hardware

When it comes time to install drawers in cabinets, you can hang them like furniture builders have done for centuries on wooden drawer slides. The trouble with wooden slides is that they can be time-consuming to install and they eventually wear out as drawers rub against them. The slides can also swell in humid conditions causing drawers to bind.

A quicker and more durable solution is to mount drawers on metal drawer slides instead. Metal slides operate with virtually no friction, because the slide rails roll past one another on nylon wheels or lubricated ball bearings. Slide hardware also keeps drawers from tipping when they are pulled out too far. Depending on their construction, slides allow different amounts of drawer projection, ranging from about 2/3 to the full drawer length. Some hardware even

allows a drawer to be extended beyond its length for cabinets with particularly deep countertop overhangs.

There are several styles of drawer slides, but the most common variety are mounted along the drawer sides. Side-mounted slides can be fitted to frameless or face frame cabinets, and they come in extension lengths that range from 10 in. to 28 in. Slides are also available that tuck beneath the drawer so they are hidden from view.

Side-mounted slides take two forms depending on where the hardware attaches to the drawer. The first variety has a telescoping-style action and mounts midway across the width of the drawer sides. The components of each slide roll on ball bearings. This tele-

scoping slide can bear more weight than other styles, up to 100 pounds or more per slide. The hardware requires 1/2 in. to 3/4 in. of clearspace on each side of the drawer to operate.

A second form of side-mounted slide wraps around the bottom edges of the drawer sides, cradling the drawer from beneath. Instead of ball bearings, the cradle-style slides roll on a pair of nylon wheels, one mounted in front and the other in back. These slides have a much lower load rating than the ball-bearing variety, but they are a good economical choice for light-duty drawers. They also come in several different colors to make the hardware less conspicuous.

Hanging shelves

It's a good design practice to make cabinet shelves adjustable. In reality, most shelves aren't repositioned all that often, but adjustable shelves are nevertheless more versatile than fixed shelves. To make shelves adjustable, cabinets are outfitted with metal shelf standards, shelf pins or plastic clips. Metal shelf standards come in strips of different lengths and finishes, and they are punched with holes along their length to hold metal clips. Pairs of standards can be attached flush against the inside face of each cabinet side with brads or small screws. A less conspicuous approach is to recess the standards into shallow dadoes. Either way, standards provide ample shelf support at reasonable cost.

Shelf pins and clips are a more subtle approach to hanging shelves than metal standards. You determine the

pin locations by drilling rows of holes into the cabinet sides. When the doors are open, all you see are the extra holes for the pins. Holes for the pins usually are drilled 1 to 2 in. apart, and you can drill as few holes as you like to make them even less conspicuous. Shelf pins come in a few different metal finishes, but they are all about the same length and diameter. Most pins have a flat, paddle-shaped end to support the shelf and keep it from rolling forward. Wood dowels also make suitable and inexpensive shelf pins. For added strength, shelf pins holes can be reinforced by pressing metal sleeves into the holes.

Shelf clips are another option. They're commonly made of plastic and insert into holes in the cabinet sides just like shelf pins. The difference is that shelf clips have a tab above and below to lock the shelf in place. Plastic clips aren't as strong as metal shelf pins, but they are sturdy enough for medium-duty shelving.

Metal shelf standards

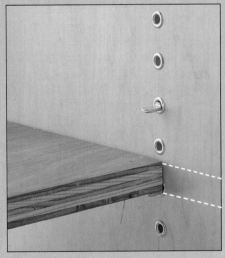

Shelf pins outfitted with metal sleeves

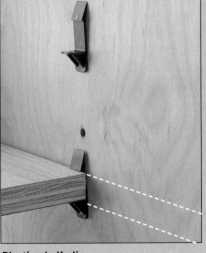

Plastic shelf clips

Vanity cabinets provide a nice combination of style and storage. Shorter than kitchen base cabinets, they're often installed in banks and can be topped with a double-bowl countertop for two-sink installations.

VANITY CABINETS

Vanity cabinets are installed in much the same manner as kitchen sink base cabinets. Like sink cabinets, they're usually open in the back to provide access for plumbing. And instead of a countertop with a sink set into a cutout, the typical vanity top is an all-in-one unit formed from cultured marble (although it's not too unusual to install a kitchen-style countertop with a bathroom sink).

Most bathrooms are small enough that a single vanity cabinet is the best option. But in larger bathrooms, it's becoming more common to install a bank of vanity cabinets, as in the photo at the top of this page. This is often done during bathroom remodels where a double-bowl vanity is chosen.

Because the selection of vanity cabinets is a bit limited compared to kitchen cabinets, it's sometimes tempting to install the kitchen version with a vanity top. There is no particular problem with this, other than the fact that vanity cabinets are 4 to 6 in. shorter than kitchen cabinets. If you have mostly taller adults in your family, they appreciate the extra height. but it can be a fairly uncomfortable stretch for children and shorter adults.

When planning a vanity cabinet installation, it's best to select the top first, then find a cabinet that's sized to accommodate the top.

Vanity tops are generally made of cultured marble or solid-surfacing material, with an integral sink, countertop and backsplash.

Center the cabinet on the drainpipe stub-out. Start by drawing a reference line directly beneath the centerpoint of the drain, then measure out half the width of the cabinet in each direction from the reference line.

Make sure the cabinet is level. Test with a level and adjust by slipping shims under the low side or by using adjustable leveler legs. Gaps of ¼ in. or less between the cabinet bottom and the floor can be concealed with caulk. If the gaps are larger, consider trimming out around the cabinet base with base trim molding, such as quarter-round or base-shoe.

Medicine cabinets aren't just small boxes with mirrors anymore. Most home centers carry a wide range of models, including highly decorative tri-mirror units like the one above.

MEDICINE CABINETS

The medicine cabinet is one of the most used and most useful cabinets in just about every home. All you need to do is open one up and try to find a spot for your new can of shaving cream to realize exactly how heavily used the medicine cabinet is. For this reason, replacing an old, cramped medicine cabinet with a newer, more spacious model is a quick and easy remodeling project that offers instant rewards.

When selecting a medicine cabinet, the basic choice is between recessed and surface mounted (See below). Beyond that, you'll need to consider basic styling, the number of doors and whether or not it has a built-in light source (side lights are preferable to top-mounted).

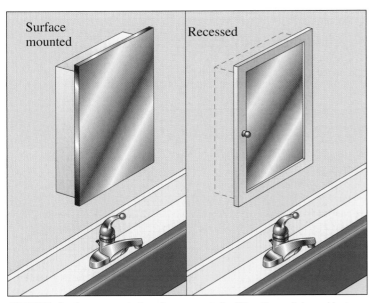

OPTIONS: Surface-mounted and recessed. Traditionally, medicine cabinets are recessed into the bathroom wall above the sink or vanity (right). While this may offer some minor space-saving advantages, most homeowners and builders today prefer to install surface-mounted cabinets (left) and avoid cutting into the wall. Many new medicine cabinets can be installed either way.

Replacing a medicine cabinet

Remove the old medicine cabinet, then lay out the installation area for the new cabinet. Mark cutting lines for the new wall opening. Center vertical lines at stud locations. If you will be cutting a wall stud, extend the lower cutting line so it's 1½ in. below the rough opening to allow for a 2 × 4 sill.

Ends of cutting area should fall over wall studs

Remove the wallcoverings, then frame in the rough opening for the cabinet. Cut out wall studs in the opening with a reciprocating saw (if removing more than one, you'll need temporary ceiling support—check with your building inspector). The rough opening should be ½ to 1 in. larger than the cabinet in both directions to allow for leveling and shimming.

Patch the wall with new wall covering material. Be sure to follow local codes when installing wallcovering materials in a wet area. Tape and sand the patched area. In most cases, you'll want to paint or finish the wall before installing the medicine cabinet.

Install the medicine cabinet. Check with a level and shim as needed to make sure the cabinet is level and plumb. Secure the cabinet with 16d casing nails or 2 in. wallboard screws driven through the cabinet sides and into the trimmer studs on the sides of the opening.

Kitchen islands have enjoyed a boom in popularity in recent years. They can be freestanding (or in some cases, rolling) or attached permanently to the floor. Many are plumbed with full-size kitchen sinks or smaller bar sinks for food preparation. Larger islands can also house major kitchen appliances and be used for seating.

KITCHEN ISLANDS

These days, just about every kitchen remodel includes a new kitchen island. From a single base cabinet with a countertop, to elaborate, multifunction and multilevel construction projects, an island adds food preparation, storage and seating capacity, reducing the pressure on your already-overcrowded countertops. Even a smaller kitchen can usually accommodate a modest island, especially if the other room elements are relocated to make room.

Convert a base cabinet

Standard kitchen base cabinets can be converted for use in an island setting by adding a matching back panel to the cabinet. If the cabinet manufacturer does not offer back panels, make one from ¼ in. plywood that has a veneer face matching the wood species of the cabinet.

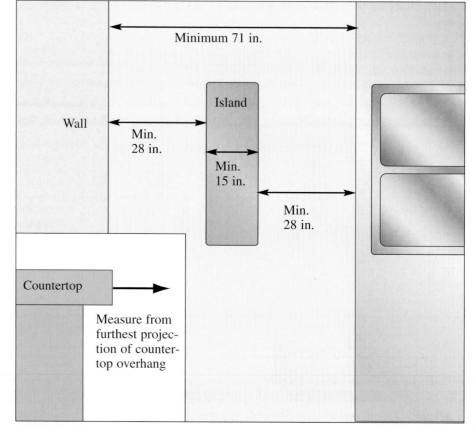

Minimum clearances. A minimum of 71 in. of clear space from countertop edge to the nearest wall is needed to install a kitchen island. With this amount of space, you can just squeeze in a 15 in. wide island surface (the minimum useful size), with a minimal passing distance of 28 in. on each side of the island. When measuring the available space in your kitchen be sure to measure from the furthest projection of each element: for example, measure from the countertop edges, not the cabinets (inset).

Appliance panels allow dishwashers, ovens and refrigerators to blend in with your new cabinetry. They can be custom-ordered from the cabinet manufacturer to fit just about any size or model appliance. *Photo courtesy of Kraftmaid Cabinetry.*

Open shelving is an option on some base cabinets. A decorative top rail and finished interior create a neater look than if you simply eliminated the cabinet door. *Photo courtesy of Kraftmaid Cabinetry.*

Organizers such as the pull-out pantry shown at left can help you maximize the storage capacity of your cabinets. But don't get too carried away with creating a special place for everything you plan to store: your needs may change, and someday you'll want to sell your home. *Photo courtesy of Kraftmaid Cabinetry.*

Pull-out worksurfaces (above) and storage (left) add valuable prep and storage space. Pull-out worksurfaces also allow a chair or wheelchair to fit below, making them a good addition to a barrier-free room. *Photos courtesy of Kraftmaid Cabinetry.*

Supporting the countertop. For corner cabinets that are not full-depth, set the cabinet in place and level it, then install the base cabinets on each side. With the cabinet leveled, cut nailing strips to attach to the wall at stud locations, level with the top of the cabinet.

Cabinet jacks. Build a cabinet jack to support wall cabinets during installation. The jack shown above is made from plywood and dimensioned to support upper wall cabinets at the correct height when it's placed on the countertop below. If the wall-hung cabinets are not above a base cabinet, use a pair of 2 × 4s for temporary support.

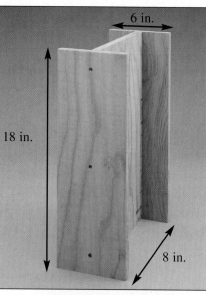

6 in.

18 in.

8 in.

Installing base cabinets. Base cabinets are leveled then screwed through the top, back rail and into the wall at stud locations. Frameless models (above) are also attached to one another by driving short screws through the adjoining cabinet sides. Cabinets with face frames (right) are attached to one another with screws driven through the adjoining face frame stiles. In either case, clamp the cabinets together before joining them, be sure to drill pilot holes, and use screws that are ¼ to ½ in. shorter than the combined thickness of the parts being joined.

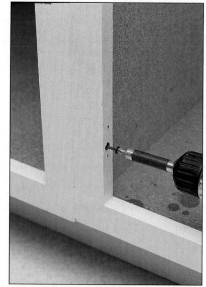

Hanging tip. French cleats are made by bevel-ripping a board that's at least 4 in. wide, then fastening one half of the board to the wall and the other to the back of your cabinet. The cleats distribute the load of the cabinet over a broad area, reducing the strain on individual screws and the cabinet structure.

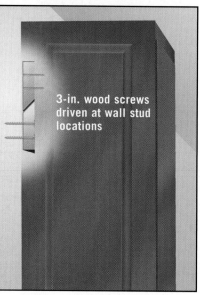

3-in. wood screws driven at wall stud locations

Remove doors for painting. Whether you're brushing or spraying (or even rolling) paint or finish onto your cabinet doors or drawer fronts, you'll get better results if you remove them from the cabinets and apply the material with the doors lying flat.

Leveler legs. You can make a base cabinet taller by adding adjustable leveler legs. Leveler legs (sold at most hardware and woodworking stores) usually come with a pair of clips so a toe-kick can be attached to the legs without fasteners. While this takes care of the front, it won't help conceal exposed sides. One way to solve this problem is to add 1 × 2 nailing strips to the inside of the base at the sides so you can attach scribed filler strips to the sides as well. The filler strips can be painted to match the toekick or veneered to match the cabinet.

Start with a plan. Sketch your new cabinet layout carefully before ordering cabinets. Share your sketch with the millwork specialist at your building materials or home center. He or she may have some suggestions to help you plan a layout that meets your needs and doesn't require custom-sized cabinets.

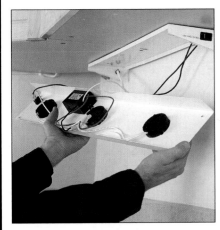

Undercabinet Lights

Undercabinet lights introduce useful work light right where you need it the most; on your countertops. They are available in numerous shapes and profiles. Most have either halogen or fluorescent bulbs. Some styles are hard-wired to your electric supply, and others are plugged into a 120-volt outlet.

COUNTERTOPS

There are many suitable materials from which you can fashion a kitchen counter or a bathroom vanity top, but each has its own strengths and drawbacks. Take ceramic tile, for example. A popular countertop option these days, ceramic tile is highly attractive, available in a wide range of colors and styles and can be installed by just about anyone with a little bit of do-it-yourself ability. But on the negative side, the higher-end quality tiles are fairly expensive (and naturally these are the ones we always choose first at the tile store); the grout lines between tiles can allow water penetration; and the tile surface itself is hard to the point of being unforgiving (you don't need to knock over your favorite coffee mug too many times to find this out).

Nevertheless, by making a careful evaluation of your needs and tastes you can find the countertop solution that works best for you and your budget.

If you are conducting a large remodeling project, wait as long as you can before installing the new countertops. Most countertop materials are relatively delicate and difficult to repair if they're damaged while you work on other parts of the room. But keep in mind that one of the most important functions of a countertop, be it in a bathroom or kitchen, is to support the sink, so if you're anxious to revive your supply of fresh water, go ahead and install the countertop as soon as the base cabinets are in.

Postform accessories

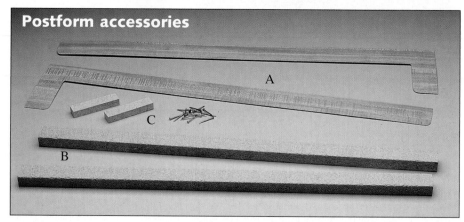

End-cap kits for finishing exposed postform ends include: matching laminate profiled to cover the backsplash and the countertop edge (A); build-up strips that are glued to the underside of the countertop before the end caps are attached (B); and small filler strips that fit along the ends of the backsplash (C).

Tile supplies

Tools and materials for installing a ceramic tile countertop include: tile cutter (A); notched trowel (B); grout sealer (C); grout float (D); grout (E); latex grout additive (F); thinset mortar (G); grout sponge (H); cementboard (I); fiberglass seam tape (J); tile spacers (K); rod saw for cutting tiles (L); and tile nippers (M).

Plastic laminate supplies

Tools and materials for working with plastic laminate include: contact cement—the nonflammable types are better in an enclosed area, while the original oil-based contact cement tends to provide a slightly stronger bond (A); a rubber J-roller for smoothing out the laminate (B); a paint roller with a short-nap adhesive sleeve for applying contact cement to broad surfaces (C); a flush-trimming laminate bit for router (D); sample chips for choosing color and style (E); disposable bristle brush for applying contact cement to smaller surfaces (F).

Postform connectors

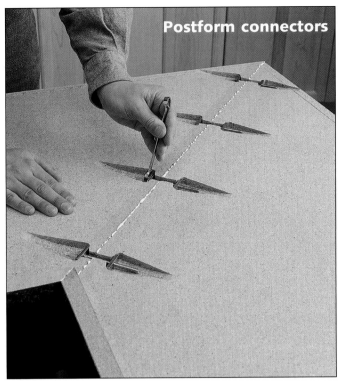

Joining postform sections. If you've purchased premitered postform countertop sections, like those shown here, simply apply glue along the joint, press the sections together upside-down on a flat surface, then insert mechanical fasteners at the premortised locations. Tighten the fasteners enough to draw the sections together, but do not fully tighten them yet. If you're cutting your own miters, use a straightedge guide and cut with a circular saw and jig saw. It's important to get a clean cut for a smooth seam, so use a very sharp blade (a hollow-ground planer blade is a good choice for the circular saw portion of the cut). Unless the cut is exceptionally straight and clean, it's a good idea to go over it with a belt sander and 100-grit paper to smooth it out. Make a template and use a router with a straight bit to cut the mortises. Or, use a drill and a wood chisel. Join the sections as described for the premitered sections.

Cutting laminate

Planning your plastic laminate countertop project: For kitchen and bathroom countertops, 36 in. wide laminate can be used very efficiently. The substrate for the laminate is normally 25½ in. wide (in fact, you can buy particleboard precut to this dimension at countertop materials distributors). Allowing ½ in. overhang for trimming on each side, covering the surface of the substrate requires a 26½ in. wide piece. You'll also need a 2 in. wide strip for the front edge (to be trimmed to 1½ in. after application); and if you're making a backsplash you'll need additional strips of about 5 in. and 2 in. Allowing for cutting kerfs, this will allow you to barely squeeze out these four strips from one 36 in. wide strip of laminate (So cut carefully!). In most cases, it's easier to make seams at corners at right angles than to miter-cut the laminate. Just make sure the laminate seam is not directly over the substrate seam.

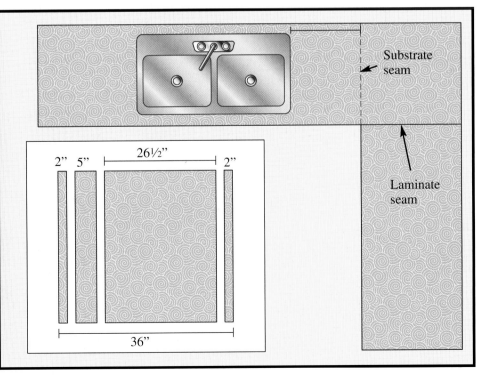

Countertop Material Options

Plastic laminate

- Durability: Okay; little water penetration on surface, but can be vulnerable at edges and back; generally has a harder surface than postform
- Cleanability: Good; gap at backsplash can create problems if not well caulked; some textures streak easily
- Heat resistance: Low
- Style variety: High
- Cost: Low to medium

Plastic laminate has endured an undeservedly bad reputation at times because it tends to be confused with lower-grade tileboard that was designed for shower stalls and other vertical applications but is often misused as an inexpensive countertop or tabletop material. Real plastic laminate is made by impregnating layers of kraft paper under pressure with plastic resin to form a hard, durable substrate. A paper color/pattern layer is bonded to the substrate, then coated with a layer of protective clear melamine to complete the manufacturing process. The plastic laminate is glued to a subbase of particleboard or medium-density fiberboard. It is available in dozens of styles, patterns and textures.

Postform

- Durability: Okay; minimal seams reduce water penetration but thin surface coating is vulnerable to scratching and other forms of damage
- Cleanability: Good; hard washable surface with minimal seams and gaps
- Heat resistance: Low
- Style variety: Low (but can be custom-ordered in many colors and styles)
- Cost: Low to medium

Postform countertops are made from sections of particleboard with preattached laminated surfaces and integral backsplashes. Postform pieces are carried in-stock at most building centers in various lengths and standard countertop width (25½ in.). Premitered sections are generally sold as well, along with straight sections that have no backsplash. Postform is the cheapest common countertop material and is very easy to install. The primary drawback is in selection: most building centers will carry only a couple of colors and styles in stock. But if you can wait a few weeks, there is almost no limit to the colors and patterns, as well as the size, that can be custom-ordered.

Solid surfacing material

- Durability: High
- Cleanability: High (scratches can be sanded out)
- Heat resistance: Good
- Style variety: Limited but improving
- Cost: High

Photo courtesy of Avonite

Solid surfacing material for countertops is known best by its popular brand names, particularly Corian by DuPont. Other brand names include Avonite, Gibraltar, Surell and Swanstone. Formed by binding resins and natural minerals together under heat and pressure, countertops made from solid surface materials will stand up to all types of abuse, while offering a seamless, high-end appearance. But they are quite costly and manufacturers of the solid surfacing panels do not recommend that homeowners work the material themselves. In fact, most factory warranties require that the product be installed by a certified technician. See page 103.

Countertop Material Options

Ceramic tile

- Durability: Good; tiles themselves are very durable but grout joints can be problematic; some risk of cracking
- Cleanability: Okay; smooth glazed tiles clean up well, although grout lines don't; cleanability decreases as texture increases
- Heat resistance: High
- Style variety: Medium
- Cost: Medium to high

Ceramic tile is a truly unique material when used for countertop installations. The individual tiles can be positioned to adapt to just about any shape or size, yet when the surface is completed it has a monolithic quality as if it were fashioned from a single piece of tile. Use thicker floor tiles for kitchen countertops. For bathroom vanities and noncountertop surfaces you can use thinner (cheaper) wall tiles. Avoid mosaic sheets for countertop applications since the small size of the individual tiles results in too many vulnerable grout lines. Also avoid larger 12 × 12 tiles, which can result in awkward shapes and irregular grout lines. For most applications, 4 × 4, 6 × 6 or 8 × 8 tiles are best.

Poured concrete

- Durability: Depends on quality of installation and other variables; if properly installed can last for generations
- Cleanability: Okay; when troweled smooth and sealed will resist staining, otherwise can absorb stains
- Heat resistance: High
- Style variety: Medium
- Cost: Low (materials only)

Poured concrete is not traditionally counted among the most desirable countertop building materials, but that is changing quickly. While it has been employed as counter and tabletop material for centuries in some parts of the world, it is just beginning to gain acceptance here in the United States. When pigmented and properly troweled to a smooth, deep finish concrete can offer advantages no other material can claim: it is truly seamless and it is, literally, as hard as rock. But the success of this material depends entirely on the manner in which it is installed. A good job will create a counter that will last indefinitely; a poorly installed countertop can crack and crumble almost immediately.

Other countertop materials

The countertop types featured in this section represent the most common selections for building your own kitchen cabinet countertops and vanity tops. But there are numerous other materials that have been adapted for use as countertops, and some quite successfully. Here are a few additional countertop material options you may want to consider:

Wood (Butcher block): Because it is not water-resistant, wood is seldom used to make countertops any more—especially in areas near sinks and other sources of water and heat. But in the right spot (for example, a kitchen island with no sink or cooktop cutout) a butcher block top can provide an unmatched blend of warmth, style and function.

Stainless steel: A very common countertop surface in commercial applications, stainless steel is one of the hottest materials in residential kitchen design. The advantages are many, particularly when it comes to hygiene and dramatic contemporary styling. But it is a very expensive material that must be custom-fabricated by a professional.

Natural stone tile: Has most of the same advantages and disadvantages as ceramic tile, but tends to create uneven surfaces that create awkward situations. But on the positive side, in the right spot natural stone can outclass any other building material on sheer appearance.

Cultured marble: A very common surface material used mostly to make vanity tops with integral sinks.

Granite or marble slabs: If you can afford them, these monolithic countertops are the absolute top of the line.

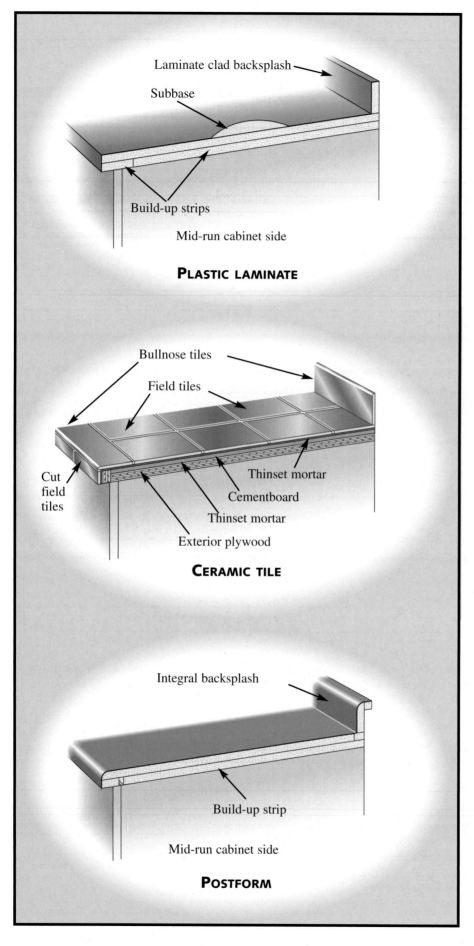

Plastic laminate. PLASTIC LAMINATE

Subbase

Laminate clad backsplash

Build-up strips

Mid-run cabinet side

Bullnose tiles

Field tiles

Cut field tiles

Thinset mortar

Cementboard

Thinset mortar

Exterior plywood

CERAMIC TILE

Integral backsplash

Build-up strip

Mid-run cabinet side

POSTFORM

Plastic laminate. Plastic laminate is bonded with contact cement to a subbase of particleboard or medium-density fiberboard. Build-up strips are glued and screwed to the bottom of the subbase at the front and sides and beneath any seams in the subbase. Build-up strips also are attached to the tops of the cabinet sides for support and to provide surfaces for attaching the countertop to the cabinets. The front edge can be covered with strips of laminate or other decorative treatments. A backsplash is adhered to the back edge.

Ceramic tile. The subbase for a tile countertop is more complex than for most other countertop materials, but far less time consuming to create than the solid mortar beds used in the old days. Today, most installers employ ¾ in. thick exterior plywood as a base, then bond sheets of 5⁄16 in. thick cementboard to the plywood with a layer of thinset mortar. Then another, thicker layer of thinset is applied to the cementboard and the tile is set into this layer. Finally, grout is used to fill the gaps between tiles.

Postform. Postform countertops don't require a subbase: they rest directly on particleboard build-up strips that are tacked to the tops of the cabinet sides. The countertop is secured by driving screws up through the build-up strips where possible, and through blocking at the top corners of the cabinet cases.

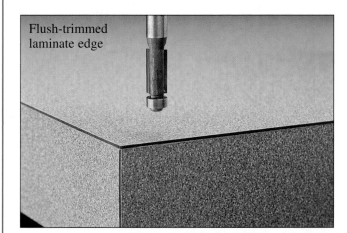

Flush-trimmed
laminate edge

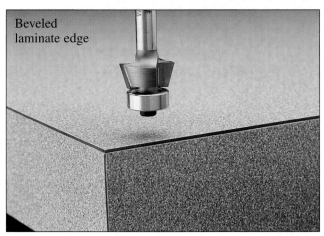

Beveled
laminate edge

Finish treatments for laminate

One advantage to building your own countertop is that you can choose whichever edge and backsplash style you prefer. Among the more popular edge treatments are laminating the edges and shaping a flush seam or a decorative beveled seam, and attaching hardwood strips to the edge. A profile can be cut into the hardwood edge strip with a router to enhance the decorative effect.

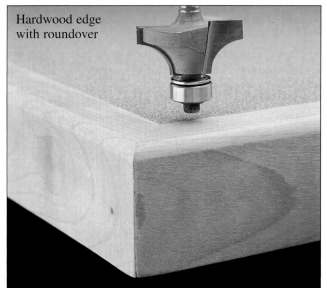

Hardwood edge
with roundover

Backsplash options

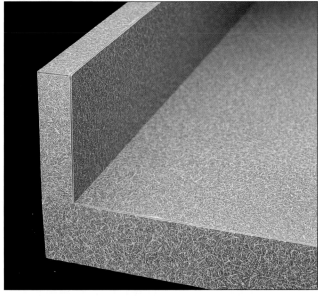

A strip of particleboard clad with the same laminate used on the counter-tops is the most basic backsplash option. Apply the tops and side pieces first, trim to fit, then apply the front strip. Trim and attach to countertop or wall with silicone adhesive.

A slight cant can be created simply by building tapered edges for the backsplash sides and bevel-ripping the bottom of the assembly to a low angle (8 to 10°). For best results, bevel-rip the top to the same angle. Then, simply apply the laminate as with a straight backsplash.

FASTENERS, ADHESIVES & CAULK

No matter how carefully you cut project parts and no matter how painstakingly you form the joints, without good gluing and fastening techniques your project likely will fail. Successful gluing is a matter of choosing the best adhesive for the job, making sure the mating surfaces are properly prepared, and applying the correct amount of glue. From bonding retaining wall blocks together with construction adhesive to applying cabinet veneer, gluing is a skill every handyman should possess.

Fastening is an easy project step to rush through. By the time you're ready to nail, screw or bolt your project together, the last thing you want to do is spend additional time fussing with pilot holes, counterbores and bolt patterns. But take the time—there's no more discouraging shop experience than to see a project fail because you neglected to choose the proper fastener for the task or install it correctly.

For projects that must endure the effects of the elements or where water resistance is necessary, caulks and other sealants will keep water problems at bay for years. Whether you are repairing an asphalt driveway, sealing the rim of a tub or replacing a few panes of window glass, the sealant industry likely has a caulking product to suit your needs. And as technology develops in this area, sealants are constantly becoming more durable and easier to apply.

This section will show you a wide variety of fasteners, adhesives and caulking products that are available for consumer use. There are far more specialized items than room allows on the pages that follow, but the selection of products covered here will provide a good overview of your options in these areas.

Nails & staples

Nails have been around for centuries, and they are arguably the quickest method for joining two workpieces together. Most types of nails, especially finish and common nails, are sized using the pennyweight system (See chart, below). You'll know a pennyweight-sized nail when it is represented by a number next to a letter "d" (which stands for penny). The higher the number, the longer the nail and, eventually, the thicker the shank. Manufacturers often list the the nail length on the box as well. Smaller nail varieties, such as brads and wire nails, are sold by length rather than pennyweight.For general construction applications, 16d, 10d, 8d, 6d and 4d nails are most useful to keep on hand. For installing trim and other light-duty woodworking, 3d, 4d, 6d and 8d finish nails will be suitable for nearly any task.

You may not reach for the staple gun often, but it helps to keep a selection of staples on hand for tacking up plastic sheeting, fastening insulation batts to wall framing or making that next batch of garage sale signs.

Nail sizes

Pennyweight	Length		Diameter	
	(in.)	(cm)	(in.)	(cm)
2d	1	2.5	.068	.17
3d	1¼	3.2	.102	.26
4d	1½	3.8	.102	.26
5d	1¾	4.4	.102	.26
6d	2	5.1	.115	.29
7d	2¼	5.7	.115	.29
8d	2½	6.4	.131	.33
9d	2¾	7.0	.131	.33
10d	3	7.6	.148	.38
12d	3¼	8.3	.148	.38
16d	3½	8.9	.148	.38
20d	4	10.2	.203	.51

Standard staple sizes

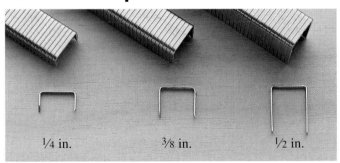

¼ in.　　　⅜ in.　　　½ in.

Staples are used mostly for attaching insulation, building paper and housewrap in home remodeling projects. They're also used for tacking drop cloths and protective plastic sheeting in place. You'll find staples available in both brass and galvanized steel for weather resistance. Size is dictated by the length of the staple prongs.

Types of nails

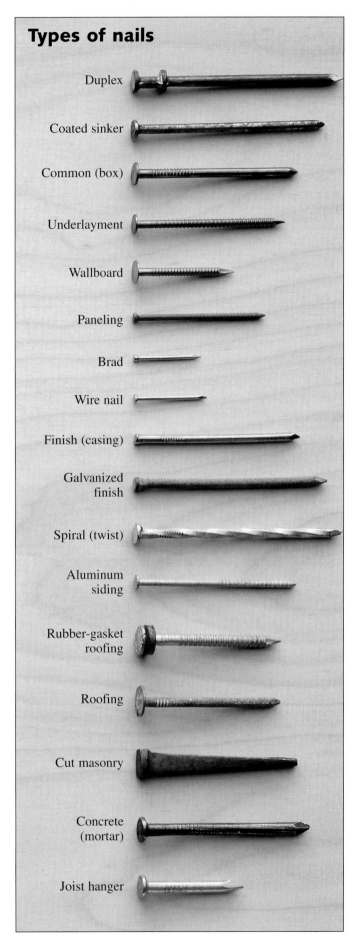

Duplex

Coated sinker

Common (box)

Underlayment

Wallboard

Paneling

Brad

Wire nail

Finish (casing)

Galvanized finish

Spiral (twist)

Aluminum siding

Rubber-gasket roofing

Roofing

Cut masonry

Concrete (mortar)

Joist hanger

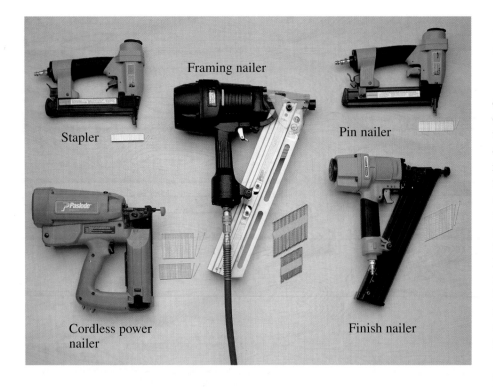

Framing nailer

Stapler

Pin nailer

Cordless power
nailer

Finish nailer

Pneumatic nailers & fasteners

Compressed-air-powered fasteners can dramatically decrease the amount of time you spend on a project. Many tools will fire fasteners as fast as you can pull the trigger. Most air nailers require a ½ to 1 hp compressor with tank capacity of at least 3 gallons of air. Smaller air nailers and staplers usually run on 2 to 5 cubic feet per minute (cfm) or air volume at a pressure of 70 to 90 pounds per square inch (psi). Larger framing nailers can require as much as 9 cfm and 100 to 120 psi. Recently, a similar tool to air nailers, the cordless power nailer, has become available for home use or for rental (See description below).

Pneumatic staplers: Air-powered staplers can drive crown-style staples from ¼ to ½ in. wide, and up to 2 in. long. Smaller staplers are useful for installing carpeting, roofing felt, floor underlayment and insulation. Larger capacity staplers can attach fence boards, strip flooring and even roof decking (check with your local building codes first).

Framing nailers: The "big boy" of air-powered fasteners, these powerful, high-capacity tools will drive nails up to 3½ in. long for all types of frame construction. The magazine can hold upwards of 100 nails.

Pin nailers: Drive brads up to 1¼ in. long. Used to attach trim, carpet strips and moldings. This lightweight tool allows you to nail one-handed, a real help when aligning trim molding pieces.

Finish nailer: Drives finish nails from ¾ to 2 in. long. Useful for installing siding, flooring, door and window casing and most types of finish carpentry.

Cordless power nailer: Relies on battery power and disposable fuel cells instead of compressed air. Require special fasteners, generally 16 gauge, from 1½ to 3¼ in. long, depending on the model. Each fuel cell will drive from 1200 to 2500 nails, depending on length, and a single battery charge will drive up to 4000 nails.

Fasteners for metal

Joining metal with mechanical fasteners is much the same as joining wood. The trick lies in doing careful layout and preparation work, drilling pilot and guide holes accurately, and selecting the right fastener for the job. Whenever possible, select hardware made from the same type of metal as the parts being joined.

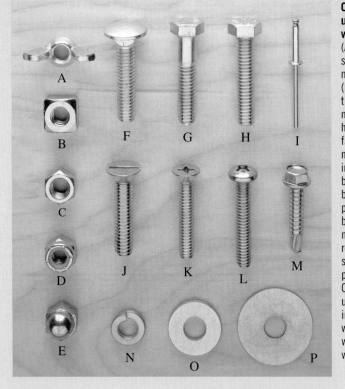

A

B

C

D

E

F

G

H

I

J

K

L

M

N

O

P

Common nuts used in metal-working include: (A) wing nut; (B) square nut; (C) hex nut; (D) stop nut (locks down when tightened); (E) cap nut (conceals bolt heads). Common fasteners used in metalworking include: (F) carriage bolt; (G) machine bolt; (H) tap bolt; (I) pop rivet; (J) stove bolt; (K) flathead machine screw; (L) roundhead machine screw; (M) self-tapping metal screw. Common washers used in metalworking include: (N) lock washer; (O) flat washer; (P) fender washer.

Screws

Screws are classified according to the type of slot, the shape of the head, the diameter and the length.

Slotted screws: Flathead screws are the oldest type of screws and have a straight slot in the head. These screws started showing up in the late 1700s and were made entirely by hand. Mass-production machines were invented in the mid 1850s and the flathead screw has been pretty much unchanged up to the present day.

Phillips-head screws: Phillips screws have largely replaced slotted screws since about the 1950s. They provide a more positive drive and will grip better in a drill/driver or screw-driver so you don't need to support them with your free hand.

Square-drive screws are a more recent screw-type innovation than Phillips screws, even though they were invented in the early 1900s in Canada. They require a square-drive bit, and will drive you nuts if you don't have one. They are the modern screw design of choice. A hybrid design that's a combination of phillips and square drive (called Torx) may also be encountered, although they are far less common than the other screw drive styles.

In addition to driving method, screws vary in the shape of the head. They may be flathead, pan-shaped, domed or tapered. Pan-shaped and dome-shaped lay above the wood, while tapered, bugle-head screws are countersunk below or flush to the surface. Flathead can be either flush or counter-sunk. The diameter of the screw is indicated by the gauge numbering system, with most woods screws falling between 6 and 12 gauge (designated by a # sign). The length is expressed in inches, from the tip to the top of the head. Common lengths are between ¾ and 3½ in.

Screws need a pilot hole so they won't split the wood when they're installed, especially near an end. Use a drill bit that's roughly the same diameter as the shank.

Countersinks & counterbores

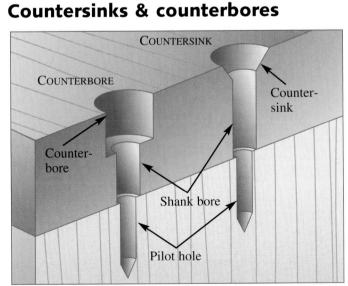

A counterbore hole has a cylindrical top intended to accept a wood screw plug; a countersink hole has a beveled top just deeply enough for the screw head to be driven below the wood surface, creating a small recess to be filled with wood putty.

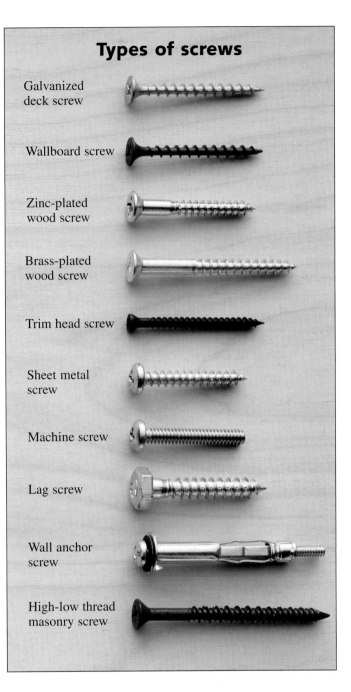

Types of screws

- Galvanized deck screw
- Wallboard screw
- Zinc-plated wood screw
- Brass-plated wood screw
- Trim head screw
- Sheet metal screw
- Machine screw
- Lag screw
- Wall anchor screw
- High-low thread masonry screw

Screw counterbore sizes

Gauge	Head bore	Shank bore	Pilot hole
2	11/64	3/32	1/16
3	13/64	7/64	1/16
4	15/64	7/64	5/64
5	¼	1/8	5/64
6	9/32	9/64	3/32
7	5/16	5/32	7/64
8	11/32	5/32	7/64
9	23/64	11/64	1/8
10	25/64	3/16	1/8
12	7/16	7/32	9/64
14	½	¼	5/32

DECK SCREWS

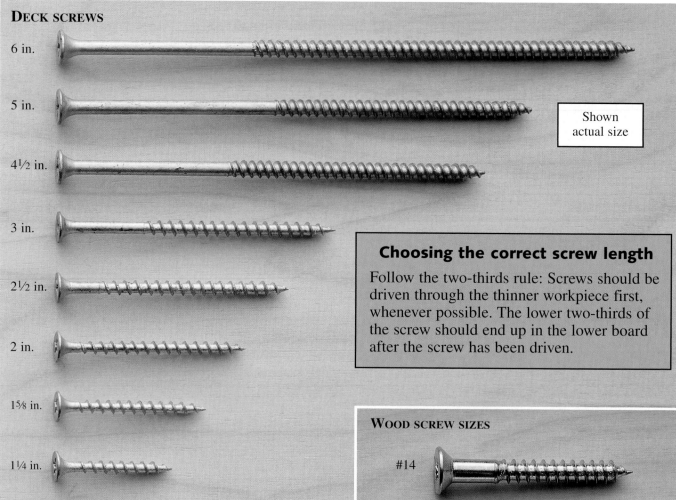

6 in.

5 in.

4½ in.

3 in.

2½ in.

2 in.

1⅝ in.

1¼ in.

Choosing the correct screw length

Follow the two-thirds rule: Screws should be driven through the thinner workpiece first, whenever possible. The lower two-thirds of the screw should end up in the lower board after the screw has been driven.

Deck screws (above) are well-suited for exterior applications. Because they have widely-spaced threads, they often can be driven without drilling pilot holes and hold well in softer framing lumbers. The thickness of the screws is uniform, but lengths vary from 1¼ to 6 in. Deck screws are available with galvanized and teflon-based coatings or made of stainless steel.

WOOD SCREW SIZES

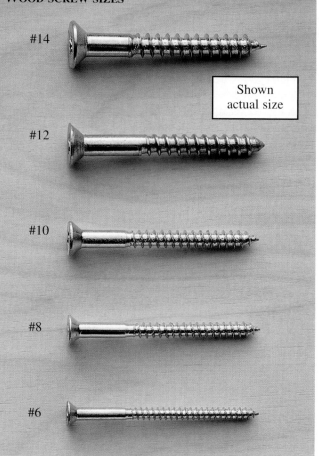

#14

#12

#10

#8

#6

Wood screw sizes

GAUGE NO.	DIAMETER		SMALLEST LENGTH	
	(in.)	(mm)	(in.)	(mm)
0	0.060	1.52	3/16	4.8
1	0.070	1.78	¼	6.4
2	0.082	2.08	5/16	7.9
3	0.094	2.39	3/8	9.5
4	0.108	2.74	7/16	11.1
5	0.122	3.10	½	12.7
6	0.136	3.45	5/8	15.9
7	0.150	3.81	¾	19.1
8	0.164	4.17	7/8	22.2
9	0.178	4.52	1	25.4
10	0.192	4.88	1¼	31.8
12	0.220	5.59	1½	38.1

Wood screw sizes (above): are listed by gauge (thickness) and length. Gauge is expressed by a "#" symbol, and length is expressed in inches.

"knock-down" fasteners provide easy disassembly

Minifix-brand fittings are two-part fastening systems similar to those used on mass-produced knockdown furnishings. The cam fits into a 15-mm hole drilled into the horizontal member and the screw assembly is fitted into an 8-mm hole in the vertical member. The screw head is inserted into the cam, and a set screw in the cam is tightened to twist the cam and draw the parts together. A decorative cap is then snapped over the cam opening.

Screw assembly

Cam

Blum-brand barrel-type two-part fasteners are used mainly to attach shelves in cabinets. The threaded nylon barrel is fitted into a 25-mm hole in the cabinet side, then the collared screw is driven into the end of the shelf so the duplex-type head projects out. The head fits into the barrel, which is tightened by turning a screw-activated metal gripping plate.

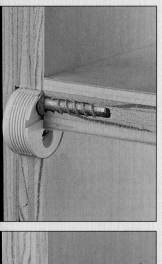

Tite Joint-brand fasteners are especially useful for joining two sheet good panels end to end, as with countertops. The heads of the fastener are mortised into adjoining panels. The mortises are connected by a groove or a guide hole that houses a threaded shaft. The sphere (the left head above) contains grip-holes so it can be spun with a scratch awl or small allen wrench to tighten the joint.

Cross-dowel fasteners can be used to reinforce right-angle corners and to support shelving. The threaded steel dowel is screwed into a barrel cam that's mortised into the horizontal member. With cross-dowels, joints can be fastened and unfastened repeatedly without stripping the screw guide hole.

Corrosion-resistant fasteners for outdoor projects

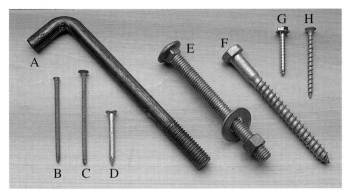

Fasteners for outdoor projects include: (A) J-bolt; (B) galvanized finish nail; (C) coated sinker; (D) joist-hanger nail; (E) carriage bolt with nut and washer; (F) lag screw; (G) hex-head screw; (H) deck screw.

Fences, decks and other exterior structures should be built with galvanized or stainless-steel fasteners to help resist corrosion. Galvanized nails, screws and bolts are far more common than stainless-steel, and more affordable too. Here is a sampling of the most common exterior-grade fasteners:

• *J-bolts* (also called L-shaped anchor bolts) with nuts and washers are used to attach post anchors to concrete footings. These are installed while the concrete is still wet.

• *Lag screws and washers* are used to join larger framing components, such as 2× beams to the sides of posts, railing posts to the sides of the deck, as well as certain types of hardware, such as metal stair cleats. They're often used in conjunction with lead lag screw shields to attach ledgers to masonry walls or concrete foundations.

• *Hex-head machine bolts, nuts and washers* have some of the same applications as lag screws but provide a stronger connection.

• *Galvanized nails* of various sizes provide the least expensive means of assembling exterior components, but they also make the weakest connection. Common nails have more holding power than box nails but are more likely to split the wood at board ends. Galvanized finish nails are used to attach decorative trims and moldings, where nail heads would be unsightly.

• *Galvanized deck screws* (See facing page) have perhaps the widest variety of exterior construction applications and provide a stronger connection than nails. Coarse, aggressive threads and a bugle-head design enable you to power-drive the screws flush to the wood surface without the need of predrilling pilot holes, as you would for conventional wood screws.

LIGHT DUTY:
Plastic sleeve tapped into pilot hole

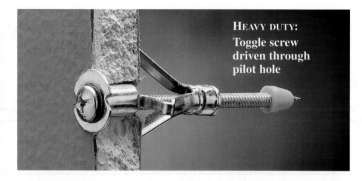

HEAVY DUTY:
Toggle screw driven through pilot hole

MEDIUM DUTY:
Self-tapping plastic anchor threaded into pilot hole

Wallboard & masonry anchors

When hanging heavy pictures or other art, wall studs aren't always conveniently located where you need them for driving the attachment nails or screws. In these instances, reach for one of three types of wallboard anchors to provide additional support. Light-duty **plastic sleeves** expand when a screw is driven through them to grip the wallboard around the sleeve guide hole. **Self-tapping anchors** with deep screw-style threads will bear far more weight, and **toggle screws** provide maximum support by gripping wallboard from behind like a nut and bolt.

Attaching sole plates for stud walls in the basement or garage and tacking furring strips to your foundation wall when insulating are just two of many do-it-yourself projects that require the use of masonry anchors. Here are a few of the most commonly used systems for screwing or bolting to concrete.

Lead sleeve. Driven into large guide hole before sole plates or furring strips are positioned. Threads of lag screws dig into soft lead as screws are driven. Sleeve expands to create pressure fit inside the guide hole. Excellent holding power.

Bolt sleeve. Requires same size guide hole for board and for concrete, so the anchor can be driven through the board and into the concrete at same time. Bolt causes sleeve to flare and grip guide hole as nut is tightened. Excellent holding power.

Self-tapping masonry screws. Driven into pilot holes in board and concrete. Hex-head and slotted, countersink versions. Good holding power, fast to install.

Powder-actuated fasteners. Gun powder charge drives hardened masonry nail through framing and into concrete. Driver can be rented. Good holding power, fast to use, but the charges are loud and the impact can split the framing.

Concrete nails. Driven with a hammer into pilot holes. Relatively good holding power, but nails bend easily.

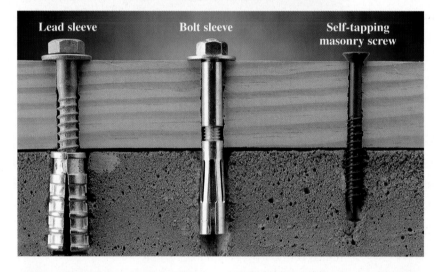

Lead sleeve   Bolt sleeve   Self-tapping masonry screw

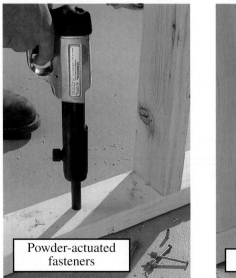

Powder-actuated fasteners

Concrete nails

Polyurethane glue

White glue

Yellow glue

Liquid hide glue

Contact cement

Construction adhesive

Two-part epoxy

Hot glue

Instant glue

Selecting the best adhesive for your bonding task

White glue: Used on wood, paper or cloth. Interior use only. Dries in several hours and has a moderately strong bond. Poor resistance to water and heat. Emits no harmful odors. Cleans up with soap and water.

Yellow glue: Used on wood, paper or cloth. Interior use only. Dries faster than white glue and has a slightly stronger bond. Moderate resistance to water and heat. Emits no harmful odors. Cleans up with soap and water.

Liquid hide glue: Ideal for fine wood furniture or musical instruments. Interior use only. Sets slowly. Has good bond and is resistant to solvents and wood finishes. An eye irritant. Will clean up with soap and water.

Polyurethane glue: Used to bond a variety of materials including wood, metal and ceramics. Sets quickly and produces a strong bond. Waterproof. Warning: this glue can cause immediate and residual lung damage. This product should only be used with excellent ventilation. Asthmatics and people with chronic lung conditions should not use this product. Cleans up with acetone or mineral spirits.

Construction adhesive: Used on framing lumber, flooring and roof sheathing, plywood and paneling, wallboard, masonry. Dries within 24 hours and has a very good bond. Cleans up with mineral spirits.

Contact cement: Joins laminates, veneers, cloth, paper, leather, and other materials. Sets instantly and dries in under an hour. Produces a bond that is not suitable for structural applications. Very flammable and an irritant to eyes, skin and lungs (non-flammable contact cement is also available). Cleans up with soap and water.

Hot glue: Joins wood, plastics, glass and other materials. Sets within 60 seconds. Strength is generally low, but depends on type of glue stick. Good resistance to moisture, fair to heat. Heat will loosen bond.

Two-part epoxy: Joins wood, metal, masonry, glass, fiberglass and other materials. Provides the strongest bond of any adhesive. Bond has excellent resistance to moisture and heat. Drying time varies. Warning: fumes are very toxic and flammable. Cleanup sometimes possible with acetone.

Instant (cyanoacrylate) glue: Bonds smooth surfaces such as glass, ceramics, plastics and metal. Has excellent strength, but little flexibility. Dries in just a few seconds. Has excellent resistance to moisture and heat. Warning: toxic and flammable, and the glue can bond skin instantly.

General-duty caulks & sealants

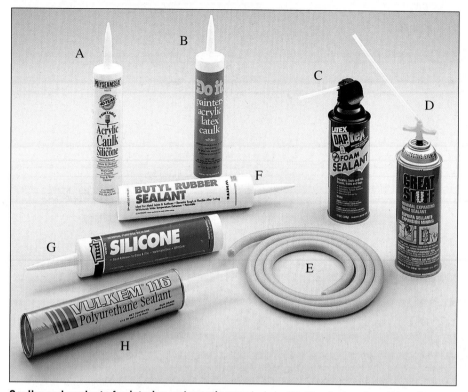

Caulks and sealants for interior and exterior use include: (A) siliconized caulk combines the economy and workability of acrylic or latex with the elasticity and sealing power of silicone; (B) acrylic/latex caulk is a good choice for general chores because it is inexpensive, workable and easy to clean up; (C) latex-based expandable foam fills voids and gaps and is easy to clean up; (D) polyurethane-based expandable foam; (E) caulk backer rod is stuffed into large gaps before applying caulk; (F) butyl rubber-based caulk is used primarily for gaps around metal or masonry; (G) 100% silicone caulk for "invisible" caulk lines with high durability and adhesion; (H) polyurethane-based caulk has become very popular in the building trades for its durability and excellent adhesion.

What's the right way to dispense caulk?

The key to achieving a good caulk bead (and it is a bit of an art form) is to maintain even pressure from the plunger and to work at a steady pace. "Should I push or pull?" is perhaps the most commonly asked question concerning caulk application. While some people may have strong opinions about which works better, the real answer is that it's purely a matter of personal preference. Try it both ways and see which way works better for you.

Also, make sure the angled nozzle tip is oriented correctly, and be sure you're delivering enough material to fill the gap being caulked. If you mess up, wipe off the evidence with a rag dipped in the appropriate solvent (See the tube label) and try again.

Type: Acrylic or Acrylic/latex
Applications: General purpose interior caulk; can be used on exteriors, if painted.
Durability: 3 to 10 years
Elasticity: Fair
Adhesion: Fair, bonds to most surfaces.
Comments: Inexpensive, fast-drying, paintable. Use to fill small cracks and joints; do not use on moving joints. Available in colors.

Type: Siliconized acrylic
Applications: General interior and exterior uses. Adheres to most surfaces.
Durability: 5 to 10 years
Elasticity: Good
Adhesion: Good
Comments: One step up from acrylic caulks above. Reasonable price combined with relatively long life.

Type: Butyl rubber
Applications: Exterior use, good for exterior metal-to-masonry joints, gutter seams, flashings, storm windows, below-grade applications. Paintable.
Durability: 5 to 15 years
Elasticity: Fair
Adhesion: Excellent
Comments: Moderately priced, excellent water resistance, paintable. Use for narrow cracks only. Messy to work with, must be cleaned off tools and hands with mineral spirits. Takes a week to cure.

Type: 100% Silicone
Applications: Use anywhere.
Durability: 20 to 50 years
Elasticity: Excellent
Adhesion: Excellent
Comments: Popular, high-performance, versatile caulk. Generally cannot be painted. Clear types used where an "invisible" joint is desired. Moderate to expensive in cost.

Type: Polyurethane
Applications: Most interior and exterior surfaces.
Durability: 20 to 30 years
Elasticity: Excellent
Adhesion: Excellent
Comments: Superior adhesion qualities, combined with good elasticity; often used as construction adhesive, especially for bonding dissimilar materials. Expensive.

Other specialized adhesives & sealants

Concrete/mortar repair caulk fills small cracks in concrete surfaces, stucco or mortar joints up to ½ in. wide. The caulk is elastomeric (flexible) when it cures so it can resist minor movement in the finished joint. It dries to a gray color to help blend into the surrounding concrete.

Gutter lap is a siliconized caulk formulated to create watertight joints between the parts of metal or vinyl gutter systems. Use it like glue to adhere connecters and downspouts to other gutter components. It can also be used to patch small leaks in older steel gutters.

Construction adhesives bond wallboard to wall framing, keep subfloor sheathing from squeaking and can generally be used as an all-purpose glue for most wood-to-wood joints. You can buy construction adhesive in a variety of formulas to suit different applications, installation conditions and drying times.

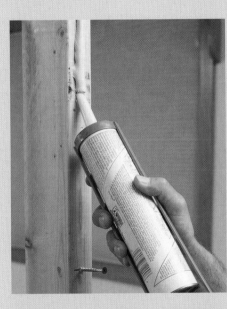

Asphalt sealing compounds are made primarily of liquid rubber and can be used to fill cracks up to 1 in. wide in asphalt driveways and walks. Most of these sealing compounds are formulated not to shrink once dry, reexposing the cracks beneath.

Roofing cement is the glue that creates watertight seals beneath shingles and around metal roof flashing. You'll find it sold in caulk tubes, which are handy for smaller projects and repairs, as well as larger cans. Use it to bond replacement shingles to other shingles as well as to seal around the heads of exposed roofing nails. It can be applied in either wet or dry conditions.

Window glazing can be purchased in cartridge tubes to make application easier. Use it to fill the recess in a window frame before installing the glass. Glazing will act like a cushion to prevent the glass from rattling in the window frame. Once the glass is in place, apply a second bead of glazing where the glass and frame meet to form a weathertight seal.

PLUMBING

If you own a home, you will have plumbing issues to deal with. A dripping faucet, a clogged drain, a broken fixture, a kitchen or bathroom remodeling project...there is just no way to avoid it. When that time comes, you'll have two options for taking care of the problem: calling an expensive plumber to replace that ten-cent washer, or fixing it yourself. If you choose the latter route, you'll generally find that plumbing is not especially complicated. It can be messy, and some of the basic skills, like sweating copper pipe, require practice. But if you have the determination and the know-how, along with the right tools and materials, you can accomplish most home plumbing projects.

While this section of *The Handyman's Guide to Building Materials* is not a tutorial of plumbing skills, it will serve as a valuable survey of the tools, pipes, fittings and other materials you'll need for tackling nearly any plumbing task. Hopefully, this section will demystify the bewildering array of plumbing supply options available to you so you can make more informed choices. Use it to help you plan your next plumbing project, and carry it with you when you shop to use as a quick-reference guide.

The basics of residential plumbing

Plumbing is simple, in principle. Water is delivered to appliances and fixtures by supply and distribution pipes. Wastewater is removed by gravity through a ventilated system of drain and waste pipes called the drain, waste, and vent (DWV) system.

As a way of preparing yourself for future plumbing projects or even the occasional plumbing emergency, get to know the plumbing systems in your home. Don't be shy about contacting professionals or even your local building inspector if you have a question or if the systems in your home don't match the information you find in plumbing reference books. Nearly every home has a few quirks, especially if previous plumbing work was done without a permit or by a novice.

Supply and distribution. A main water supply line comes into the house under pressure through a water meter and one or two shutoff valves. If you have a private well, water is pumped into a pressure tank. The pump automatically keeps the tank pressure within a set range. No meter is needed on a pressure tank, but a shut-off valve will exist on one or both sides of the pressure tank. The cold-water distribution pipes branch as much as necessary to carry water to the fixtures (sinks, toilets, baths) and appliances (washing machines, ice makers, boilers) of the house. Soon after entering the house (or exiting the pressure tank) a line branches off to the water heater. Branching hot-water distribution pipes from the water heater then parallel to the cold-water distribution pipes to appliances and fixtures in the house.

In a modern, code-compliant house, all fixtures and appliances have individual shutoff valves. These can be straight or angled, chromed, plain brass or plastic. Tub and shower shutoffs may be accessed through a panel or from below. Sinks typically have angle stops directly below the basin.

The drain/waste/vent (DWV) system. After the water is used it enters drain or waste pipes, which carry it by gravity to the sewer or septic system.

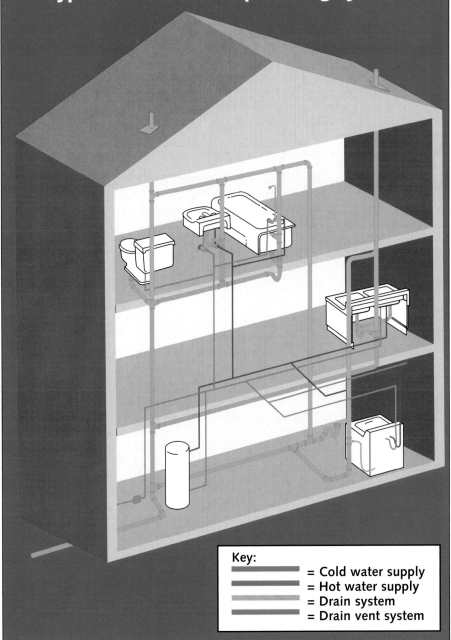

Typical whole-house plumbing system

Key:
= Cold water supply
= Hot water supply
= Drain system
= Drain vent system

Since sewage generates noxious and even explosive gasses, each point of entry into the drainage system must be blocked with a low bend of pipe filled with water. This bend is called a "trap". Every appliance and fixture that is drained must have a trap that always remains filled with water. All drain lines need to be vented through a separate set of pipes out of the building, usually through the roof.

Branch drains from fixtures on upper floors must either drop steeply or vertically to the horizontal building drain or run almost horizontally (at a ¼ in. drop per foot) to a soil stack. In-between slopes can cause clogs, since the water would rush away leaving solids stranded to snag more debris. On the slab or at basement level, stacks from upper floors enter the building drain. Fixtures and appliances on the ground or basement level empty into the building drain through vented horizontal branch lines. The building drain runs at a gentle slope to a municipal sewer or to the sewer line leading to a private septic tank.

Supply pipes

Flexible copper tubing is used mainly for gas, but the narrow water supply tubes to fixtures and appliances may be made of flexible copper tubing. Cuts with a tubing cutter or hacksaw. Joins with soldered, compression, or flare fittings.

Rigid copper is the most common water distribution material. Type M (with red lettering) is the lightest type and is used most commonly above ground in residences. Joins with soldered fittings. Cuts with a copper-tubing cutter or a hacksaw. Compression fittings may be used if joints are exposed.

CPVC (Chlorinated polyvinyl chloride) is a rigid plastic tubing used in hot and cold-water distribution. CPVC is popular among DIY-ers since its joints can be solvent welded. Check local codes before using. CPVC is solvent-welded into fittings, or grip fittings are used. Cut with a PVC tubing cutter, hacksaw, or miter box and saw.

PEX (Cross-linked polyethylene) is a flexible plastic tubing used in hot and cold-water distribution. Check with local code officer before using. PEX joins with insert fittings and crimp rings or with grip fittings. PEX cuts with a flexible plastic tubing cutter, shears, or a knife. PEX should not be left exposed to direct or indirect sunlight indefinitely.

Galvanized steel is found in older dwellings and is susceptible to water pressure loss due to scale buildup. You may transition to another material with the appropriate transition fittings when extending water distribution lines. Joins with threaded fittings. Cuts with hacksaw, reciprocating saw, or ferrous pipe cutter.

PE (Polyethylene) is a cheap, rugged, flexible plastic pipe used for cold water. Common uses include water supply to the house, irrigation, and cold water supply to an outbuilding. PE is joined with PVC insert fittings and hose clamps. It cuts with a flexible plastic tubing cutter or a sharp knife. For irrigation, a cheaper utility grade PE tubing is used.

PLUMBING MATERIALS

Pipe and tubing are the most basic plumbing materials. The materials and their characteristics have evolved over the years in response to changing technology, availability, cost and health concerns.

You will most likely encounter one of seven kinds of water distribution pipe in your house. Identifying and measuring them correctly is critical to purchasing the right fittings and valves. Identify newer pipe by the codes printed on the pipe. The nominal diameters of copper supply and distribution pipes are about equal to the inside diameters of the pipes. The nominal diameters of copper and plastic water pipe are ⅛ in. less than the outside diameters. Small diameter supply tubes beneath fixtures and appliances are measured by their outside diameters (except synthetic and woven flexible tubes). You may switch pipe materials on a job if you use the appropriate transition fitting.

Take samples, measurements, and written information from the sides of the pipes when going to a plumbing supply store for fittings. The lettering on the sides of pipes says everything. Red lettering on copper indicates type M pipe, the thinnest wall thickness grade and the kind you are most likely to use. "NSF-PW" and "NSF-DWV" mean the National Sanitation Foundation has rated the pipe for pres-

Standard pipe diameters

MATERIAL	INSIDE DIA.	OUTSIDE DIA.
Copper	¼	⅜
	⅜	½
	½	⅝
	¾	⅞
	1	1⅛
	1¼	1⅜
	1½	1⅝
Galvanized steel	⅜	⅝
	½	⅞
	¾	1
	1	1¼
	1¼	1½
	1½	1¾
	2	2¼
Plastic (Schedule 40 PVC)	0.5	0.845
	0.75	1.050
	1	1.315
	1.25	1.660
	1.5	1.9
	2	2.375
	3	3.5
	4	4.5
Cast iron	2	2.35
	3	3.35
	4	4.38

surized water or drain-waste-vent, respectively. The only kinds of plastic pipe currently installed for hot and cold supply and distribution are CPVC and PEX. Plastic water pipes follow the sizing convention established for copper water pipe. The outside diameter of a CTS (copper tube size) pipe is ⅛ in. greater than its nominal diameter. On copper pipe, nominal and inside diameter are about equal.

Old houses may have cast iron or terra cotta pipe joined together with flared hubs and straight spigots. These joints will be packed with hemp or oakum and sealed with lead. More recent cast iron and terra cotta pipes are "no hub." No-hub pipe and fittings are the same diameter end-to-end and are joined with stainless steel clamps over rubber sleeves. No-hub cast iron is still used extensively in modern construction because it is quiet, durable, and it won't burn.

Threaded galvanized steel pipe and soldered copper were used extensively in DWV systems for branch lines before the advent of plastic. Schedule 40 plastic DWV pipes share the same outside diameters as steel pipes of the same nominal size. Most residential drain systems now are partially or wholly made of black ABS plastic or white PVC plastic. These light, strong pipes are easily cut and cemented together using hubbed fittings.

Plumbers putty (left photo), **pipe joint compound** and **Teflon tape** (right photo) are three products you'll use extensively in residential plumbing. Generally, joint compound is applied to female threaded fittings, Teflon tape is applied to male threaded fittings and plumbers putty is used to create a waterproof seal around fixtures in wet areas (for example, between a sink rim and countertop).

DWV pipes

Galvanized steel was once (and sometimes still is) used for DWV branch lines. It is joined with threaded fittings. Galvanized cuts with a ferrous pipe cutter or reciprocating saw. It is threaded and joined with fittings or with threaded union fittings.

Copper is rarely used for DWV branch lines or traps anymore. It is joined with solder and sometimes with banded clamps over rubber sleeves. Copper may be cut with a tubing cutter, a reciprocating saw, or a hacksaw. Banded couplings can be used to join other pipes and tubing to copper drain and waste pipes.

ABS (Acrylonitrile Butadiene Styrene) plastic is used in modern plumbing. It is cheap and easy to work with but it will burn and it dampens less noise than cast iron. Cut with a tubing cutter, plastic saw, or miter box and saw. Join with ABS solvent cement.

PVC (Polyvinyl Chloride) plastic is the most commonly used DWV pipe material. It is resistant to damage by heat and chemicals. PVC is cheap and easy to work with but will burn and is loud. Cut with a tubing cutter, plastic saw, or miter box and saw. Join with PVC solvent primer and cement. Schedule 40 PVC is shown here.

Cast iron was once common for drains, particularly the main drain stack and the floor drain. The outside pipe (inside hub) diameter is from 1/4 to 3/8 in. greater than the nominal (inside) diameter. Pipe marked XH is 3/8 to 1/2 in. bigger than nominal. Iron pipe cuts with a snap cutter and may be joined with solid banded couplings with rubber or neoprene sleeves inside.

Couplings, fittings & adapters

Couplings, fittings and adapters are used to join the various components of your plumbing system together. Whether they're copper, PVC, brass or another plumbing material type, they all look pretty much the same in shape and relative size. The examples shown on these two pages are copper and brass fittings, all of which are soldered to copper pipe on one or both ends. If you are installing or working with PVC, galvanized or another pipe material, look for fittings made for that material. The different configurations are designed to make bends in the lines, make transitions and extend pipe on longer runs.

Trap adapters

Trap adapter

Trap adapters are a kind of compression fitting that secures tubular pipe inside standard pipe. Tubular pipes are measured by their outside diameters, so they can slip inside DWV pipes, which are measured loosely by their inside diameters. Accessible traps, like those under sinks, are made of tubular brass or plastic and are held in the drainpipe stub with a trap adapter. The trap adapter may have female threads and be screwed to an iron drainpipe stub, or it may have a female slip cup and be solvent welded to a plastic stub out. Trap adapters can also be attached to most DWV pipe ends with a mission coupling.

Soldered copper and Schedule-40 plastic traps, such as those found in concealed spaces under tubs and showers, often have standard, not tubular, DWV dimensions. In such cases, the trap adapter is used to secure the tubular tub tailpiece into the trap inlet. If the trap is accessible, through a panel or under a sink, a Schedule 40 trap may still have a union nut for cleanout purposes just like a slip nut tubular trap. The trap arm is held to the galvanized waste line with a mission coupling.

Supply fittings

Compression fittings

Retainer nut

Ferrule

Union

Ferrule

Retainer nut

Compression fittings are useful where connections are not permanent. Plumbers use compression fittings mainly to attach small diameter water supply tubes to stop valves beneath sinks, lavatories, toilets and appliances. Code usually prohibits concealing compression fittings in walls, since they are more prone to failure than soldered or solvent welded joints. Do not use compression fittings where they will be subject to vibration, which could loosen the compression nut.

Flare fittings

Flare nut

Flare union

Flare nut

Flare fittings work something like compression fittings, except instead of a brass ferule, the flared end of the pipe itself is compressed between the fitting and the nut. Flair fittings are not used much with water supply pipes and tubes anymore, but they are still popular with copper gas and fuel lines.

Drop eared elbow. The drop eared elbow (also called a drop-eared 90) is commonly used when working with plumbing fixtures. It lets you transition from a vertical pipe in the wall to a horizontal copper stub out, brass nipple, or shower arm. The ears let you screw the elbow to blocking, adding stability and strength to whatever attachment extends outside the wall. To the right is a ½ in. cup × FIP (female iron pipe) drop-eared elbow that transitions from copper pipe to a threaded brass nipple.

Repair coupling. When you are doing repair work or adding a branch line, it is often necessary to insert a fitting or assembly into fixed pipes. Couplings without stops (also called "repair couplings) are needed here to allow the coupling to slide out of the way onto a leg of the pipe while you insert the new pipe. Couplings without stops may be purchased for PW and DWV piping in both plastic and copper.

Threaded Adapters. Threaded adapters can be soldered to copper or solvent welded to plastic, enabling you to make a connection with threaded pipes or nipples. The threaded side of the adapter can be screwed to another threaded fitting or to a threaded pipe. Threaded adapters provide a safe, strong way to transition from copper to plastic. It is preferable (and frequently required by code) that the plastic adapter have the male end and the metallic adapter have the female end. This is because threaded pipe and fittings are tapered, and screwing a hard metal male end into a soft plastic female socket can break the female fitting apart. The Plastic MIP adapter should be wrapped clockwise with four layers of Teflon tape. Apply a pipe joint compound that is compatible with the plastic material on the metallic female threads.

Female

Male

Stop coupling. When you need to joint two straight runs of pipe in a new installation, use a stop coupling to make the connection. Unlike the smooth repair coupling, the stop coupling has internal ridges that the mouth of each tube press against when inserted, strengthening the bond when the parts are soldered or solvent-welded.

Street or male-end fittings. Sometimes you need to insert one fitting directly into another fitting or valve without any pipe in between. The inserted fitting must be "streeted"—that is, it must include a port that shares the same outside diameter as a pipe. Street fittings are common with DWV pipes, where wide pipes need to change direction in small areas. In water supply, you may need copper street elbows to join a single-handle tub and shower valve to the hot and cold water supply

Unions are a secure mechanical coupling for pipes that can be taken apart with wrenches without twisting the pipes themselves. You may use unions at water heaters, whole house filters, or in other situations where you want a joint that can be opened but that provides a higher level of security than a compression fitting. When cutting your pipe for a union, make sure to allow for the gap that will be occupied by the union fitting.

Reducing fittings. Often, the openings on an elbow, tee, or coupling will require different sized cups. Reducing fittings are available in a broad range of configurations, with tees and couplings having the greatest range of options. To the left is a ¾ × ¾ × ½ tee fitting.

Transition fittings: exploded view

Transition fittings connect two different pipe materials, such as galvanized to copper, CPVC to galvanized and CPVC to copper. A galvanized-to-copper union fitting (called a dielectric union) contains a non-metallic spacer so that the two materials don't react electrochemically and corrode.

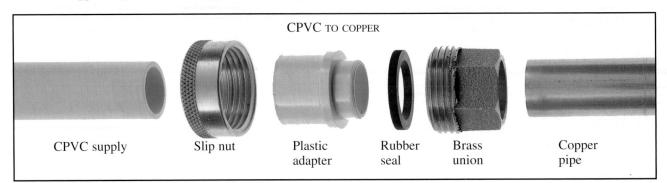

CPVC TO COPPER

| CPVC supply | Slip nut | Plastic adapter | Rubber seal | Brass union | Copper pipe |

CPVC to copper

When attaching CPVC to copper tubing, a four-piece union is needed. First, solder the brass union to the copper tubing. Let the brass cool before inserting the rubber seal. Then attach the plastic adapter to the CPVC pipe with solvent glue. Make certain the slip nut is in place before gluing. After the glue has set (at least 30 minutes), tighten.

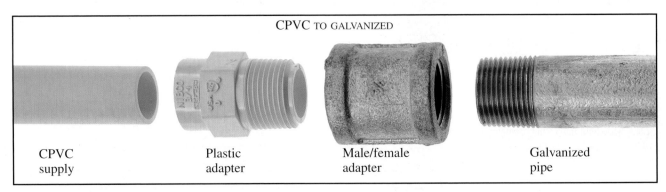

CPVC TO GALVANIZED

| CPVC supply | Plastic adapter | Male/female adapter | Galvanized pipe |

CPVC to galvanized

Connect galvanized pipe to CPVC pipe with male and the female threaded adapters. The plastic adapter is attached to the CPVC pipe with solvent glue. Threads of metal pipe should have a coating of pipe joint compound or teflon tape. The metal pipe is then screwed directly to the adapter.

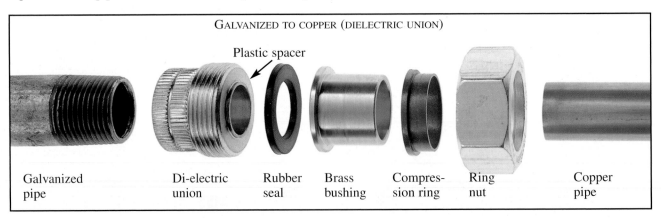

GALVANIZED TO COPPER (DIELECTRIC UNION)

Plastic spacer

| Galvanized pipe | Di-electric union | Rubber seal | Brass bushing | Compression ring | Ring nut | Copper pipe |

Galvanized to copper (Dielectric)

A dielectric union is needed to connect copper to galvanized steel. The union is soldered to the copper and threaded onto the steel. The dielectric union has a plastic spacer that prevents corrosion caused by an electro-chemical reaction between the different metals.

Prevent pipe corrosion by connecting galvanized and copper pipes with a dielectric union fitting. The pipes above show what will eventually happen if you connect these two metals with a standard union fitting. When connecting copper pipe to galvanized iron pipe, you need to install a dielectric union between the two materials. That's because if copper and iron come in contact with each other, a chemical reaction between the metals will increase corrosion. The dielectric union will prevent this corrosion from occurring.

Electrical grounding tip for dielectric unions & PVC pipe

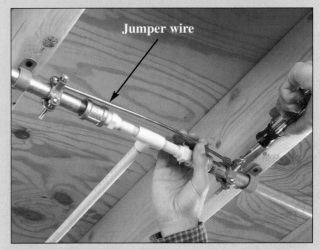

Jumper wire

If you insert dielectric unions or PVC plumbing into an existing metal line, bridge the metal pipe ends with a jumper wire in case the pipes are used as an electric ground. Use 6-gauge copper wire for the jumper, and tighten the jumper wire lugs securely.

More transition fittings

Hot water nipple
Designed mainly for use with water heaters, the hot water nipple has expandable seals on each threaded end to help it stay watertight throughout dramatic temperature changes. Typically a galvanized nipple with two male-threaded ends, it is best used with a hot water transition fitting (right).

Hot water transition fitting
A threaded adapter lets you transition from a hot water heater nipple to plastic water pipe. Special adapters are needed here since different materials expand at different rates when exposed to heat. The fitting transitions from ¾ in. iron pipe to a ¾ in. CPVC solvent-weld slip.

Banded couplings join pipe to pipe or pipe to tubular trap pieces and tailpieces. To accommodate different thickness pipes, buy a coupling where the rubber or neoprene sleeve beneath the band changes thickness. **Mission couplings,** such as the one shown here, have stickers with abbreviations for plastic (PL) and cast iron (CI) after the listed nominal diameter. Plastic trap adapters and Schedule 40 plastic traps go by the PL designation, as does galvanized steel, which has the same outside diameters as plastic DWV. "Tube" means the fitting is for tubular brass and plastic, which includes tubular PVC, ABS and chromed brass trap arms and tub tailpieces. Sometimes this will be described as a "bathwaste tailpiece" size.

Brass Nipple
The brass nipple is not technically a fitting, but it is invaluable for transitioning from a water heater or a drop-eared 90 in the wall to an angle stop or tub spout. To save money, some plumbers will use galvanized steel nipples instead of brass, which leads to galvanic corrosion and clogged valves.

Types of supply valves

Pressure-reducing valve is installed after your main shutoff valve to reduce chattering and other negative effects of having the water pressure too high in your supply lines.

Ball valve (copper to copper) is a useful shutoff valve for supply pipes with limited access. In less than one revolution, handle cranks to block water flow with a chrome-plated ball.

Stop & waste valve (copper to copper) is soldered between two copper supply pipes. Remove the handle mechanism before soldering to prevent damage to internal neoprene parts.

Gate valve (threaded) closes gate inside valve to arrest water flow. A popular shutoff valve for use with galvanized supply pipes. Similar valve made for copper to copper connections.

Hose bib is an inexpensive spigot with a male threaded nozzle that accepts garden and appliance hoses. Attaches to threaded supply pipe. Not recommended for exterior use. (See sidebar, this page, for examples of external hose bibs.)

Saddle valve is clamped around a copper supply pipe to create a branch supply line for appliances, such as ice makers. The T-handle drives down a piercing spur and compresses a rubber washer to prevent leaks.

Valves

Valves are plumbing fittings that can be adjusted to control the flow of water. Faucets are considered valves, as are shut-offs and essentially any other fitting with a handle or lever that can be opened and closed.

Following are descriptions of the most common types of valves for home plumbing (excluding kitchen and bathroom faucets, which technically are also types of valves).

Frostproof sillcocks

Exterior hose bibs (often called "sillcocks") are vulnerable to freezing and require an anti-freezing mechanism. To prevent the water supply leads for sill-cocks from freezing and bursting, homeowners in colder climates should install a frost-proof sill-cock. These devices are equipped with shutoff gates that are located far enough back into the supply lead that they stop the water flow inside the house. Most also have integral vacuum breakers to stop any backflow from drawing wastewater into the supply line and cross-contaminating your home's potable water supply.

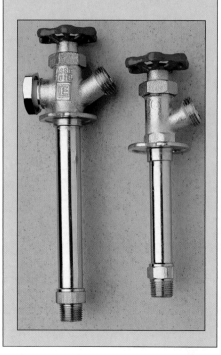

Shutoff valves

Shutoff valves can be a little bit tricky since one side connects to a pipe in the wall or floor and the other side connects to a supply tube that goes to the sink or toilet. These are not only different diameter pipes, but may use different kinds of connections as well. When specifying dimensions and joint types, the wall/floor side is called the "inlet" and the supply-tube side is called the "riser outlet." The supply stop itself is called a straight stop or an angle stop, depending on whether it is straight (for a pipe coming out of the floor) or takes a 90° turn (for a pipe coming through a wall).

Here are some terms and concepts you need to know when buying a shutoff valve:

FIP (Female Iron Pipe): The female side of a threaded joint using iron pipe size.

IPS (Iron Pipe Size): A thread standard used with any material, not just iron.

MIP (Male Iron Pipe): The male side of a threaded joint using iron pipe size.

Compression Fitting: A kind of fitting that let's you connect to a smooth pipe without solder. A compression fitting includes a threaded nut and a brass ring called a compression ring that's pressed between the pipe and the nut.

Nipple: This is a short section of IPS threaded pipe.

Nominal (Named) Diameter: All pipes are given a size name, like "½-in. copper pipe." Supply and distribution pipe sizes are named roughly by their inside diameter. This distinguishes pipes from tubes, which are narrower inside than their named tube size.

OD (Outside Diameter): Supply tubes to fixtures and appliances and tubular traps and drain tailpieces are named by their outside diameters (braided supply tubes are an exception).

ID (Inside Diameter): Water pipes, including the nipples and stub outs that come out of the wall and floor, are named roughly by their inside diameters.

Angle stop. Used when the water supply pipe enters the room through a wall. The 90° angle of the outlet to the inlet allows you to make supply tube connections without kinking the tubes.

Straight stop. Used when the water supply pipe enters the room through the floor. Very common for toilet hookups.

COPPER PIPE

If applied correctly, solder makes a strong and enduring joint between copper pipes and fittings. The most important keys to soldering success are proper preparations of the surfaces and heating the pipes and fittings to a hot enough (but not too hot) temperature with a propane torch.

Before soldering, polish all surfaces to be joined to remove oxidized copper. You may use emery or plumber's sanding cloth, or buy a brush tool that cleans the inside of the fitting and the outside of the pipe. Using the wrong kind of abrasive can remove too much copper or leave shavings that can interfere with the flow of molten solder.

If you are working on an installed supply line, shut off the water and open the valve drain cock, flush the toilets, and empty lines by opening low and high faucets including the outside sillcock. If you shut off and drain the hot water system, make sure you also turn off the water heater. Mark where your new or old tubing sections are to be cut with a small hacksaw. Cut the ends off new lengths of tubing, which may be misshapen. Measure new tubing to fully insert in the fitting sockets, but not so long that the pipe will be compressed or cocked.

Copper supply pipe and tubing is lightweight, easy to cut, corrosion-resistant and the joints formed by soldering two pieces of copper are extremely strong and durable when made correctly.

Copper pipe fittings

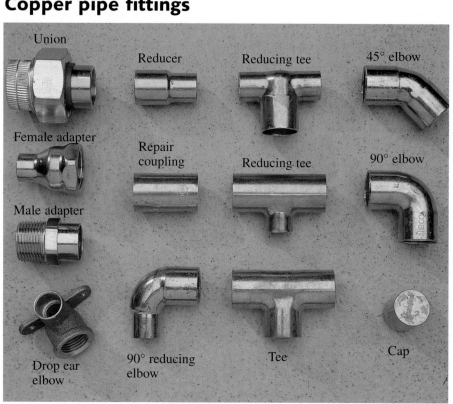

Union
Reducer
Reducing tee
45° elbow
Female adapter
Repair coupling
Reducing tee
90° elbow
Male adapter
Drop ear elbow
90° reducing elbow
Tee
Cap

The most common fittings for joining copper pipe and tubing are shown above. Make sure the inside diameter of the fitting matches the outside diameter of your tubing.

Types of copper tubing

There are two basic types of copper tubing: *rigid* and *flexible*. Rigid pipe is used for most of the water supply system. It comes in three grades, ranked according to the thickness of the pipe walls. *Type M* is the thinnest and cheapest copper pipe. It's suitable for most household plumbing uses. *Type L* is generally used for commercial applications, and *Type K* is the thickest rigid copper and is not used in residential plumbing. Flexible copper tubing can be used for water supply lines in some cases, but is used most commonly for gas lines.

Supplies for cutting & soldering copper pipe

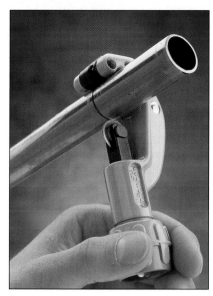

Tubing cutter uses a cutting wheel and a pair of rollers to straddle copper pipe and score it cleanly all around. Swivelling the cutter around the pipe and gradually tightening the tension on the cutting wheel eventually shears the pipe cleanly in two.

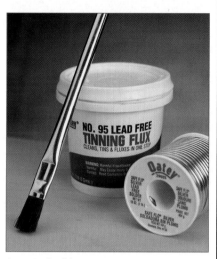

An auto-igniting propane torch can help you solder more quickly and efficiently. The torch produces a flame with the push of a button, saving fuel and allowing you to work faster. A propane torch with an auto-igniting starter is also safer than a manually-lighted torch. There is less chance of a flare-up when starting and the flame is eliminated when you release the button. To solder, you'll need flux, solder wire and a brush to apply the flux.

Pipe brush: Copper pipes, tubing and fittings must be clean and burr free before soldering. A pipe brush allows you to clean both the inside and outside surfaces, and to scuff the copper slightly, creating a bonding surface for the solder.

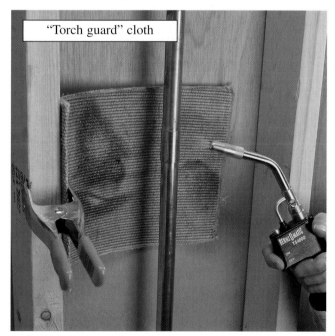

"Torch guard" cloth

Heat block: A propane torch can easily ignite nearby flammable materials when soldering. If you are working on pipes near anything flammable, use a heat block. An effective block can be fashioned out of sheet metal (at least 26-gauge). Clamp the metal to nearby studs. Be warned, however, that the metal can become very hot. Another option is to use specially designed "torch guard" cloth behind pipes you are soldering.

PLASTIC PIPE

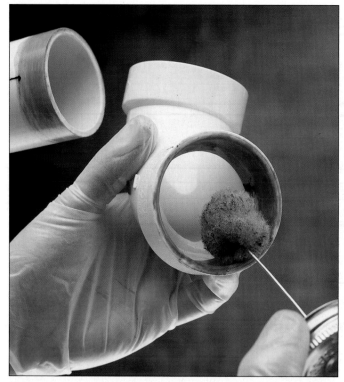

PVC and other types of plastic pipe are more popular today than ever before. As a building material, PVC pipe is inexpensive, easy to work, lightweight and relatively forgiving. To join PVC pipe and fittings, scuff and degloss the mating surfaces with emery cloth, then coat them with primer and solvent glue. The primer is colored so you can see when full coverage is achieved. Be sure to wear vinyl or latex gloves to protect your hands from the solvent glue.

Except for flimsy plastic drain trap parts, which are joined with slip nuts and nylon washers, plastic pipe is connected by solvent welding. Solvent welding is a lot like welding metal. Your goal is to liquefy the pipe and fitting surfaces then let them harden together. Primer makes the surface of the pipe and the inside surface of the fitting soft or liquid. Cement helps keep the pipe material liquid, but it also has PVC, CPVC, or ABS suspended in it, which fills in any gaps. Naturally, the cement has to be applied when the fitting and pipe are still damp with primer, so that the plastic on the joining surfaces is receptive to the cement. With ABS, which is more reactive, the solvent in the cement is enough to dissolve the plastic and no primer is used.

Joining rigid plastic drain pipes can be difficult. Expect that you'll make some mistakes at first and have to cut out and redo some joints. ABS drainpipe tends to set quickly. It's a good idea to have a friend to help twist the pipes into place. PVC set time is extremely temperature dependent. In cool weather you may have to hold the pipe three minutes for the larger drain pipes to set. In hot weather you will barely have time to get the joint in position before it sets up. Keep PVC in the shade in hot weather. Before using plastic pipe, bring it close to room temperature. Protect plastic pipe from extended exposure to direct sunlight. Eventually, the UV radiation can weaken the material.

PVC pipe fittings

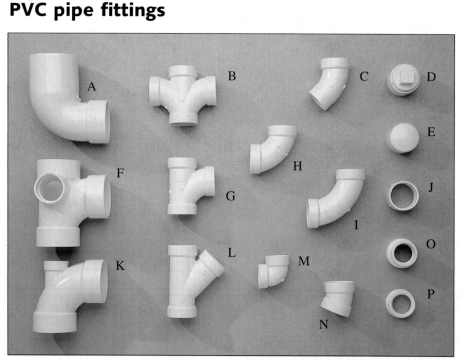

(A) closet bend; (B) waste cross; (C) 45° reducing elbow; (D) cleanout plug; (E) cap;
(F) waste tee with side inlet; (G) waste/sanitary tee; (H) 90° elbow; (I) long-sweep 90° elbow; (J) coupling;
(K) 90° elbow with side inlet; (L) wye fitting; (M) vent elbow; (N) 22° elbow;
(O) reducer; (P) reducing bushing.

Methods for cutting PVC pipe

Plastic tubing cutters. A PVC ratchet cutter will make short work of smaller PVC pipes. This tool is especially useful if you have a large variety of plastic pipes to cut.

Power miter saw. If you have a lot of plastic pipe to cut—and you want to make neat cuts very quickly—use a power miter saw fitted with a fine blade that has a high number of teeth per inch.

PVS pipe saw. To cut PVC pipe by hand, a PVC pipe saw will give you better results than an ordinary hacksaw. Make certain to hold the pipe securely in a vise and keep the saw blade straight while cutting.

Materials for solvent-welding PVC

When working with PVC pipe, make certain you use the correct materials. Solvent and primer should be labeled for PVC pipe (ABS requires ABS cement and no primer). Colored solvent and primer allow you to inspect more easily to make sure all parts are coated. Sandcloth or emery paper is used to smooth rough edges. Primer helps degloss the pipe's slick surface, ensuring a good seal. If you buy more than a quart of cement, transfer some to a quart container for application, since the cement is extremely volatile. Wear protective clothing, especially gloves, and follow the manufacturer's instructions carefully.

Code tips for working with plastic pipe

• Hose bibs and nipples for tub spouts and other fixtures need to be connected to metal components anchored to the building.

• Plastic pipe should not be exposed to direct sunlight in its installed location. The exception is plastic vent chimneys, which may be protected with latex paint.

• If you insert plastic fittings or piping into an existing metal line, your local plumbing code may require that you affix a permanent sign to the electric service panel: "This building has non-metallic interior water piping."

GALVANIZED PIPE

Galvanized pipe is rarely installed in new construction today for one main reason: it's time-consuming to install. Compared to soldering copper tubing, or solvent-welding plastic pipe, putting together galvanized pipe is slow work. However, replacing a section of old galvanized pipe with new galvanized pipe is a reasonable project for the do-it-yourselfer.

Galvanized pipe is connected with threaded fittings and a combination of pipe joint compound and Teflon tape. When shopping for replacement pipe, specify the nominal diameter of the pipe you need. Pre-threaded pipes, called nipples, are available in lengths up to 1 ft. or longer. For longer runs, have the store cut and thread the pipe to your dimensions.

You can also thread your own by renting pipe threading equipment from larger home and rental centers. You'll need to rent a pipe vise, a reamer and a threader to thread your own galvanized pipes. Get a threader with a head that is the same nominal diameter as the pipe you are threading.

One warning: Galvanized iron pipe, which has a silver color, is sometimes confused with "black iron" pipe. Black iron pipe is used only for gas lines. Never use it for water. It lacks a protective coating inside and will begin to corrode immediately when wet.

Prior to the increased use of copper tubing, galvanized pipe was the standard material choice for residential plumbing. However, the galvanized coating, which resists corrosion, eventually fails and the pipes will become encrusted with rust and other mineral deposits. Eventually, accumulated deposits inside the pipes will lead to reduced water pressure.

Galvanized pipe fittings

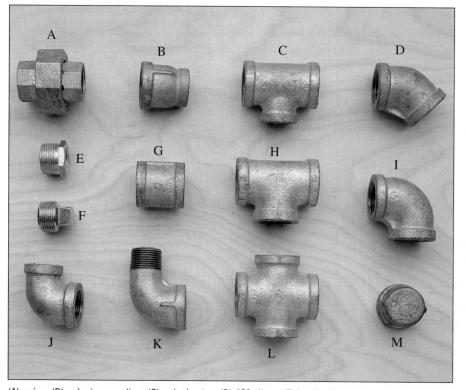

(A) union; (B) reducing coupling; (C) reducing tee; (D) 45° elbow; (E) hex bushing; (F) square head plug; (G) coupling; (H) tee; (I) 90° elbow; (J) 90° reducing elbow; (K) 90° street elbow; (L) cross connector; (M) cap.

Supplies for sealing galvanized pipe joints

To join galvanized pipe, apply joint compound to the female threads (those inside fittings) and wrap four layers of teflon tape around male threads for best seal.

SUPPLY PIPES & TUBES

Supply pipes bring water from the water main to the shutoff valves at plumbing fixtures. Regardless of whether they are copper, plastic or galvanized steel, they are either ½ or ¾ in. in diameter. From the shutoff, water is sometimes distributed to the fixture via smaller supply tubes. The type of connection between the supply pipe and the shutoff depends on the material the pipe and fitting are made of. These days, supply tube connections tend to be made with compression fittings.

Because supply pipes are pressurized and connected to a virtually inexhaustible source of water, a leak or burst supply pipe has the potential for causing catastrophic damage. Pay attention to them and be sure you know where the main shutoff is in case of a problem.

Supply tube types

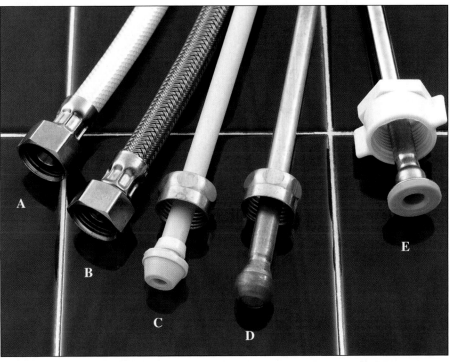

Supply tubes carry water from the shutoff valve to the fixture. You may find any of the following types in your home: (A) Vinyl mesh with integral nut; (B) Braided steel with integral nut; (C) PEX (cross-linked polyethylene) with "acorn" and slip nut; (D) Copper tubing with "acorn" and slip nut; (E) Chromed brass with ballcock coupling nut.

Typical supply pipe & tube diameters for common plumbing fixtures

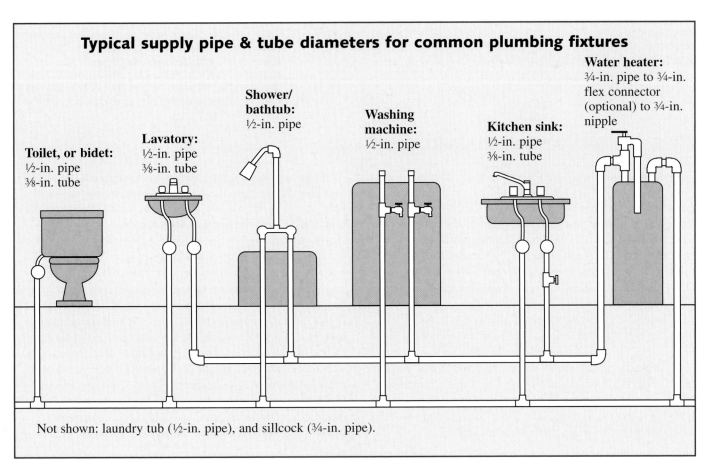

Water heater: ¾-in. pipe to ¾-in. flex connector (optional) to ¾-in. nipple

Shower/bathtub: ½-in. pipe

Washing machine: ½-in. pipe

Lavatory: ½-in. pipe ⅜-in. tube

Kitchen sink: ½-in. pipe ⅜-in. tube

Toilet, or bidet: ½-in. pipe ⅜-in. tube

Not shown: laundry tub (½-in. pipe), and sillcock (¾-in. pipe).

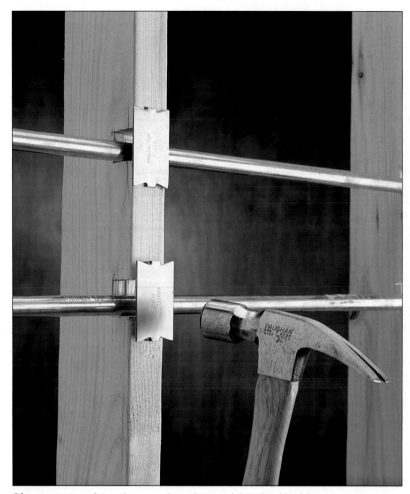

Pipe protector plates. In cases where pipes notch into the side of framing members, protect them with metal pipe protector plates before attaching wall coverings. The plates protect pipes from being pierced later on by nails.

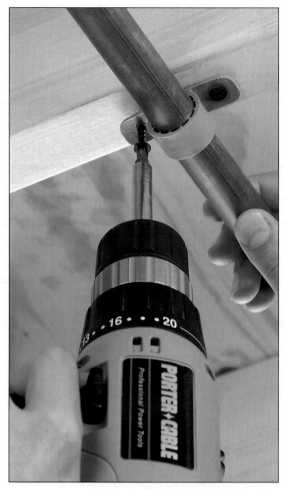

Split, two-hole plastic hangers can be used to suspend copper or plastic pipe. They will not have any negative reactions with the metal, plus they allow the pipe to expand or contract and they don't rattle against metal pipes, as loose metal hangers can. Do not use them if they'll be exposed to direct sunlight or to suspend DWV pipe near a dishwasher or washing machine.

PIPE INSTALLATION MATERIALS

Whether you're adding a shower riser or correcting a sag in a DWV branch line, you'll need to work with pipe hangers, clamps, or straps. Keep in mind the "needs" of your pipe. Plastic pipe requires the most support (See chart, next page). A PVC or ABS DWV pipe running from a hot dishwasher or washing machine should be supported along its full length with wood or metal; the heat softens these plastics. Horizontal plastic water pipe should be supported every two or three feet.

Plastic pipe generally should be allowed to move through the hangers without abrasion, since plastic is subject to significant expansion and contraction. For this same reason, flexible plastic tubing should be snaked through stud bays and rigid plastic should generally not be secured immovably at elbows where pipes change direction. When securing DWV or water plastic pipe, stay aware of what happens when the pipe grows or shrinks by a few inches.

If you need to add pipe hangers to water pipe, use a split, two-hole flat strap secured with hex-head bit-tip screws or a split, two-hole, high-eared strap secured with the same. They hold the pipe off the framing, which reduces sound and makes insulating the pipe easier. They also allow the pipe to move lengthwise: an important feature with plastic pipe that can also keep copper hot water pipe from ticking.

If you use metal hangers, use the same metal as the pipe or make sure two unlike metals (like copper and steel) are protected from contacting each other with plastic or insulation. Felted galvanized steel straps insulate against sound, can be used with copper piping, and are appropriate in high stress areas or where plastic hangers will be degraded by sunlight. Pronged wire hangers may back out of joists, so avoid these or use extras to compensate for ones that fail. If running pipe through a stud wall, attach metal protector plates to the wall studs to shield pipes from puncture.

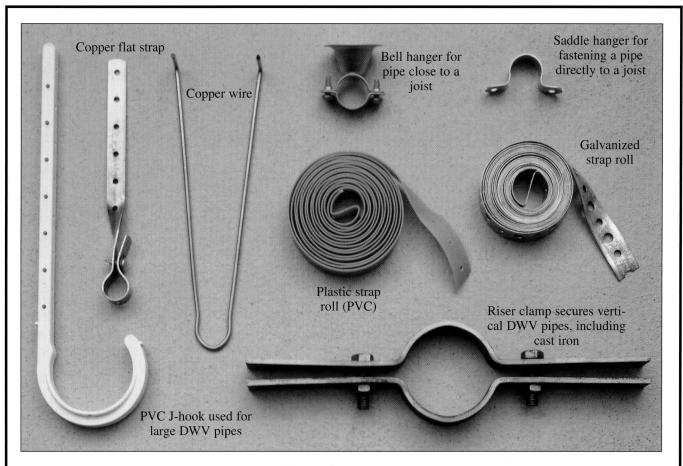

Copper flat strap

Copper wire

Bell hanger for pipe close to a joist

Saddle hanger for fastening a pipe directly to a joist

Galvanized strap roll

Plastic strap roll (PVC)

Riser clamp secures vertical DWV pipes, including cast iron

PVC J-hook used for large DWV pipes

Pipe hangers

Always use special-purpose pipe hangers when running pipe in your home, and make sure the hanger you choose is the best one for the pipe type, size and installation area.

• **Two hole hangers** (See previous page, top right, and the bell and saddle hangers above) can be used with copper, CPVC, PEX, and PB water pipe. These permit hot water pipes to slide during expansion and contraction, prevent pipe rattling, and provide room for pipe insulation. Secure them with screws. Do not use plastic in areas exposed to sunlight. When securing plastic pipe, allow room for expansion and contraction by not securing too close to a change-of-direction fitting.

• **Flat straps** made from solid copper (not plated), or galvanized steel can be used with like-metal pipe in sunlight-exposed areas and where extra strength is needed. Insulated straps may be used with plastic and hot water pipe. Install with No. 6 or 8 stainless steel sheet metal screws. Don't overtighten on hot water pipes, where pipes need to slide lengthwise.

• **Strap rolls** are perforated for ease of use and can be cut to any length you need. They are made from any of the primary materials pipe is made from. Use steel and copper tape with like-metal pipes and plastic tape with plastic pipe or lighter metal pipe. Use heavier galvanized tape on large cast iron drainpipes. Select screws or nails with heads that fill the holes. Consider that plastic drainpipes can bow on long runs, requiring support from above as well as below.

• **Hanger wire** is intended to be driven directly into joists, but has a tendency to loosen or fall out.

• **J-hooks** are used to hang plastic DWV pipe from joists or in walls, where the DWV pipe passes through over-sized holes. Use them to keep the pipe falling at a constant 1/4-in.-per-ft. pitch. J-hooks are easy to adjust.

• **Riser clamps** support vertical metal and plastic DWV pipes where they pass through wall plates and subfloors. Additional riser clamps are useful when you need to cut into a stack, leaving the upper portion unsupported. Use with blocking.

Allowable distances between pipe hangers

MATERIAL	SUPPORT SPACING
ABS	4 ft.
Galvanized	12 ft.
Copper	6 ft.
CPVC	3 ft.
Cast iron	5 ft.
PVC	4 ft.
PB pipe	32 in.

Faucet types

Ball faucets

Found on single-handle faucets, ball-type mechanisms include a hollow ball that fits into a dome-shaped housing. Rotating the housing and ball causes inlet holes in the ball to align with outlets in the faucet body, letting water flow up through the ball and out the spout.

Cam

Cam washer

Ball

Valve seat & spring

Compression faucets

Most two-handle sink faucets use compression-style operating parts. These have a threaded stem that raises and lowers a washer to control water flow through an intake port. The most common causes of leaks in compression faucets involve failure of the O-ring or stem washer.

Stem

O-ring

FAUCETS

Faucets for kitchen and bathroom sinks are selected and replaced for aesthetic reasons as much as any other purpose. Replacing an out-of-date or worn faucet with a newer, more stylish one is a quick and inexpensive way to freshen up a room. Whether you're dealing with a single-handle kitchen faucet or a two-handle lavatory faucet (or a bar-sink faucet, laundry-tub faucet or exterior sillcock, for that matter), pay attention to the type of sink the faucet is installed on and make your choice accordingly.

Look for high quality and reputable brand names when buying replacement faucets. Lower-end units tend to be made with cheaper materials that fail at a much quicker rate. Solid brass under the chrome finish is a good sign, as are solid brass or stainless steel washers and nuts. Avoid handles and faucet bodies made of chromed plastic. These will wear faster than brass, rendering high-use parts such as handles useless. If you do receive plastic or brass-plated steel washers and mounting nuts with your faucet, consider replacing them with solid brass or stainless steel versions of these parts purchased separately.

Faucet types. Most of the faucets manufactured and sold today fall into one of four basic categories, based on the mechanical characteristics of the faucet valve component that regulates the flow of water. The four types are *compression, ball, disc and cartridge* (See inset photos, these pages). While certain brand names often associate with particular

Disc faucets

Disc faucets use a single handle to rotate perforated ceramic discs within a barrel-shaped cartridge. The relative alignment of the holes in the upper and lower discs controls the flow of water.

valve styles, you will not always know what's under the handle until you take it off. But the general shape and size of the visible parts can provide some good clues, as you can see in the photos below. Keep in mind that some modern faucets utilize features of more than one valve style (in particular, compression-style faucets that include a removable cartridge).

Mounting options. There are two mounting configurations for sink faucets: *deck-mounted* (also called center-set) and *widespread*. Deck-mounted faucets sit above the sink or counter and attach from the bottom with mounting nuts. Usually, deck-mounted lavatory faucets fit into two holes that are four inches apart on-center, with a third and sometimes smaller hole in the center for the pop-up stop lever rod. Kitchen sinks have a hole under the spout for the sprayer hose attachment and a hole off to the right of the faucet holes for a sprayer handle for a total of four holes. Most faucet valve holes in kitchen sinks are spaced 8 inches apart on-center, for the left and right tailpieces, which usually drop through the first and third holes from the left. Make sure you measure between hole centers on your existing sink before buying a new faucet.

Deck-mounted faucets are sold in single-handle and two-handle models, and you'll generally find your choice of mechanical internal components (ball, cartridge, compression or disk).

Widespread faucets offer greater flexibility than standard deck-mounted faucets, as well as an alternative appearance. Because they are composed of three independent parts (a

spout, a cold-water valve and a hot-water valve) they are not confined to the limitations of an integral base plate and can be installed in virtually unlimited configurations. The valves can be spread up to 16 in. apart, since they are connected beneath the sink with tubing, not fixed to the body of the faucet. Since most sink basins are manufactured with predrilled holes, opting for a widespread faucet is frequently a matter of appearance. But on older basins with nonstandard hole spacing they may be your only option.

Fixing leaky faucets

Leaks in kitchen and bathroom faucets are generally easy to repair. In most cases, spouts drip and handles leak when washers, rings, and seals inside the faucet fail. By far the most common remedy for a leaky faucet is to replace the internal parts. Hardware and plumbing supply stores carry generic replacement parts as well as kits for specific brands of faucets. Whenever available, choose repair kits or parts made by the original faucet manufacturer.

Cartridge faucets

Cartridge mechanisms are employed in both single and two-handle faucets. Because the moving parts are all contained within the cartridge, repair is generally a matter of removing and replacing the entire cartridge.

Widespread faucets

Widespread faucets do not have a faucet body containing the handles and spout. Because the valves are independent of one another, they can fit sink basins with nonstandard hole configurations. Widespread faucets are generally available for bathroom vanities, although they are used increasingly in contemporary kitchen sink styles. Since the hot and cold water valves are separated from one another, widespread faucets usually contain the same internal components as compression-style deck-mounted faucets.

Sink styles

Sink basins and lavatories are essentially reservoirs installed between the water supply and the drain system. Installing them typically involves both plumbing and carpentry skills.

Bathroom vanity cabinets are fitted with an integral sink basin and countertop, usually fashioned from cultured marble.

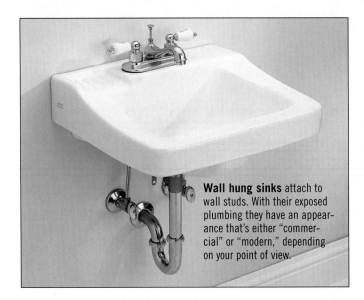

Wall hung sinks attach to wall studs. With their exposed plumbing they have an appearance that's either "commercial" or "modern," depending on your point of view.

SINK BASINS

The vast majority of kitchen and bathroom sinks installed today are self-rimming, drop-in style fixtures. Lighter weight sinks (such as stainless steel kitchen sinks) are attached to the countertop with clips that hold them in place. Heavier sinks, like cast-iron kitchen sinks, rely mainly on their own weight and the stabilizing effect of the plumbing connected to them to stay put. A bead of adhesive caulk between the rim of the sink and the countertop helps a little, but it's primary purpose is to block water from seeping under the rim. If you are installing a new sink, attach the faucet body to the sink before you mount the sink.

Sink basins themselves require very little maintenance. Refreshing of the caulk seal between the sink rim and counter and backsplash is about the extent of sink basin upkeep, other than regular cleaning. But whether it's due to wear or changing design tastes, swapping out your old sink with a fresh new model is a very popular home improvement project.

When choosing a new sink or lavatory, variables you'll need to take into account are: size (make sure the new sink will fit your existing counter opening, if you wish to keep it intact); depth (standard kitchen sinks are 8 inches deep, but many deeper models are available and may well be worth the extra cost); predrilled hole configuration; and type of material the sink is made of.

Pedestal sinks have "vintage" styling that somehow manages to give bathrooms an updated appearance. The sink basin is supported by the fixed pedestal in newer models. On older models, the sink is attached to the wall and the pedestal serves only to conceal the plumbing.

Sink material options

Stainless steel: Very popular in kitchens because they do not chip, as enameled metal sinks can, and many are very low-priced. Quality is generally a factor of the thickness of the steel. Modern versions are all self-rimming. Available in a brushed "satin" finish or brighter mirror finish.

Enameled steel: Pressed steel sink basins are coated with enamel or porcelain glazing in a selection of color options. Weight depends on the thickness of the metal. Most are self-rimming and easy to install. Finish prone to chipping.

Cast iron: Heavy-weight enameled sink basins made for both kitchens and bathrooms. Due to their weight, retainer clips usually are not needed for self-rimming installation.

Composite: Designed for both kitchens and bathrooms, composite sinks are relatively new on the market. They are lighter than cast iron or solid-surface sinks, but equally thick to deaden sound and provide insulation for hot water. The color is solid throughout, making it easy to disguise scratches.

Solid-surface: Made from the same material as solid-surface countertops, these sinks frequently are rimless (mounted from beneath the countertop) or integral with the countertop.

Vitreous china: Sinks made from vitreous china are relatively lightweight, inexpensive and easy to maintain. They are too fragile for kitchens, however.

Cultured marble: Most bathroom vanity cabinets are fitted with cultured marble basins molded into the countertop surface. Also too fragile for kitchens.

Kitchen & lavatory sink drains

Basket strainer sink drain

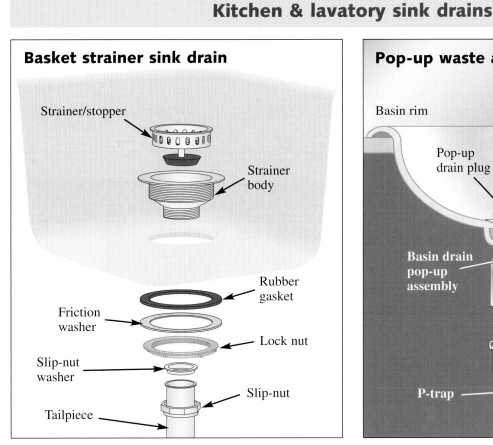

Pop-up waste assembly

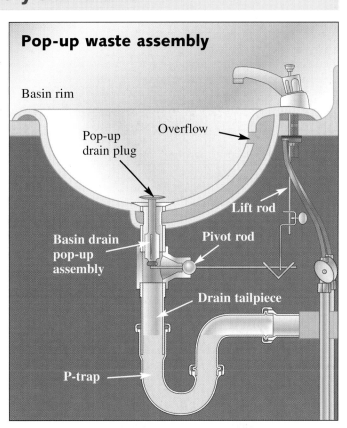

Basket strainers serve the double purpose of plugging the kitchen sink and straining food wastes when draining the sink. The strainer body is secured to the sink with a large lock nut. A rubber gasket above the lock nut helps to prevent leaks between the sink and the strainer body, but the strainer body should also be bedded in plumbers putty where the sink and body meet. The bottom of the strainer body is threaded to receive the slip nut that attaches the tailpiece to the drain. Basket strainer assemblies are available in stainless steel or several colors of plastic to match the sink.

Lavatory sinks are usually plugged with a pop-up stopper that's lifted and lowered with a knob on a lift rod behind the spout . The heart of this mechanism is the waste body, a hollow tube that contains the pop-up stopper. The waste body has openings where it crosses the overflow channel under the basin. Water flowing down through the overflow channel can enter the waste through these openings. The stopper itself is on a post that is pushed up and let down by a pivot rod. The pivot rod runs through a pivot ball that sits behind the waste body. A beveled nylon washer keeps water from leaking out around the pivot ball. The pivot rod is levered up and down by a lift strap (immediately above the pivot rod) that is pushed up and down by the user with the lift rod.

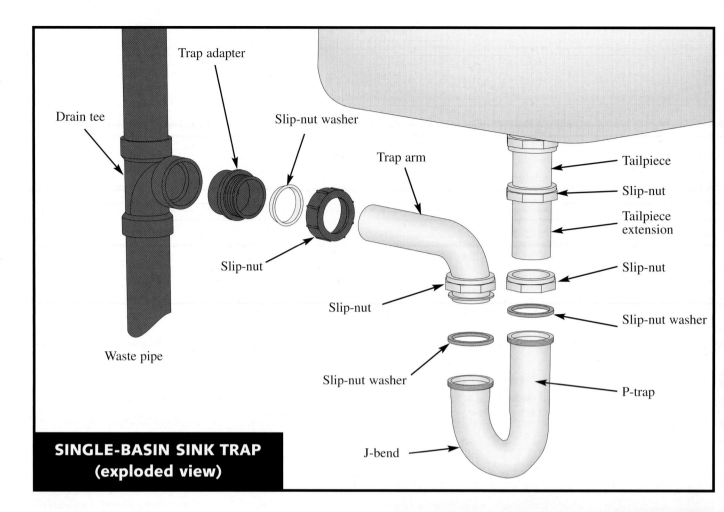

Trap adapter

Drain tee

Slip-nut washer

Trap arm

Tailpiece

Slip-nut

Tailpiece extension

Slip-nut

Slip-nut

Slip-nut washer

Slip-nut

Waste pipe

Slip-nut washer

P-trap

J-bend

**SINGLE-BASIN SINK TRAP
(exploded view)**

SINK TRAPS

Replace sink and lavatory traps that leak or become corroded. In most areas, you can use ABS (a black plastic), PVC (a white plastic), or chromed brass trap fittings. Some localities permit only metal traps since plastic traps will burn in a fire and give off toxic fumes. Because sinks and lavatories are easily accessible, code permits you to join the components of your trap system with slip nuts. This also allows you to easily take apart the trap to clear out clogs.

Lavatories generally have 1¼ in. trap systems and kitchen sinks generally have 1½ in. trap systems. Double lavatories move up to a 1½ in. trap size, but double basin sinks stay at 1½ in. If you are wondering what size trap you are replacing, measure the outside diameter of the sink tailpiece or trap arm (See photo, right). Tubular trap pieces are sized according to their outside diameters. This allows you to insert the trap arm inside the pipe stub in the wall, since DWV pipes are sized by their inside diameters.

If you will be replacing a sink tailpiece and the trap arm, measure the length of these so you know what the minimum size is that you must get. It's okay to buy these pieces long since they can be cut back, but make sure you get them long enough to span the gaps, including the overlaps. You want

(Continued, on page 244

Sink trap components are made from a number of materials. Some local codes place restrictions on which types may be used, so be sure to check with your building department if you're not sure. Perhaps the most common material today, particularly when replacing a trap with a store-bought kit, is lightweight plastic (PVC) tubing (A). It is inexpensive and easy to cut and make connections with. But it is also the least durable and the connections are the most prone to coming apart. Chromed brass tubes (B) are also very popular among do-it-yourselfers. Like plastic tubing, chromed tubes are fitted together with slip nuts and are relatively easy to cut (although more touchy than plastic). Chromed tubes also are prone to corrosion and deterioration. Schedule 40 ABS pipe (C) and Schedule 40 PVC (D) are very durable and are joined with tough solvent-welded connections.

Sink trap fittings, extensions & adapters

Chromed brass vs PVC sink trap fittings

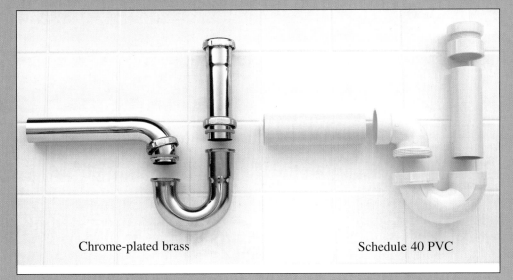

Chrome-plated brass   Schedule 40 PVC

Most homeowners prefer to work with chromed or lighter-weight plastic sink trap fittings that are joined with slip nuts and washers. Because they can be easily accessed, the occasional (and inevitable) leaks that develop when the slip nuts slip are not difficult to fix. But many professional plumbers prefer to use heavy-duty schedule 40 PVC trap components that are joined by solvent-welding, not slip nuts (the J-bend to trap-arm joint, however, is made with a slip nut so the trap can be disconnected and unclogged if needed).

Tailpiece extensions

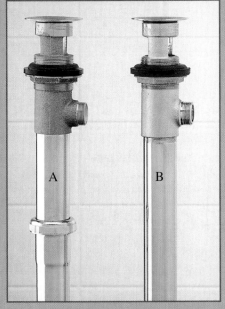

Often, the tailpiece from a pop-up stop waste or a basket strainer isn't long enough to reach the trap. To solve the problem, purchase a longer tailpiece for the basket strainer or pop up stop, or buy a tailpiece extension. The extension on the left in this photo (A) is a slip-joint extension that is simply added to the original tailpiece with a slip nut. The fitting on the right (B) is a 12-in.-long, threaded, extension that screws into the drain body to replace the original tailpiece.

Transition fittings/trap adapters

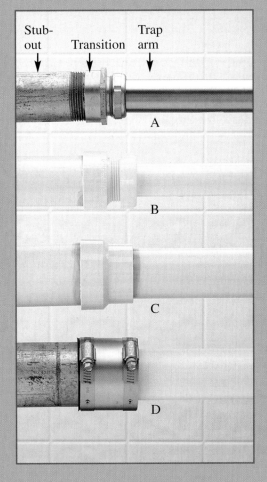

Stub-out   Transition   Trap arm

You may already have a trap adapter with a slip nut on the stub-out in your wall. If not, you can purchase the appropriate fitting if you measure and/or identify the pipes to be joined. Identify nominal DWV pipe sizes by their larger-than-nominal outside diameters. Tubular sizes, used with most trap parts, are equal to the outside diameter.
(A) This trap adapter transitions from a 1½ in. tubular chromed brass trap arm to a 1½ in. threaded galvanized steel pipe.
(B) This trap adapter transitions from a 1½ in. tubular PVC trap arm to a 1½ in. Schedule 40 PVC pipe. (C) This solvent-welded adapter transitions from 1½ in. Schedule 40 PVC to 2 in. Schedule 40 PVC. (D) Mission coupling to join any narrower trap arm to a wider stub-out.

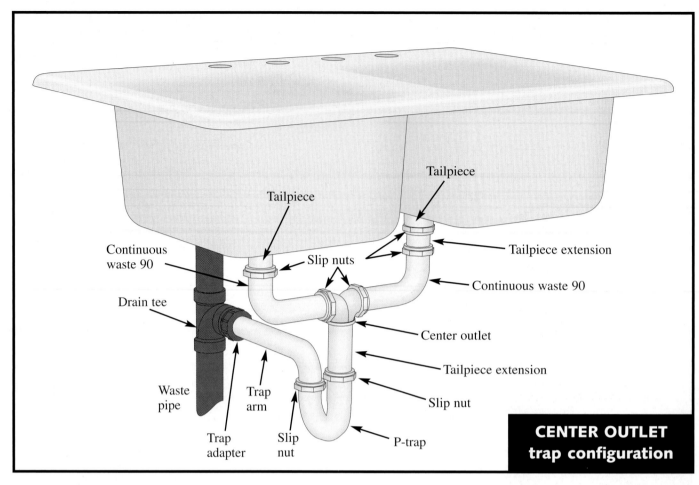

Continuous waste 90

Drain tee

Waste pipe

Trap adapter

Tailpiece

Slip nuts

Tailpiece

Tailpiece extension

Continuous waste 90

Center outlet

Tailpiece extension

Slip nut

Trap arm

Slip nut

P-trap

CENTER OUTLET trap configuration

(Continued, from page 242)

the tailpiece of the sink or lavatory to penetrate the trap as much as possible. You also want close-to-maximum penetration of the trap arm into the trap adapter and stub in the wall.

Sink trap code issues

Before starting work on your trap system, check with your local building inspector to determine if you will need two traps for a double lavatory (this usually depends on how far the most distant sink is from the waste stub-out in the wall). Also check to see if you will need a baffle in the tee if you are using a single trap. (A baffle keeps waste from one sink from flowing into the other sink.) Finally, see what types of materials are allowed for building the trap system. Some local codes restrict the use of plastic drain piping outside the wall. Note that a stub-out from the wall must have at least a 1½ in. inside diameter to receive waste from a double lavatory.

If you're simply replacing trap and waste components, take measurements off the old parts to cut new ones.

*Important: Not all sink traps are tubular size. Schedule 40 plastic traps and some metal traps are pipe size, which means the nominal diameter is the same or smaller than the inside diameter. Solvent-welded Schedule 40 plastic is often used with disposers so the joints won't be shaken apart. With pipe-size traps, a trap adapter or Mission coupling must be used on the sink side of the trap to transition to the tube-size tailpiece.

Double sinks and lavatories. If one sink is more or less in front of the waste stub-out in the wall, then you will want to install an end outlet tee. The line up doesn't need to be perfect since you may swing the J-bend on the P-trap one way or another and still have the trap arm approach the wall square. You will attach a trap to the one sink in front of the stub out as you would trap a single sink, except the tailpiece of the sink will be interrupted with a tee. A long pipe with an elbow on the end will run from the side inlet of this tee over to the other basin. This long pipe is called a continuous waste 90 since it's continuous with the other waste and has a right angle on the end. If the drain stub-out is between the two sinks, then you will want to use a center outlet tee. With a center outlet, both sinks attach to the same tee with continuous waste 90s.

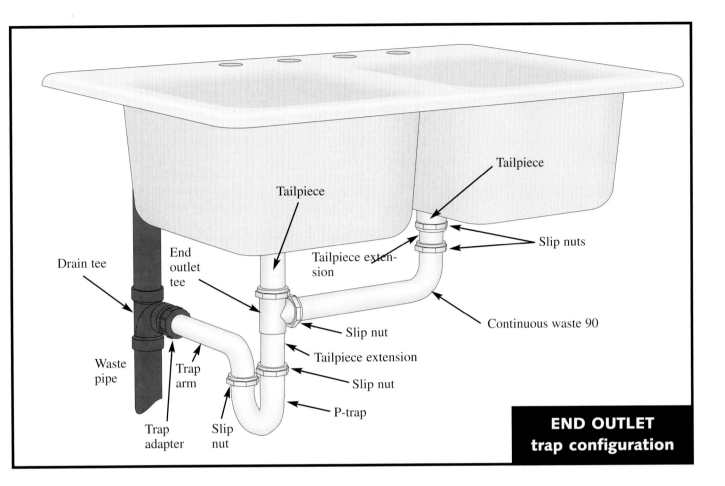

Tailpiece

Tailpiece

Slip nuts

Drain tee

End outlet tee

Tailpiece exten-sion

Continuous waste 90

Waste pipe

Trap arm

Slip nut

Tailpiece extension

Slip nut

P-trap

Trap adapter

Slip nut

Sink/disposer/dishwasher hook-up schematic

B

A dishwasher requires a hot-water supply hookup (A) and a drain line with an air gap (B). An air gap is a ventilated chamber installed on the deck of the sink that elimi-nates the risk of the dish-washer sucking dirty water out of the disposer or waste pipe and into the dishwasher. A ⅝-inch drain hose from the dishwasher (C) drains into a larger, ⅞-in. drain hose (D) at the air gap. The larger hose then drains into the disposer or the tail-piece of a basket strainer. The air gap can sit in the hole for a sprayer or in any free punch-out hole on the sink.

A garbage disposer (E) suspends from the second opening of a two-basin sink on a mounting assembly (F) that replaces the basket strainer. Attach the disposer discharge tube (G) directly to your trap or to an end-

D

F

E

G

C

A

outlet slip-joint tee with a slip washer and nut. Attach the larger air gap hose to the dishwasher inlet nipple on the disposer with a hose clamp.

TUBS & SHOWERS

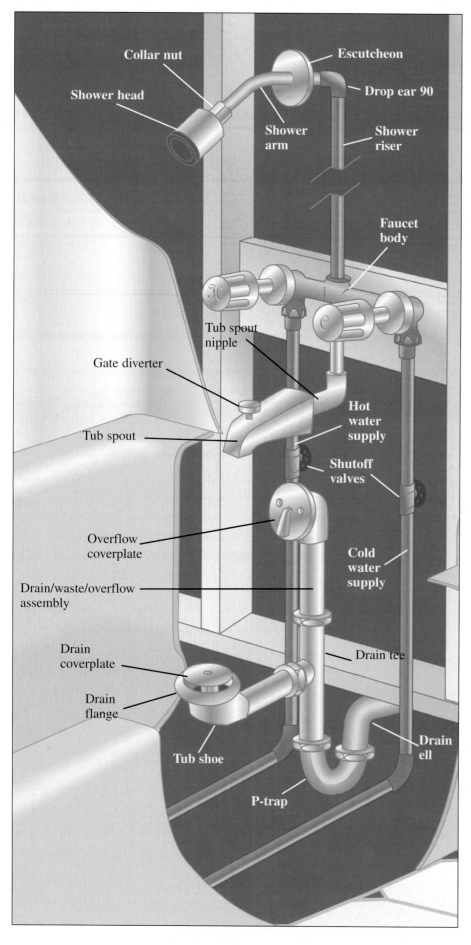

Collar nut

Shower head

Escutcheon

Drop ear 90

Shower arm

Shower riser

Faucet body

Tub spout nipple

Gate diverter

Tub spout

Hot water supply

Shutoff valves

Overflow coverplate

Drain/waste/overflow assembly

Cold water supply

Drain coverplate

Drain tee

Drain flange

Tub shoe

Drain ell

P-trap

Installing bathtubs and showers has gotten much easier over the years. It wasn't too long ago that any shower required a custom-poured mortar base with metal reinforcement. Drains were fashioned from oakum and other hard-to-handle materials. Today, the availability of do-it-yourselfer friendly kits has greatly simplified the process. And new advances in plastics and polymers have brought us newer, lightweight alternatives to traditional cast iron and porcelain. Bathtubs, for example, are now made from polymers that have many of the same properties of much heavier materials. You'll also find tubs made of plastic, fiberglass, and lightweight pressed steel.

Shower and tub surrounds are almost always installed as kits these days, compared to the clunky, site-built efforts that always seemed to leak or lose their surfacing. Along with these advances, some new accessories have been developed, including prefabricated glass doors that are a breeze to mount.

Preparing for the task

Even though replacing a bathtub, shower or combination tub-and-shower is getting easier, these projects will still require more than a beginner's level of carpentry skills as well as tools. You will also need a helper—from removing the old tub through attaching the waste and positioning the new tub. Potentially high levels of demolition (and therefore, reconstruction) are involved. You will need to remove at least some of the old tub surround, possibly floor tiles, and even sections of wall and ceiling from rooms adjacent to or below the bathroom. You may need to cut a tub-sized hole in the wall to remove the old tub and bring in the new unit.

Changing from an open tub to an alcove tub is easy enough if you know how to construct a partition wall. Alcove tubs are popular because the shower curtain can be replaced with easily cleaned, translucent sliding doors.

You may replace a tub without replacing the hot- and cold-water plumbing. However, if you want to convert a tub to a tub with a built-in shower, you must open the wall to replace the faucet and add piping to the showerhead.

As a general rule, install a new faucet and the piping for a new shower before installing the tub. This will involve some demolition and the installation of horizontal blocking for the new hardware. Whichever valve style you purchase, avoid "fishing at the bottom of the barrel," since defective or worn out shower valves are not easily replaced. Buy quality fittings as well.

If you've had problems with banging pipes when turning off the old tub or shower, consider installing commercial or home-made air chambers on your tub and shower supply pipes. These can tee off the supply pipes just above the shut-off valves. Use copper stubs and 90° elbows to extend the air chambers past and above the level of the valve body.

Today's popular pressed steel or fiberglass tubs are manufactured to be installed in alcoves with manufactured tub surround panels to form the shower. An alcove was created for the tub in the top photo by building a partition wall at the end. Shower stall kits (right photo) come in many shapes and styles. Both tub surrounds and shower stalls are designed to be DIY-friendly to install.

Diverters & faucets

Shower and tub faucets are larger versions of sink and lavatory faucets, with the exception that combination tub/showers have manual diverter valves to switch water flow between the tub spout and the showerhead. The diverter valve may be controlled with a handle in the wall or with a lever on the spout. Three common styles include: one handle hot/cold control with a diverter valve on the spout; two-handle hot and cold control with the diverter on the spout; and three-handle hot, cold, and wall-mounted diverter control.

Diverter types

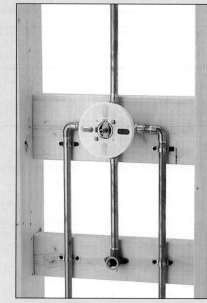
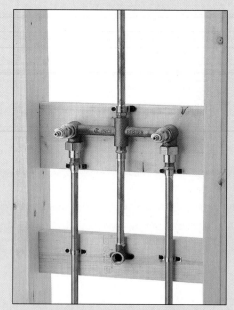
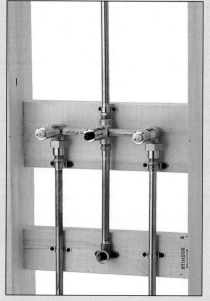

One-handle hot/cold control with a diverter valve on the spout.

Two-handle hot and cold control with the diverter valve on the spout.

Wall-mounted diverter control.

Tips for basic tub & shower faucet repairs

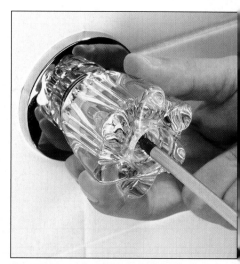

Seal behind escutcheon plates with plumbers putty whenever you remove them to service tub and shower faucets. Pack the back of the escutcheons with putty or form a coil of putty on the wall and press the plates into the putty. Without a watertight seal around these plates, water can seep into the wall openings and damage the wallboard and framing behind.

Plastic faucet controls will eventually crack and break or become discolored after years of exposure to detergents and hard water. Replace them by popping off the decorative plastic or metal cap that covers the center of the handle with a screwdriver. The handles should be held in place with a single screw. Most home centers will stock a wide selection of replacement handles.

Adding a shower

You can convert a tub to a tub-and-shower with a flexible-hose shower adapter. Purchase a quality shower head or shower massager. The shower head can be mounted for shower traditionalists or it can be hand-held for greater control and spray force. A spout with a diverter valve allows you to switch easily from tub spout to shower.

Hand-held showers use water more efficiently than fixed shower heads. Flexible showerhead tubes with mountable heads can be added to a regular shower arm as well as to a shower-adapter tub spout with vacuum breaker.

Spout with vacuum breaker

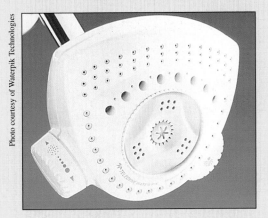

Low-flow showerheads

New showerheads are required by law to be low-flow. This will save the average household about 12,000 gallons of water a year. Lower quality heads or flow-restricting washers tend to atomize the water into an ineffectual mist. High-quality low-flow showerheads keep water droplets from becoming too small, delivering a shower that feels voluminous. Water massage showerheads pulsate the water flow—an action that saves water while producing a forceful shower. Showerhead shutoff valves reduce flow to a trickle with the flick of a lever, saving water while the bather lathers. Shutoffs can be purchased separately and are sometimes built into better showerheads.

When a showerhead leaks or doesn't hold its position, unscrew it from the shower arm and the swivel fitting. Replace the neoprene O-ring inside. Coat the new O-ring with heatproof grease to seal it and keep it from tearing during reassembly. Hand tighten the swivel fitting to the head with the collar nut, then reinstall the showerhead.

The best insurance against leaks around threaded fittings is to use a combination of Teflon tape and pipe joint compound. Wrap tape around the male threads, working clockwise. Coat the female threads with compound. For threaded plastic, be sure to use pipe joint compound formulated for use on plastic threads.

Leaking valve stem cartridges on tub faucets can often be repaired by changing the O-rings that seal the cartridge in the faucet body. While you are at it, change any interior springs and seals as well. Plumbing suppliers or the faucet manufacturer may have repair kits that contain all the parts you'll need. If this doesn't stop the leak, replace the whole cartridge.

The physics of flushing. When a traditional gravity-flush toilet is flushed, a lift wire or rod raises the flapper that covers the valve leading from the tank to the toilet bowl. With the flapper raised, the water in the tank rushes into the hollow rim of the toilet, where it cascades into the bowl through a number of jets in the toilet rim. The sudden influx of water causes the water in the bowl to overflow the bowl trap and rush down toward the drain. The rushing motion of the water creates suction that quickly empties the toilet bowl. At this moment, the flush valve closes and the tank and bowl begin to refill. The method of refilling the tank depends on the style of flush-&-fill mechanism (See below).

TOILETS

Replacing a toilet is not as difficult as many people think—as long as the closet flange and floor around the base of the old toilet are in good shape. Once you have removed the old fixture, inspect these areas closely for signs of damage or rot. If you spot any problems, you'll definitely want to take care of them before installing the new toilet.

Even if your current toilet is working just fine, you may want to consider replacing it with a modern low-flow model, typically using only 1.6 gallons of water per flush (compared to 3 gallons or even more on some older models). The savings on your water bill may not completely offset the cost of the new unit, but it's an environmentally responsible act of remodeling. And in many localities, low-flow toilets are now required by building codes.

When buying a new toilet, don't simply rush out and get the cheapest one off the floor at your local building center. Certainly there are times when this approach might make sense, but consider your options. There are many factors to evaluate. Whichever style toilet you choose, make sure it will fit your space. The distance from the closet flange (drain) to the wall determines what size you should purchase. Measure the distance from the bolts to the wall. If there are four bolts, measure from the bolts that are attached to the flange. This "rough-in" distance determines which size toilet you must buy (12 in. is the minimum distance and most common these days).

Styles of toilet tank flush-&-fill mechanisms

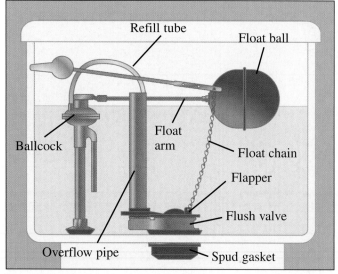

Float ball style: Most older toilets in use today employ this familiar system for flushing and filling the toilet tank. A float ball is connected to a plunger with a metal arm. When the toilet is flushed, the float ball sinks down to the lower water level, then gradually returns upward as the water level rises. When the tank is full, the float arm depresses a plunger on top of the ballcock, causing the inlet valve to close.

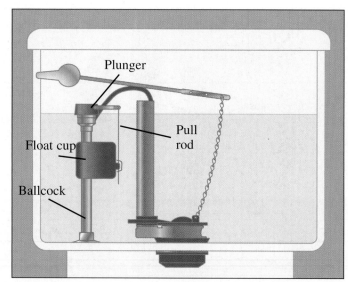

Float cup style: This variation of the float ball mechanism is becoming increasingly popular because it's more reliable than the float ball system. The basic principle is the same, but instead of a detached float, a plastic float cup mounted on the shank of the ballcock moves up and down with the tank water level. A pull rod connected directly to the plunger controls the flow of water into the tank. It also comes with an anti-siphon valve, which is now required by code for new construction toilet installations.

Toilet styles

The close-coupled toilet has a tank joined to the back of the bowl with gaskets and bolts. It's the most typical toilet design for residences, using gravity to flush wastes from the bowl into the drain. Low-profile toilets include the tank and bowl in one unit. They are less efficient flushers than close coupled designs for the same reason that, on a given size river, a low waterfall is less powerful than a tall waterfall.

Today's emphasis on water conservation means that close-coupled toilets have to use water more efficiently. Now most parts of the country require 1.6 gallon toilet tanks, compared to tanks that held as much as 8 gallons a generation or two ago. The best low-flush toilets have tall, narrow tanks to take better advantage of gravity. Some low flush toilets let you adjust for a longer, slightly more voluminous flush by using an adjustable float on the flush valve chain than can be positioned to hold the flapper open longer.

Low-volume, pressure-flushed tank toilets are also available now for residences. Like the "flushometer" toilets used in public buildings, pressure-flushed tank toilets blast out the bowl with pressurized water. While a flushometer toilet taps the water-supply pressure directly, a pressure flushed tank toilet stores pressure from the water system in a tank, making it look like a conventional close-coupled toilet. These toilets flush effectively with only 1.6 gallons of water. However, pressure-flushed tank toilets are expensive and prone to failures that are expensive to fix.

Two-piece toilets, also called "close-coupled" have a separate tank bolted to the back of the stool. This makes them easier to transport but also creates a potential problem area in the seal between the two parts—leaks can occur and moisture can get trapped in the seam. But all of the lower-priced toilets on the market are two-piece, making them considerably more common.

One-piece toilets, also called "low-profile" or "low-boy" generally are considered more attractive, and the absence of a mechanical joint between tank and stool makes them easier to clean and less prone to leakage. But they also tend to be weaker flushers and more expensive than two-piece fixtures. Parts also can be more expensive and difficult to find.

Exposed trap   Concealed trap

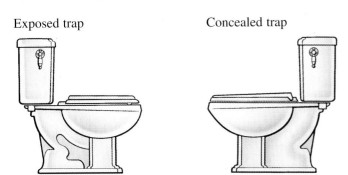

Concealed or exposed trap? Most toilets on the market today have a revealed trap: you can see the profile of the drain trap on the outside surface of the stool. For a sleeker appearance and ease of cleaning, some manufacturers produce smooth-sided toilets, but they tend to be more expensive.

Round or elongated seat? The shape of the bowl determines the shape of the seat. If you have space and a few extra dollars to spend, consider a toilet with an elongated bowl and seat for greater comfort and enhanced sanitation.

Round   Elongated

Adding oomph to the flush

Assisted-flush toilets have a pressurized tank that compresses air when it fills with water. The compressed air forces the water out of the tank into the bowl with greater force than an ordinary gravity-assisted tank. The increased flushing power minimizes the number of "multiple flush" experiences associated with smaller 1.6 gallon tanks. Assisted-flush tanks are louder and costlier than their gravity-flush cousins.

Photos & illustrations courtesy of American Standard

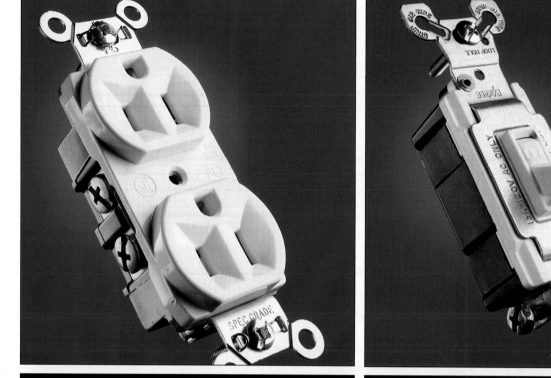

WIRING MATERIALS

Working with wiring is not diffi-cult. But even the most experi-enced handymen often draw the line at doing electrical work. Likely as not, it isn't the complexity of the task or the labor involved that gives us pause, it's fear. To some degree, fear of electricity is a good thing: Never forget that each time you apply a tool to your electrical system you're taking a risk, and take all available precautions to minimize that risk.

This section on wiring will give you a broad overview of the most common materials involved in accomplishing most home wiring tasks. As with many

Safety apparel

• **Wear safety glasses.** When cutting wire, if you snip a small piece off the end of a wire, it shoots out like a rocket ship. It could fly up and into an eye. When you work overhead, dirt or debris can fall into your eyes, or an arc from a shorted wire could send a brand into your eyes.

• **Consider wearing rubber gloves** (such as dishwashing gloves) when working with electricity, but never assume they'll give enough protection to handle a hot wire.

• **Always wear rubber-soled shoes** to prevent your body from making a complete circuit with the earth, should you touch a hot wire. The thicker the soles the better.

Removing current from the line

Power to a specific circuit can be removed by simply turning off (or removing) the overcurrent protection device for that circuit, be it a circuit breaker (left) or fuse (top). If you are working with circuits controlled by a fuse box, be sure to remove the fuse completely from its holder and set it aside. Fuses that are unscrewed but left in their holders sometimes can vibrate back in and make contact, re-energizing the circuit.

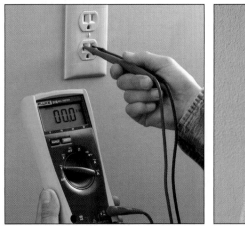

Test the circuit with a current testing device before even going as far as removing a faceplate. The plug-in circuit analyzer (right) is a popular device for this purpose because it is so inexpensive. But a digital multimeter (left) is much more reliable and can detect lower level current the plug-ins could miss.

areas of home improvement, there are scores of wiring products available to you at your local home center. Some will provide years of safe and reliable service, while others are of poor quality and will not. Without a resource to help explain your options, buying the right and best quality cable, receptacles and switches can be confusing. Installing the wrong switch or an inferior receptacle can be dangerous.

Use this section in conjunction with a good reference book on wiring techniques to help plan, shop for and carry out your wiring projects. Be sure to follow all applicable local building codes as well. Most wiring tasks that go beyond the scope of replacing an existing fixture, switch or receptacle will require a building permit. This is so that your work can be checked by a building inspector. Electrical permits may seem like an inconvenience, but they are required in order to ensure that you are working safely.

The safest way to work around electricity is to have all power removed from the area you are working in. This can be done by throwing the main breaker or pulling the main fuses. In some cases, it is wise to have the power company shut off service to your home while you work. When shut-

ting off the power, be sure to do it in the daytime when possible and have a flashlight ready for emergency light.

A more convenient way to remove power is to throw off the breaker or unscrew the fuse that regulates the circuit you are working on.

NM CABLE

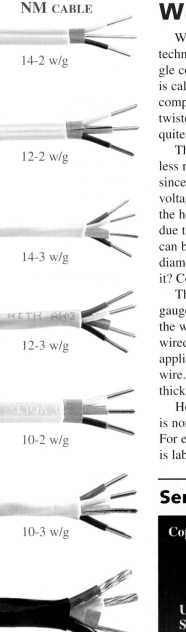

14-2 w/g

12-2 w/g

14-3 w/g

12-3 w/g

10-2 w/g

10-3 w/g

6-3 w/g

UF CABLE

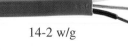

14-2 w/g

12-2 w/g

WIRE & CABLE

What we normally call wire and cable are technically known as conductors. Usually, a single conductor is called a wire and group of them is called cable. However, large conductors are composed of many individual conductors, usually twisted together, so the terms are interchanged quite often.

The larger the diameter of the conductor, the less resistance it creates. Less resistance is good since resistance opposes the current and inhibits voltage getting to the load. If more than 10% of the household voltage doesn't make it to the load due to too much resistance, motors and fixtures can burn out. So why not just use very large diameter wire everywhere and don't worry about it? Cost.

The diameter of a wire is described by its gauge. The larger the gauge number, the smaller the wire. Most 120-volt home wiring circuits are wired with 14 or 12-gauge conductors. Small appliances or lamps may contain 18 or 20-gauge wire. On the bigger end, you can find wire as thick as 2/0 and even up to 4/0 in a home.

How do you tell the two gauge cables apart? It is normally written on the sheathing of the cable. For example, the aforementioned 12-gauge cable is labeled on its sheath, 12-2 w/g NMB. The 12 is

the gauge, the 2 means there are two insulated conductors, and w/g simply means "with ground." The NMB means nonmetallic sheath with a 90° Centigrade temperature rating. Almost all interior wiring today is done using NM cable (popularly called Romex).

When purchased in 50 or 100-foot rolls, cable is relatively inexpensive, even if it's heavier 12-gauge cable. If the cable will be exposed instead of covered by a wall in a stud or joist cavity, it should be run through conduit to protect it from

Common wire gauge uses

End use	Wire gauge
Wall outlets	14
Overhead room lights	14
Gas dryer	14
Basement/garage lights	14
Dishwasher	12
Attic fans	12
Gas range	12
Clothes washer	12
Refrigerator and freezer	12
Garbage disposals	12
Workbench outlets	12

Service entrance cable (SEC)

Copper SEC

USE cable in conduit

U-style
SE cable

Aluminum SEC

4/0-gauge

2/0-gauge

Common types of copper service entrance cable (SEC) are: the U-style, with two hot conductors wrapped in a braided wire neutral and bound by thermoplastic sheathing (above left); and USE cable (above right), which is created by running strands of insulated 1/0 conductor through conduit. One USE strand is taped white for neutral and the other two strands are hot. Aluminum SEC is also safe for use in residential applications, provided the exposed connections are coated with a noncorrosive compound.

Size requirements for service entry cable

SERVICE	COPPER	ALUMINUM
200-amp	2/0 gauge	4/0 gauge
150-amp	1 gauge	2/0 gauge
100-amp	4 gauge	2 gauge

18-gauge

16-gauge

14-gauge

12-gauge

10-gauge

8-gauge

6-gauge

4-gauge

1-gauge

2/0-gauge

Aluminum wire

From approximately 1965 to 1972, 2 to 3 million homes were constructed with single-strand branch circuit aluminum wiring. Unfortunately, the homeowners soon learned that aluminum wiring exposed to air will produce a surface barrier chemical reaction that can act as an insulator, destroying wiring connections and increasing resistance. In addition, the screws that held the wires down would become loose after a period of time. As a result, codes today restrict the installation of new aluminum wire. Exceptions are made for large diameter wire, like service entry cable.

But even large diameter aluminum wiring can be problematic unless the exposed conductors have been coated with a noncorrosion compound and the terminals are kept tight.

If you have single strand aluminum wiring feeding the receptacles and switches in your home, you have a major problem. In addition to its tendency to corrode, it is difficult to splice and breaks easily. Also, most electrical fixtures are UL-approved for copper wire only. The best solution is to simply rewire the house. If that is not an option, some companies do manufacture wire connectors they say will splice copper to aluminum. Switches and receptacles for aluminum wire are sold at large electrical supply houses.

damage. Some codes still allow armored cable to be used in interior situations. Armored cable is manufactured with flexible metal coil sheathing. But generally, you'll find it easier to work with nonmetallic cable fed through conduit than to handle and cut armored cable. And the cables will also be better protected.

Exterior wiring is normally done with underground feeder cable (UF), which is constructed like NM cable except the sheathing is made of a much more rugged material and wraps around all conductors individually. In certain situations, UF cable should be run through exterior-rated conduit.

Use the correct wire connector

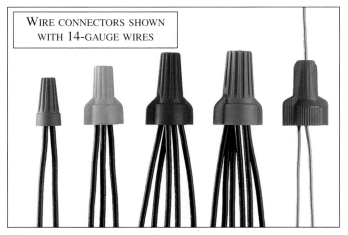

WIRE CONNECTORS SHOWN
WITH 14-GAUGE WIRES

Wire connectors are color-coded to indicate the number of wires of various gauges they can connect so you can easily choose a connector that is neither too large nor too small for your job. An orange connector handles up to two 14-gauge wires. Yellow accepts three 14-gauge or two to three 12-gauge wires. Red connects four to five 14-gauge or four 12-gauge wires. Gray or blue connects six 14-gauge or five 12-gauge wires. Green wire connectors are used with grounding wires. They can handle two to four 14-gauge or 12-gauge wires. Some green connectors have a hole in the tip allowing one grounding wire to pass through and connect to a grounding screw terminal, so an extra pigtail isn't needed. Wire connector packages should list the number of all wire gauge sizes and combinations they can safely connect.

Types of wire

Household receptacle and switch wiring. Here your choice is simply 14 or 12-gauge cable. If you are not on a tight budget, always opt for the heavier 12-gauge. For general residential circuits, 14-gauge is the smallest diameter wire allowed by the NEC. As you might think, 14-gauge conductors can create problems, so they must be used only where there is low current draw. Because home builders usually don't know where you will be using your heavy electrical items, it's common to find 14-gauge cable almost everywhere in newer homes, except the kitchen area, bath and utility room, where the NEC requires 12-gauge.

Service entrance cable. In most cases, the largest wire in a residence will be the service entrance cable (SEC)—the very thick wires that bring power from the transformer connection to the service panel in your home. If you're working with SEC, copper wire generally is a better choice than aluminum because it's smaller in diameter so it is easier to bend and fits better into conduit.

Electric stove wire. Copper stove wire is normally 6- or 8-gauge, making it the heaviest wire coming out of most main service panels. Aluminum could be used here (6- or 4-gauge) but many local codes forbid it because it is susceptible to corrosion.

Electric dryer wire and electric water heater wire. Both typically need to carry 4000 to 5500 watts, so they are a hefty 10-gauge copper in most cases.

Metal conduit & fittings

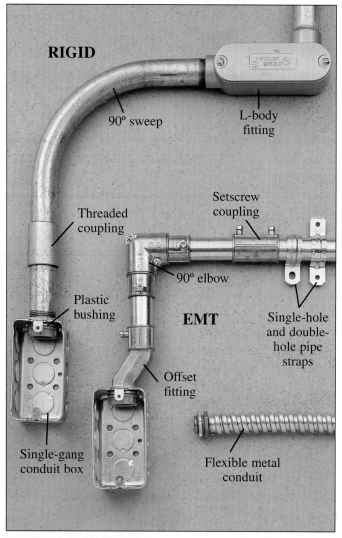

RIGID

90° sweep

L-body
fitting

Threaded
coupling

Setscrew
coupling

90° elbow

Plastic
bushing

EMT

Single-hole
and double-
hole pipe
straps

Offset
fitting

Single-gang
conduit box

Flexible metal
conduit

Metal conduit and fitting types used in home wiring are Rigid for exterior use and EMT (Electrical Metal Tubing) for interior, dry locations.

CONDUIT

Conduit is used to protect wires in exposed locations, such as on masonry surfaces in a basement. Conduit rated for exterior use can be used to install circuits outdoors. Check with your local electrical inspector to determine the type of conduit your project requires.

Metal conduit

Metal conduit is available in three types. EMT (Electrical Metallic Tubing) is lightweight and easy to work with, but because of its thinner tubing, EMT shouldn't be installed where it could easily be damaged. IMC (Intermediate Metallic Conduit) has thicker, galvanized walls to withstand rougher treatment. It also is a good choice for outdoor installations when used with weatherproof fittings. Rigid metal conduit provides heavy-duty protection, but it is the most expensive and also requires threaded fittings. IMC or EMT should be adequate for most of your projects. PVC conduit (See next page) is increasing in popularity because it is lighter in weight, inexpensive and easy to work with, but check your local building department first: PVC isn't

Armored cable

Armored cable is essentially pre-wired flexible conduit that was popular for use in areas that receive little traffic (like attics) but require protected cable. When running new wiring, most pros today prefer to install conduit and thread it with plain old nonmetallic cable. Conduit and cable are cheaper and regarded as easier to work with.

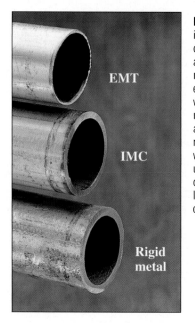

EMT

IMC

Rigid
metal

Metal conduit is the most familiar conduit material for both residential and commercial applications. The lightest gauge metal conduit (EMT) is still used extensively in exposed interior wiring locations, such as basements and garages. But it is not allowed for exterior work. IMC and rigid metal conduit, when used with watertight connectors, may be used outdoors. But they are seldom used anymore, in favor of lighter and more workable PVC conduit.

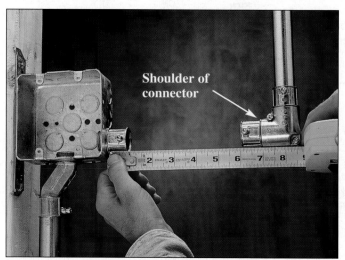

Shoulder of
connector

Measure from shoulder to shoulder. Use a tape measure to determine the length of conduit needed between locations. Measure to the shoulders of connectors to determine the distance the conduit will need to span. Then cut the conduit to length with a hacksaw.

approved for some applications and in some geographic areas.

Metal conduit fittings

Metal fittings are available to make the installation of metal conduit quite easy. Rather than bend the conduit yourself with special tools, you can purchase these connectors premade to create the conduit layout your project requires.

Threaded couplings, connectors and sweeps are used to install rigid metal conduit.

Setscrew fittings are used with EMT and IMC. The removable cover on the 90° elbow makes it easy to pull wires around a corner. An offset fitting connects conduit, anchored flush against a wall, to the knockout on a metal electrical box or to a service panel knockout.

The same metal electrical conduit boxes are used with all conduit types. An L-body fitting is used as a transition between vertical and horizontal lengths of conduit, such as when underground wires must enter a building. The cover can be removed, making pulling wires easier. Plastic bushings cover exposed conduit ends, protecting wires from damage by the rough metal edges. Metal pipe straps anchor conduit against masonry surfaces or wood framing members. Conduit should be supported within 3 ft. of each electrical box and fitting, and at least every 10 ft. in straight runs.

Flexible metal conduit bends easily and can be used for short unsupported distances where rigid conduit is difficult to install. It is frequently used to connect appliances that are hard-wired, such as water heaters. Wires are pulled through flexible metal conduit in the same manner as with other conduit. Armored cable (See previous page) is flexible metal conduit that comes with the wires prerun through the conduit. It is seldom used in new work today.

PVC conduit

Most residential building codes allow the use of PVC plastic conduit in installations requiring wire protection. Plastic conduit and fittings are lightweight and very easy to install. Sections of rigid conduit are cut and assembled with solvent glue to threaded or smooth fittings, just like PVC plumbing pipe. Two advantages to PVC conduit over metal conduit is the soft plastic can be cut more quickly than metal with a tubing cutter (See photo, right) or power miter box. PVC also will not corrode in damp conditions, as metal conduit could. Check with your local electrical inspector to find out if plastic conduit is okay for your project.

Plastic conduit is generally connected to plastic electrical boxes with fittings that come in similar shapes and sizes to those used with metal conduit. But PVC conduit can also be attached to a metal box by welding a threaded male coupling onto the end of the conduit, then securing the coupling to the metal box with a cable clamp nut.

As with metal conduit, flexible plastic conduit is also available to span difficult gaps between lengths of rigid PVC or electrical boxes. Flexible plastic conduit may or may not meet code in your area. If in doubt, contact an inspector.

Plastic conduit & fittings

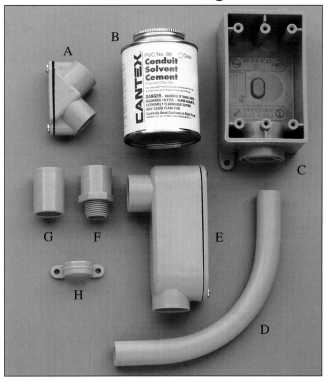

Conduit fittings for PVC (plastic) conduit include: (A) 90° connector; (B) conduit solvent compound (for solvent-welding joints); (C) exterior box; (D) 90° sweep; (E) ell fitting; (F) threaded coupling; (G) straight coupling; (H) plastic pipe strap.

Working with PVC conduit

Cut conduit sections to length using a tubing cutter (top photo). The tool blades ratchet down around the pipe and cut it cleanly in two. You can also use a power miter saw with a fine-toothed blade or a hacksaw.

Attach sections of conduit to fittings or receptacle boxes with solvent cement formulated specially for PVC conduit applications (bottom photo). In most cases, you'll need to use a threaded connector to transition from the conduit to the box.

Anatomy of a service panel

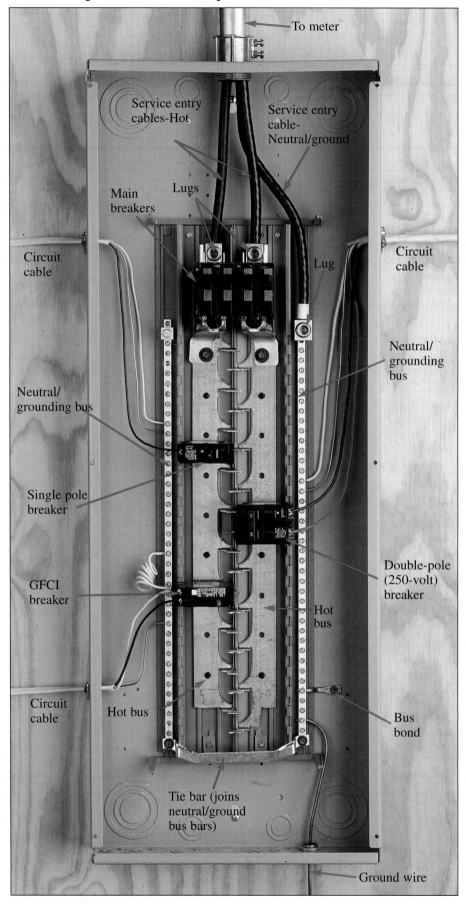

To meter

Service entry cables-Hot

Service entry cable-Neutral/ground

Main breakers

Lugs

Lug

Circuit cable

Circuit cable

Neutral/ grounding bus

Neutral/ grounding bus

Single pole breaker

Double-pole (250-volt) breaker

GFCI breaker

Hot bus

Circuit cable

Hot bus

Bus bond

Tie bar (joins neutral/ground bus bars)

Ground wire

SERVICE PANELS & CIRCUITS

All the electrical service in your house starts at the service panel (also called the load center). It is the heart of the electrical system. It also houses the main cut-off switch and contains protective devices (circuit breakers or fuses) for all the wiring in the house. Every adult in the house needs to know where this panel is and how to throw the main breaker on and off in case of an emergency.

The service panel divvies up the raw power entering your house into organized, controlled circuits. A circuit is a cable that has been installed to power a light, receptacle, appliance or area. Wiring codes are very specific about the number, size and purposes of the individual circuits originating in the service panel. Many home appliances require dedicated circuits of their own. Lights should be on their own circuit so that if an appliance overloads and trips a circuit breaker, the lights will stay on so you can find your way around the house and down to the service panel. Furnaces, garages, stoves and other major kitchen appliances generally command their own circuits.

Parts of the service panel

The main breaker. The primary purpose of having a main breaker is to limit the amount of current coming into the panel and house so that excessive current cannot damage the service entrance cable or main panel. Being current sensitive, the main senses the amount of current (amperage) flowing from the meter base into the panel and will throw the main breaker off if the amperage is over the designed limit. The designed limit is normally written on the breaker handle or the panel lid.

NOTE: *If an additional cutoff panel is ever installed between the utility meter and the main service panel, the main service panel becomes a subpanel where neutrals must be separated from the grounding system.*

General circuit breaker types include double-pole breakers (left), single pole breakers (middle) and GFCI-protected breakers (right). Double-pole breakers are used for circuits that carry larger amounts of current and for circuits where two separate hot leads are needed. Single-pole breakers are the most common, with 15- and-20-amps being the most frequent capacities. GFCI breakers protect an entire circuit from ground faults, eliminating the need for GFCI-protected receptacles on the line. In addition to the cost savings gained by using standard receptacles, GFCI breakers are increasing in popularity because they have a longer life expectancy than GFCI receptacles.

Circuit breakers. One of the purposes of the service panel is to distribute all the power to the various circuits that feed all the house loads. This distribution is done most often through mechanical/ electrical devices called circuit breakers. They plug into the two hot busses going down the panel center. When the circuit breaker is in the ON position, power flows out of the hot bus and through the breaker, into the wiring, and then to the various loads throughout the house (switches, receptacles and appliances). In the OFF position, the breaker stops the flow of power to those same loads. As the load pulls the power through the breaker, the breaker senses the amount of current and if it is more than the amount allowed on the circuit wiring, 15 or 20 amps for example, the breaker will trip and open the circuit. To reset the breaker once the excessive load has been removed, you must turn the breaker to full OFF first and then back to ON. Otherwise, the breaker will trip back off again.

You can also purchase GFCI-protected breakers to provide reliable ground-fault protection to an entire circuit. These special breakers eliminate the need for GFCI receptacles on the circuit.

Breakers come in different amper-

ages: 15, 20, 25, 30, etc. The amperage that is used for a circuit is always matched to the maximum allowed current for whichever gauge wire is used in the circuit. For example, 15 amps for 14-gauge wire, 20 amps for 12-gauge wire, and 30 amps for 10-gauge wire. Breakers can be single-pole, double-pole, slim-line or quad styles. A single pole breaker services one 120-volt circuit, measured from hot wire to ground or neutral. These are the ones with one black wire going to the load and one white wire going to the neutral/grounding bus. The hot wire (normally black) takes the power from the breaker to the load and a neutral (always white) brings it back. The neutral connects to the neutral/ grounding bus in a main service panel or to the neutral bus in a subpanel.

A single-pole breaker is the most common breaker in your panel. Double-pole circuit breakers are two single-pole circuits put together with a common trip arm. Double-pole circuits feed 240-volt loads, such as water heaters and baseboard heaters. These circuits also use the black and white wire, each of which goes to the breaker (there is no neutral) but the white wire should have a band of black tape around it to indicate it is not a neutral.

Fuse boxes

Many older homes still have 60-amp fuse boxes rather than service panels. Typically they will have two 60-amp, pull-out cartridge fuses for the main service protection, two 40-amp, pull-out cartridge fuses for the stove's wiring protection, and four glass plug fuses for individual circuits. Old fuse panels are not designed for today's many varied loads. Modern panels can distribute power to as many circuits as the service panel is designed to support (up to 40). This is a tremendous improvement over fuse boxes that can support no more than four circuits. If your home still has a fuse box and you want to add circuits, you must change it out for a service panel with circuit breakers. Most codes require updated service panels for any major electrical work or remodeling that requires extensive electrical modifications.

If slot space is at a premium in your service panel, you may be able to substitute slim-line breakers that can run two single-pole circuits from a single slot. These devices, also called two-in-one breakers, do not fit every panel.

Neutral/grounding bus bars. These are the aluminum bars where the white neutral wires and bare and green ground wires terminate. The returning neutral currents from each circuit collect on this bar, then return to the utility transformer through the grounded neutral of the service entry cable. Remember, all the current starts at the transformer and therefore must return to the transformer. You will not find this bus on a subpanel. Subpanels have a separate neutral bus and grounding bus. A tie bar connects the two neutral/ground bus bars. If the tie bar is removed, the panel may be used as a subpanel, which requires separate neutral and ground bars.

Hot busses. These are the two copper or aluminum strips,

insulated from the metal of the panel, that run down its center. The two busses match up with the two incoming hot cables that feed into the main. Each bus, sometimes called a "leg," supplies power to the circuit breakers contacting it. All breakers tied to the same bus are on the same "phase."

Bus bond. A physical connection from a neutral/grounding bus to the metal of the panel. The bus bond places the panel at ground potential so that if accidentally touched by a hot wire the breaker will kick, cutting off the power. If left unbonded, the panel can become a hot conductor if a hot wire touches it.

Ground wire. Even though the incoming neutral is grounded at the utility pole, a ground wire, usually 4 to 6-gauge bare copper, is installed at the main service panel.

When to add a subpanel

A subpanel is a panel downstream from the panel closest to the utility meter—in other words, the second panel after the meter base. For example, if your local area requires a cutoff panel immediately adjacent to the meter base, then the circuit breaker panel (main service panel) in the house is a subpanel. If there is no cutoff panel, then the main service panel is not a subpanel. But if there is a large cable feeding a panel on the other side of the house from the main panel, then that panel on the other side of the house would now be a subpanel.

The reason the code people are so picky about what is and isn't a subpanel is that subpanels are wired differently from a standard main service panel—the neutrals are isolated from the grounds. Assuming you do not have a cutoff panel, the main service panel has its neutrals and grounds connected together on the same bus or busses. It is actually called a grounded neutral because of that.

A subpanel that comes after the main service panel is not required—though normally they are installed to conserve cable if the house is very long. They are also installed as a supplement to the main service panel if all the circuit slots in the main are full (but before doing this, make sure your main service panel receives enough amperage to support the panel and new circuits).

A subpanel requires two insulated hot wires fed from a breaker off the main service panel. It will also need an insulated neutral and a grounding wire. All these wires must connect into the subpanel and connect all the way back to the main service panel. The most common subpanel size is 100 amps.

A subpanel normally doesn't require a main breaker. There are two big lugs at the top of the panel in lieu of the main breaker—this is why they are also called "lugs-only" panels. The main breaker for this panel is considered to be the breaker in the main service panel that feeds

the cables going to it.

The most important thing to remember in wiring a subpanel is that the neutral bus must float (not be connected to ground) and the ground must be connected to the metal of the panel. This means that all white neutral wires must connect to the floating bus and all bare ground wires must connect to the grounded bus.

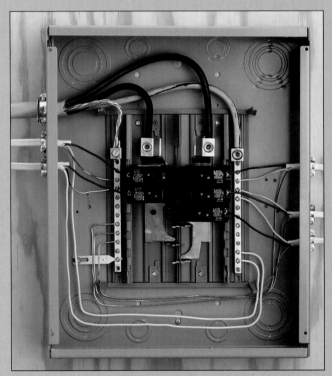

Think of a subpanel as an extension of the main service panel. It brings circuit breakers closer to the receptacles they control, such as those in a detached garage, workshop or remote storage building. Subpanels also supplement the main service panel by providing more circuit slots when the main panel is full.

Planning a new circuit

If you're planning to install a new circuit in your service panel, start by making sure you have space in the panel for a new breaker. Keep in mind that just because a knockout slot cover on the panel cover has not been removed doesn't necessarily mean that there is room for a new breaker behind it. It's not unusual for some of the lower slot covers to be positioned over nothing. You'll need to make sure the slot opening has access to the hot bus bar where the breakers connect. Also, check to make sure at least two screw holes are vacant on the neutral/grounding bus. On some panels these can fill up quickly. If you're planning to install a double pole breaker, make sure there are two adjoining slots available. In some cases, you may need to rearrange the existing breakers to create access for the double-pole.

If all the slots on the service panel are full, it may still be possible to add circuits if your panel allows you to replace existing single-pole breakers with slimline breakers. Or, you could install a subpanel (See previous page). But before you do either, make sure that a new circuit won't overload the panel. Add up the amperage of the existing circuits—you'll probably find that they already exceed the load capacity of the panel. That's okay, as long as the circuits are balanced on the two hot bus bars. If you have a 100-amp panel, you can actually load it with 200 total amps of circuitry provided that they're split evenly so neither bus is carrying more than 100 amps.

If you find that one bus is carrying more amperage than the other, you should install the new circuit so it draws from the bus with the lighter load.

TIP: *Before you go to the trouble of running new cable to the panel to create a new circuit, make sure you can find a new circuit breaker that will fit your panel. If your panel is old or made by a defunct manufacturer, locating a new*

The panel index for a main service panel is located on the inside of the panel door. The index provides valuable information about which circuits control what rooms and major electrical devices, such as electric furnaces, water heaters and ranges. Take the time to fill it out accurately on a new service panel when adding circuits. On existing service panels, double-check all the index entries to make sure they're correct.

breaker can sometimes be difficult. If you check with an electrical supply house, however, you can usually track down a compatible breaker (still, you may want to investigate the option of replacing the panel).

Guidelines for distributing circuits

Ideally, a home with fully updated wiring should have the following circuits for applicable home features:

- Six circuits for the kitchen:
  two for the small appliance counter circuits, one for the lights, one for the dishwasher, one for the refrigerator (this is not required, but some people do it anyway), and another for the optional garbage disposal.
- One or two circuits for the garage
- One or two circuits for the laundry
- Two circuits for the water heater
- Two circuits for the electric dryer
- Two circuits for the electric stove

- Two circuits for the electric oven
- Four circuits minimum for interior lights
- Four circuits for a heat pump
- Two circuits for a bathroom heater
- One circuit for bath receptacle
- One circuit for outside receptacles
- Two circuits for a welder
- Two circuits for a water pump
- Two circuits for a sewage pump
- One circuit for a sewage pump alarm
- One circuit for a gas or oil furnace
- Two circuits for each electric baseboard resistance circuit
- One circuit for a small to medium whirlpool, two for a large one

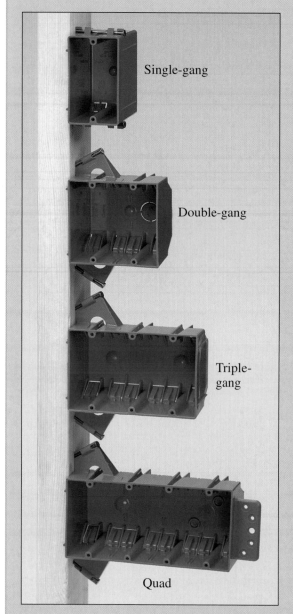

Single-gang

Double-gang

Triple-gang

Quad

Gang boxes

Switch and receptacle boxes are usually 3½ in. tall with varying depths (see next page). The width of the box is a factor of how many outlets it's intended to house. A single-gang box is usually 2 in. wide (opening dimension). A double-gang box is about 3¾ in. wide. A triple-gang box is in the 5½-in.-wide range. And a quad box measures around 7½ in. wide. If you need extra room for wires in your box, you can use a box that's one size bigger than needed, then install a single-gang box cover over the unused receptacle or switch opening.

The triple-gang box and quad box are plenty roomy, but it isn't always advisable to use them to their full capacity of outlets. There simply will be too many wires coming in and going out. It can get confusing. Instead, use a pair of double-gang boxes or a single and a double.

RECEPTACLE BOXES

The purpose of the outlet box is really twofold. Besides providing the structure to mount the outlet, it provides a place to house all the splice connections it takes to connect the outlet device. And since there are many different types of outlets, there are many different types of outlet boxes.

Whether it's during the rough-in stage of wiring your house or after the finished walls are long up, one of the most frustrating parts of wiring is to find that you don't have the right outlet box for the job. If you've ever made the assumption that a box is a box and any one that's convenient will do, just try answering these questions: Are you going to buy a deep or shallow box? Metallic or nonmetallic? Plastic, fiberglass or Thermoset? Captive nail or bracket mount? Square, rectangular or round? Single-gang, double-gang, triple-gang or quad? These are all questions you should consider before you're standing in the store aisle. If you do make a purchasing error, it's tempting to keep the box you bought and try to make it work. But that can be very dangerous—outlet boxes are an integral part of the wiring process and safety demands that care be taken to choose the right one.

Box types. The first thing you need to know when you go hunting for electrical boxes is whether you need a single, double, triple, quad or just a rectangular splice box. If all you are going to do is to install one switch or receptacle, a single box (technically called a single-gang box) is fine. If two receptacles or switches are needed, you need a double-gang box. Manufacturers also make triple-gang boxes, four-gang (quad) boxes and even larger boxes that are normally used only for switches. If the box is simply going to be used as a master splice box in an attic or crawl space, buy at least a double or triple—you want a lot of room for all the splices.

Box volume. Boxes that are the same type (e.g., all single-gang boxes) often have different volume: that is, the physical room within the box to

Double-up double-gangs to avoid confusion

Instead of installing a quad box for wiring four switches, use a pair of double-gang boxes. Doing so reduces the number of wires in each box so they're easier to identify when wiring the switches.

Box volume

The length and width of boxes is pretty much standard within a size type. Single-gang boxes, like those shown here, generally are 2 in. wide × 3½ in. high. So the volume of a box, which determines how many wires the box is allowed to accommodate, varies according to its depth. The shallowest single-gang boxes (not shown here) are the "handy boxes" which, at 1½ in. deep, have barely 10 cubic inches of volume. By deepening the box to 2¾ in., the volume is increased to 18 cubic inches, which can be loaded with up to eight 12-gauge wires. At 20.3 cubic inches, a 3¼-in.-deep box can handle nine 12-gauge wires. A 22.5 cubic inch box, which is 3½ in. deep, can hold ten 12-gauge wires.

Each non-ground conductor in sheathed cable counts as one wire. All ground wires in the box count cumulatively as a single wire.

18 cubic inches

20.3 cubic inches

22.5 cubic inches

Electrical box wire capacities*

OUTLET BOX		MAX. NO. OF WIRES		
Box size	Box shape	#14	#12	#10
4 × 1¼	Round/oct.	6	5	5
4 × 1½	Round/oct.	7	6	6
4 × 2⅛	Round/oct.	10	9	8
4 × 1¼	Square	9	8	7
4 × 1½	Square	10	9	8
4 × 2⅛	Square	15	13	12
4¹¹⁄₁₆ × 1¼	Square	12	11	10
4¹¹⁄₁₆ × 1½	Square	14	13	11
4¹¹⁄₁₆ × 2⅛	Square	21	18	16
Switch/Receptacle box		**#14**	**#12**	**#10**
10.3 cu. in.		3	3	3
16 cu. in.		8	7	6
18 cu. in.		9	8	7
20.0 cu. in.		10	8	8
21.1 cu. in.		10	9	8
22.5 cu. in.		11	10	9

hold the outlet and all the splices you will be working with. Overcrowding, or trying to force too many wires, caps and outlets into a box, has been a common problem in the past and continues to be responsible for a lot of electrical problems. The end result of using a box with inadequate volume is broken and shorted wires.

There is a better way: buy a box with enough volume to contain what you are putting into it. There is a complicated formula for finding the amount of cubic inch volume needed per conductor. But rather than work through the math, refer to the chart above. Or just use some basic common sense and buy the deepest box you can find that will fit into the installation area.

Single-gang boxes come in several volumes. However, many building centers and hardware stores (even some electrical supply houses) only stock the most popular boxes, which typically means the cheapest. These are also the ones with the smallest volume. Utility boxes (also called handy boxes) fall into the category of "cheap but small." If an installer doesn't know what box to use, it's normally the handy box

Increasing volume in tight spaces

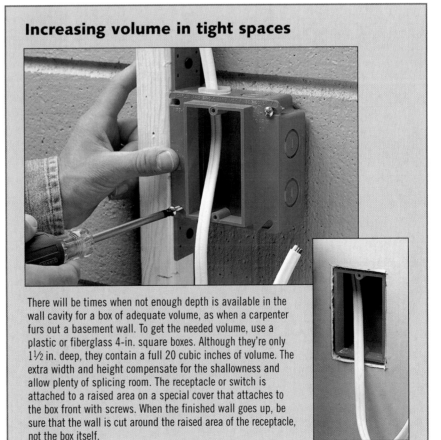

There will be times when not enough depth is available in the wall cavity for a box of adequate volume, as when a carpenter furs out a basement wall. To get the needed volume, use a plastic or fiberglass 4-in. square boxes. Although they're only 1½ in. deep, they contain a full 20 cubic inches of volume. The extra width and height compensate for the shallowness and allow plenty of splicing room. The receptacle or switch is attached to a raised area on a special cover that attaches to the box front with screws. When the finished wall goes up, be sure that the wall is cut around the raised area of the receptacle, not the box itself.

Avoid using 'handy' boxes

The most inexpensive (and, consequently, popular) outlet box is known in the trade as the "handy box." Although they're readily available, cheap and easier to fit into tight spaces than more generously-proportioned boxes, they are responsible for many of the problems that afflict a home wiring system. With as little as 10.3 cubic inches of volume, they're just too small to hold more than a single light-gauge wire and an outlet. The only way to get the cabling for most hookups into them is to force them in, usually by using the receptacle or switch mounting screws to press the wires back with the outlet as the screws are tightened. This can cause connections to fail, insulation to strip off and wires to short out against the metal box. Avoid using these boxes.

Stackability is one of the best reasons to use metal boxes. One or both sides of the stackable boxes can be removed. By removing the adjoining sides of two single-gang boxes, then fastening the boxes together, you can create an instant double-gang box in a fraction of the time it would take to go out and purchase one.

that gets drafted—obviously that's where their nickname comes from. The end result is the most common code violation in a house. To solve this problem follow the age old advice of not taking what you are offered—ask for what you want. If the first store doesn't have what you need, go to a store that does. Just be aware that it will be hard, if not impossible, to find deep metallic boxes. Such deep boxes are necessary when three 12/2 w/g cables, along with a receptacle, are being squeezed into the box (a common occurrence you need to plan for).

Box material. Outlet boxes are made from either metal or nonmetallic material, typically PVC (plastic).There are slight variations within each category, mostly related to heat and moisture exposure.

Metal boxes. Once the only box available, metal boxes are becoming supplanted by nonmetallic models because the nonmetallic versions are less expensive, install faster and are nonconductive. But there are still times where it's to your advantage to use a metal box. Use metal boxes in locations where cables and receptacles may be exposed to physical abuse, such as surface mounting in the garage or basement, or where boxes are set in concrete. Metal boxes also are available in more designs and sizes since they have been on the market longer. One useful design element that is unique to metal boxes is their ability to

For single-gang boxes, the best and safest box to use for any project has a depth of 3¼ to 3½ in. Volume wise, this is 20.3 to 22.5 cubic inches. A good rule of thumb is three 12-gauge cables or four 14-gauge cables. If you are not using the deepest box, then cut the number of cables back by one.

be stacked. Stacking allows you to increase the box volume by attaching them onto each other—simply take two boxes that have removable sides, remove two of the sides that would face each other, and screw the two boxes together. A single-gang box can be converted to a double-gang or even a triple-gang box.

All metal boxes share the same problem—they're conductive. As the receptacle or switch is inserted into the box the hot screws are only a fraction of an inch away from the metal sides of the box. If the receptacle or switch slides slightly to the side, it could short out. Therefore, always try to keep the receptacle or switch centered in the outlet box as much as possible. Problems can also arise from wires cutting their insulation on the box's sharp edges and shorting out the circuit. To

prevent the receptacle's side screws from shorting onto the metal of the outlet box, wrap some electrical tape around the sides of the outlet, covering the screw terminals.

Nonmetallic boxes. The most commonly used outlet boxes are made of plastic, not metal. Being both nonconductive and inexpensive, these boxes have taken the construction industry by storm. Made from PVC plastic, fiberglass or Thermoset (a brown/black brittle plastic), these boxes are used throughout the house wherever wires are kept within walls. Nonmetallic boxes aren't recommended for exposed areas where they may be subject to abuse, such as when surface-mounted on a wall.

PVC plastic is both economical and flexible, which is why PVC boxes are so popular. But the flexibility means the box can warp very easily—especially if nailed too tightly to the stud or at an angle. The problem gets worse as the boxes get longer—double-gang and triple-gang. Fiberglass and Thermoset boxes are much more rigid and don't warp as the plastic boxes do. Despite their rigidity, however, they are brittle—one miss with a hammer as it is being nailed into the wall could ruin the box, and the few pennies you saved by buying the cheaper box will be gone. If you want a box that doesn't warp or break buy metal boxes, which are twice as expensive.

Making safe connections in metal boxes

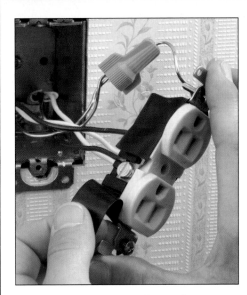

Wrap the receptacle with tape

All metal boxes share the same problem— they're conductive. As the receptacle or switch is inserted into the box the hot screws are only a fraction of an inch away from the metal sides of the box. If the receptacle or switch slides slightly to the side, it could short out. Therefore, always try to keep the receptacle or switch centered in the outlet box as much as possible. Problems can also arise from wires cutting their insulation on the box's sharp edges and shorting out the circuit. To prevent the receptacle's side screws from shorting onto the metal of the outlet box, wrap some electrical tape around the sides of the outlet, covering the screw terminals. Be careful not to wrap the top and bottom attachment screws.

Use cable clamps

Unlike most plastic boxes which have integral cable clamps, many metal boxes have knockouts only. Cable clamps, which either snap onto the box or are secured by a threaded nut, must be used to secure the cable to the box..Either clamp type may be used, as long as it is the correct size to fit the knockout opening in the box. Typically, one clamp is used for each cable entering the box. It is important to tighten the clamp so the cable is held securely, but not so tightly that the sheathing or wires are crushed or crimped.

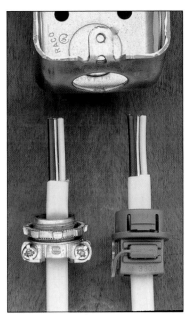

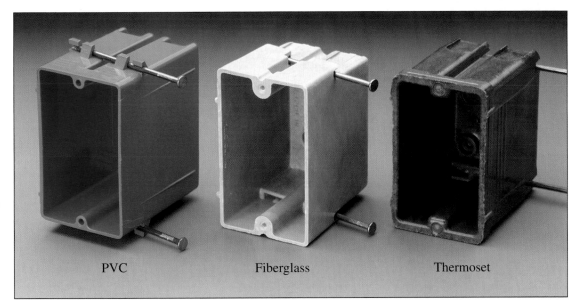

Nonmetallic boxes are generally regarded as safer to use than metal outlet boxes because the wires they contain won't short out if they happen to come in contact with the box. The most common nonmetallic boxes are made of PVC and are most often blue or gray. They're also available made of fiberglass and a more brittle material called Thermoset, which are both more rigid than PVC.

PVC   Fiberglass   Thermoset

Options for setting box depth

Depth ribs. Some boxes are made with half-round ribs along the front of each side, generally 3/8 in. long, as well as calibration marks at 1/4, 3/8, 1/2 and 5/8 in. from the front edge. Use the ribs and calibration marks to align the box to allow for the thickness of your wallcovering.

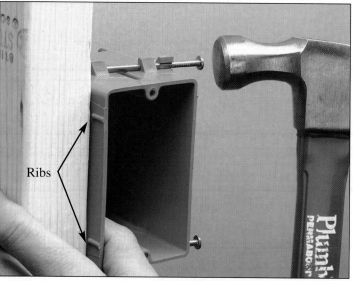

Ribs

Adjustable boxes. Some boxes have a mounting bracket with an adjustment screw attached to the box. By turning the screw, you can move the box backward and forward until it aligns perfectly. The screw is accessible from inside the box, so adjustments can be made even after the wallcovering is installed.

Spacers. Boxes with no depth-setting device can be positioned correctly using a spacer made from the actual wallcovering material. Simply hold the spacer flat against the framing member and adjust the box until the front edges are flush with the spacer.

BOXES FOR NEW CONSTRUCTION & REMODELING

Installing receptacle and switch boxes in new construction is very easy. There are no universal specifications regulating receptacle height from the floor, so it's common to install the box one hammer-length up from the bottom wall plate. Receptacles that are dedicated to a specific appliance need to be within 6 ft. of that appliance. Switches need to be no higher than 6 ft. 7 in. from the floor. It's common to mount the switch box around 4 ft. off the floor. Be sure to mount the box so the front edges extend out from the stud a distance equal to the thickness of the finished wall.

Today, the most common box-mounting method in new construction is to use nonmetallic boxes with preattached nails—called integral nail boxes. The problem with the integral nail box is that you must nail the box onto the stud at exactly the right spot, allowing for a perfect flush fit with the finished wall (some boxes come with spacers molded into the box edge as an aid in getting the distance just right). For a few pennies more you can buy boxes with a bracket that, when nailed onto the stud front, will automatically place the box at the right depth. The easiest boxes to adjust for depth are adjustable after mounting. They have a bracket that snaps around the front of the stud, along with a screw-activated depth adjuster that moves the box in and out of the wall for a perfect fit.

Boxes for remodeling

Also called old-work boxes or cut-in, these are employed in situations where the finished wall or ceiling is already in place and you would rather not remove it to expose wall studs. The cut-in boxes all have some type of gripping mechanism that can grab onto the wallcovering material to secure the box. Available in both plastic and metal, the most common cut-in boxes have drywall ears that fit against the front of the wall with some type of anchor that presses up against the back of the wall—thus the wall becomes the middle of the sandwich.

Be careful when locating the holes in the finished walls for cut-in boxes. At least some cut-in boxes cannot work properly if placed next to an existing stud wall.

All cut-in boxes have one thing in common: the need to have their access hole cut almost perfectly in dimension (the same size as the cut-in box that is going into the hole). Since you are dealing with finished walls and the coverplate is only marginally larger than the box, you'll have very little margin for error when making the cut. Some manufacturers even provide a template with the box to help you lay out the cutout just right. If the hole gets too big, the toggles or wings that are supposed to catch onto the interior surface of the wall will slip out through the hole.

Experience has shown that it is best to have several cut-in box designs on hand when dealing with finished walls. In other words, several different cut-in boxes with different physical sizes.

Typical electrical box hook-up

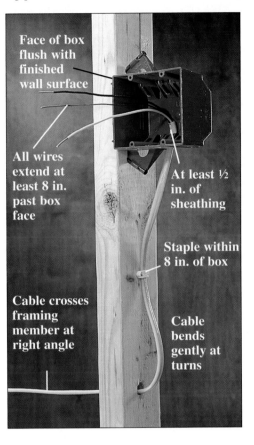

Face of box flush with finished wall surface

All wires extend at least 8 in. past box face

At least ½ in. of sheathing

Staple within 8 in. of box

Cable crosses framing member at right angle

Cable bends gently at turns

When installing new construction boxes and running wire, attach the box to a framing member so the face will be flush with the surrounding wall surface. Drill holes for running cable around 8 in. higher than the box to allow room to staple the cable to the stud. Drill the stud holes in a straight line across the wall to make pulling the cable easier. Once you've pulled the cable through the holes, bend the cable and insert it into the box allowing 6 to 8 in. of slack within the box. Go around doors and windows by running the cable into the attic, through the crawl space or within the shim space of the door or window. If the cable is run within 1¼ in. of the edge of the stud, a steel protector plate (a minimum of 1/16 in. thick) must cover the area to protect the cable from nails and screws (See below).

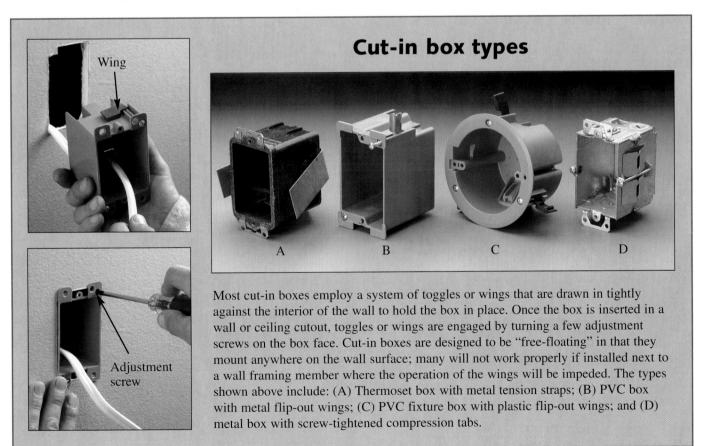

Cut-in box types

Wing

Adjustment screw

A   B   C   D

Most cut-in boxes employ a system of toggles or wings that are drawn in tightly against the interior of the wall to hold the box in place. Once the box is inserted in a wall or ceiling cutout, toggles or wings are engaged by turning a few adjustment screws on the box face. Cut-in boxes are designed to be "free-floating" in that they mount anywhere on the wall surface; many will not work properly if installed next to a wall framing member where the operation of the wings will be impeded. The types shown above include: (A) Thermoset box with metal tension straps; (B) PVC box with metal flip-out wings; (C) PVC fixture box with plastic flip-out wings; and (D) metal box with screw-tightened compression tabs.

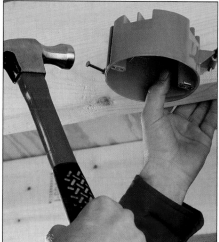

Nail-in boxes are cheap and easy to install. They can be attached to ceiling joists, wall studs or to crosspieces attached between joists or studs. For installations where the fixture box might be subject to damage, use a metal box.

Direct-mount fixture boxes are attached to joists or wood crosspieces between joists, using the same basic installation methods as with a regular wall outlet box. These fixture boxes also can be installed in walls for wall-mounted lights. The boxes shown here include: (A) a heavy-duty fan box with slot for mounting on a 2 × 4 crosspiece; (B) a nonmetallic nail-in box; (C) an octagonal metal box with nailing strap; (D) a "pancake" box with flanges for attaching to a 2× crosspiece; (E) a "pancake" box for direct mount to joist.

Ceiling fan-rated boxes

Ceiling fans and fixtures that are very heavy (in excess of 50 pounds) require heavier-duty ceiling boxes that are directly supported by a joist or crosspiece. These boxes are labeled "Approved for use with ceiling fans."Ordinary fixture boxes aren't designed to bear the weight of a heavy fan and may only be anchored to the ceiling with small nails or screws. Over time an undersized box could cause a fan to wobble, come loose on its mounts or even fall to the floor.

FIXTURE BOXES

A common light fixture can be wired to almost any type of ceiling box—and there are many to choose from. Unlike regular electrical boxes, fixture boxes are usually round or octagonal. The standard size is 4 in. in diameter, but the depth varies as with regular boxes. It's always a good idea to use the largest (in this case, the deepest) box that the ceiling joist cavity will accommodate.

Before choosing the box to install for your light fixture or ceiling fan, assess the access to the joist area. If the space above the joists is unfinished, as with an attic, you can use a box that mounts directly to the ceiling joists—these boxes are cheaper and easier to install. But if you have no access from above (and don't want to cut out a big chunk of the ceiling) you'll need to use a cut-in box designed for retrofit work.

If the fixture weights over 50 pounds then it needs to be independently supported, usually with a brace attached to a ceiling joist. Or, you can use a box that's approved for heavier weight loads (see photo, above). If you're using a metal box, you must have a way to ground it. Attach a bare wire pigtail that comes off the ground splice in the outlet box to the grounding screw on the box.

"Pancake" fixture boxes are very shallow, low-profile boxes intended to be mounted flush to a ceiling joist or directly onto a finished ceiling. The boxes are shallow enough to be covered with a domed escutcheon plate.

You do not just wire and mount a light fixture as you might assume. When you buy a light fixture it will come with a mounting strap—it is to this strap that the light attaches to, not the outlet box. The mounting strap is a piece of metal that spans across the outlet box and attaches to its two screw holes. Pull all the wires in the outlet box off to the side and screw the strap to the box (two screws are provided in the light kit).

Braced ceiling boxes. Boxes used to mount ceiling fixtures can be attached directly to the ceiling joists in situations where you have access to the ceiling joists from above. But if there's no access from above, you'll need to use a ceiling box with an attached metal brace that spans between joists. You'll also need to use a brace if you want to position the box so the fixture is located between joists. The top and bottom boxes in the photo to the left can be adjusted along the braces to get the box exactly where you want it. The tabs at the ends of the braces attach to the joists with screws or nails, so they're best suited for installations with access from above. The middle box fits on a brace that's inserted into the ceiling cutout then telescopes so the ends are held in place with pressure against the joists—making it well-suited for retrofit situations.

Exterior boxes & covers

Boxes that are installed outside of the house need to be sheltered from the rain and snow. Special exterior-rated boxes are available, usually made of either cast metal or plastic. You can also use a regular plastic or metal box for an exterior outlet as long as the box is installed inside the wall and covered with a weather-tight box cover.

Whether you use a flush-mounted exterior-rated box or an in-the-wall ordinary box depends largely on what kind of siding you have. If your exterior wall has beveled siding, install an exterior, weather-tight box that mounts to the wall, cutting away the siding so the box rests against the wall sheathing. On a flat, reasonably smooth wall you can install the box in the wall cutout, so the edges are flush with the exterior wall surface, then attach a weather-tight cover. Whichever method you use, caulk the joints where the box contacts the siding.

You'll also need to decide whether you want a standard receptacle configuration or a GFCI receptacle configuration. GFCI receptacles are a lot less expensive than GFCI breakers, but sometimes have very short lifetimes when exposed to the weather (if you opt for the standard receptacle, you'll need to install a GFCI-protected breaker in your service panel.

Exterior fixture boxes must have watertight covers, which come in two types. The spring lid cover (left photo) is only watertight when nothing is plugged into the outlet. For continuous in-use protection from the elements, install a safety outlet enclosure (above).

SWITCHES

The purpose of a typical household switch is to connect power to a load, normally a light, when you throw it to the up position. Like receptacles, switches come in different amperages. The most common switch used throughout the house is rated 15 amps at 120 volts and can be used for motor loads up to ½ HP at 120 volts. In theory, the switch can pull its full rated current except for motor loads—for that, it is limited to 80% of its capacity. Experience has shown that the typical residential 15-amp switch should be limited to currents well under its rated amount. If the current is of any significant magnitude (10 amps or more as an arbitrary figure), you might consider an upgrade to a SPEC grade or equivalent switch and perhaps even to a 20-amp switch.

The biggest problem with the low-cost, residential switches is not amperage—it's breakage. The cheap, brittle plastic breaks easily. Many break as they are taken right out of the box—others the minute a wire is tightened down on a screw. This is just one more reason to upgrade to a better type of switch.

Never use the push-in terminations provided in most low-grade switches. They have the same problem with the wires pulling out as the push-in receptacles.

Like receptacles, switches come in various grades. Most people are familiar with the low-cost version—the thin, residential grade that breaks under the lightest pressure. Better grades are available and are in the bins adjacent to the cheap grades at the larger distributors. These will have bodies twice as thick as the residential grade.

High-quality switches offer many advantages over their low-cost cousins. For example, better conductivity and less heat buildup within the switch body. Extra large sliver cadmium contacts (where the electrical connections are made internally) reduce the wear; a neoprene rocker keeps the switch working for years; and a nylon handle eliminates breaking. All these attributes are

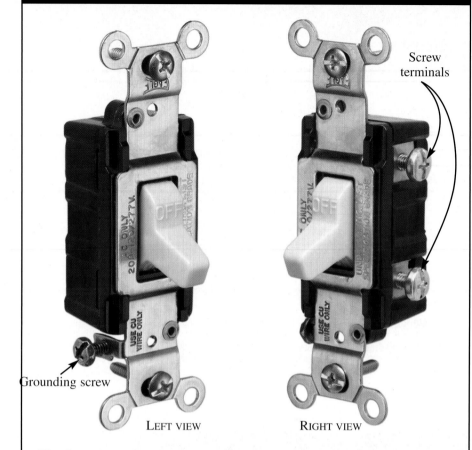

Single-pole switches

Screw terminals

Grounding screw

LEFT VIEW   RIGHT VIEW

Single-pole switches, also called snap switches, have only two screw terminals plus a grounding terminal. They are very simple to wire since it makes no difference which wire goes to which terminal. One wire brings in power and another takes it away to the load once the switch has been thrown on. When the switch lever is raised, the wires are connected electrically within the switch.

A single-pole switch is the most commonly used of all the switches—controlling primarily power to lights. The most common mistake made when wiring a single-pole switch is installing the switch upside down—so the "ON" and "OFF" designators are upside down.

As with all switches, single-pole switches are made in varying qualities. The switch shown above is of particularly high quality, with a heavy, durable plastic case and thick metal parts. Compare this switch to the cheaper alternative on page 272.

typical of a high-quality switch.

Most better switches are a one-piece design that uses no rivets, as compared to the bottom-end line. Some are color-coded—blue for 15-amp, red for 20-amp, and green for 30-amp, for example. (The 30-amp switch is what you would use at the water heater as a

cut-off switch.)

High-quality switches, like receptacles, have an automatic grounding feature that grounds the outlet if screwed into a grounded metal box. Switches, in general, share many quality indicators with receptacles.

Double-pole switches

A double-pole switch is normally used to shut off a 240-volt appliance. It is simply two single-pole switches with one handle. It will have four screws and ON/OFF indication. Normally, you connect one cable (white and black wires) to the top two screws and the outgoing cable to the bottom two screws. When the switch handle is in the down or OFF position, the switch is an open circuit to the wires—the load is disconnected from any power. When the switch is throw up like a light switch, the switch closes and 240 volts is applied to the load.

LEFT VIEW   RIGHT VIEW

Three-way switches

A 3-way switch is used in light-switching applications when the load is to be controlled from two different locations. Most common locations are at the top and bottom of staircases, both ends of long hallways, and at two different entrances to the same room. A 3-way switch has no ON/OFF indication, since the positions change relative to the other switches in the series.

COMMON terminal

LEFT VIEW   RIGHT VIEW

Dimmer switches have a habit of being noisy, so always shop for one that has some type of RF (radio frequency) filter. They also require a lot of physical space. In new installations, be sure to install a box with plenty of splicing room. In retro-fit installations, make sure there is physical room for the dimmer, and make the wiring neat to occupy less room.

Four-way switches

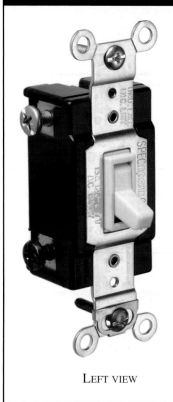 

A 4-way switch is similar to a 3-way switch—the main difference being that it has four screw terminals, not three. This allows you to control a light from switches in more than two locations.

LEFT VIEW   RIGHT VIEW

Specialty switches. Aside from the usual toggle-style switches, there are many different types of specialty switch designs on the market. Lighted switches are very nice to have in childrens' rooms—they provide a useful night-light and show the kids where to turn the lights on in case of an emergency. For temporary loads, like bathroom heaters, timer switches are available. Programmable switches are made to turn the lights and radio on at preset times so it looks like the house is inhabited when the owner may be on vacation.

Dimmer switches vary the amount of power flowing through the switch and to the light by interrupting the current flow at extremely fast rates of speed, causing the light to brighten or darken depending on the switch position. In addition to creating a pleasant mood in a room, the added benefit is that a dimmer also allows you to save money by reducing the amount of light in a room. Fan control switches work like dimmers, but are used to control the speed at which the blades of a ceiling fan rotate.

Programmable timer   Rotary dimmer   Motion-activated

Slide dimmer   Rocker   "Pilot light"

Specialty switches are becoming more commonplace as wiring technology advances, now using computer circuitry and sophisticated photo-sensitive cells for practical applications. A few of the more popular specialty switches available today include: a programmable timer switch that can turn lights and appliances on and off at scheduled times when you're away from home; dimmer switches in an amazing variety of shapes and styles (the classic rotary dimmer and slide dimmer are shown); motion-activated switches; fashionable rocker switches; and a "pilot light switch" with a neon indicator that glows when the switch is turned on.

"Economy Switches"

An economy switch is made of much lighter materials than a higher grade switch, and the assembly is held together with lower quality rivets. You'll also feel a noticeable difference in the amount of "snap" when the switch is flipped. In just about every case, you'll be better off spending a little more money on a longer-lasting, more reliable switch like the one shown on page 00.

RECEPTACLES

The purpose of a receptacle is to provide access to electrical power. The actual voltage is applied to metal fingers within the receptacle. The front of the receptacle, called the face plate, has openings or slots that allow the prongs of a plug to be inserted. When a plug is inserted into the slots, the prongs push the metal fingers apart to make contact and access the voltage. It is done this way so no one can accidentally touch a hot terminal from the front of the receptacle.

Anatomy of a receptacle. The front of a typical, modern receptacle has a narrow slot, wide slot and ground. The narrow slot allows access to metal fingers that are internally wired to the side-mounted brass colored screws adjacent to it. They, in turn, are attached to the black hot wire that comes into the outlet box—the one that receives power directly from the

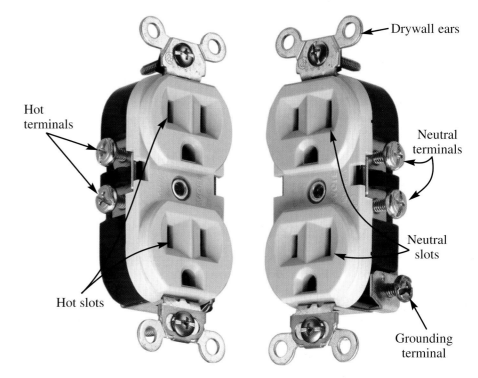

Drywall ears

Hot terminals

Neutral terminals

Neutral slots

Hot slots

Grounding terminal

A standard 120-volt receptacle has polarized slots (one—the neutral connection—is larger than the other—the hot connection). Modern receptacles also have a round plug-in hole for the grounding prong and a green grounding terminal connected to the body of the receptacle. The brass screw terminals (left photo) designate which terminal the hot (usually black) wire is connected to. The silver screw terminals are intended to accept the white neutral. Following this scheme will ensure that the polarity of your outlet is correct.

Common duplex receptacles & their uses

Two-slot receptacles, which have no third ground prong hole, should be used only if your home wiring is not grounded to the service panel—do not install a receptacle with a grounding prong hole if the circuit is not grounded.

Common 15-amp receptacles have polarized and non-polarized vertical slots and a ground prong hole. They're intended for general-duty loads around the home and must be wired with a dedicated ground wire.

A 20-amp receptacle has a horizontal leg in the neutral slot to accept a plug from an appliance requiring a 20-amp circuit. The 20-amp plugs will not fit into a 15-amp circuit.

Benchmarks of receptacle quality

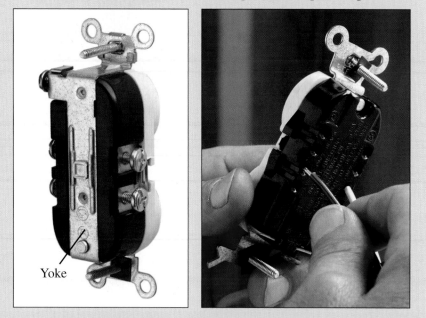

Yoke

Ever wonder why plugs fall out of receptacles? The low-cost outlet doesn't have enough metal in its slots to hold the prongs in tightly. Solution: buy better quality receptacles. Expect to pay around $2 or more for a good receptacle. Higher-quality receptacles have thicker metal and plastic components, including a metal yoke that binds the receptacle together and automatically grounds it when it is installed in a grounded metal box (See left photo). The thicker metal and higher-impact plastic increases durability and allows the receptacle to operate more smoothly and with a firmer grip on the plug prongs. Avoid receptacles with push-in wire connectors (See right photo). The connections created when the stripped wire is inserted into the push-in hole in the back of the receptacle is not as secure as that formed when the wire is anchored to a screw terminal.

Designer receptacles, also called decorator models, are becoming more popular. Internally, these are the same as standard switches—they're just fancier outside. Shop for these the same as you would the standard series—shop for quality. Don't fall into the trap of paying a high price for a cheap switch just because it has a little extra styling and color.

Buyer's Guide

If you are looking for the ultimate receptacle, look to the Hubbell 5262. This is probably the most copied receptacle in existence. It was so good when it came out in 1950 that other manufacturers allegedly copied the number just to cash in on some of the business. This receptacle has heavy-duty everything. If you have life-support equipment in your house, this is the receptacle you want it plugged into. Get it at the large electrical supply houses.

main service panel. The wide slot on the receptacle front provides access to the metal fingers that connect to the silver-colored screws on its adjacent side opposite the brass screws. These screws secure the white neutral wire and provide the return path to the main service panel for the electricity provided by the black wire. The grounding slot on the receptacle front connects to the green grounding screw on the receptacle back. The bare wire, called the equipment grounding conductor, connects here and returns any appliance fault current (hot wire shorting against a frame) to the main service panel so the breaker can trip to OFF.

A standard receptacle has two screws on each side which can connect to two conductors on each side. Since you cannot put two wires under one screw, you are limited to two hot conductors and two neutral conductors. If you have more than two wires of each color coming into the outlet box, you must splice all wires together and then run a short wire, called a pigtail, to one of the screws. Be sure to put the wire cap covering the splice on securely. Push-in wire connections are available on some types of receptacles. Do not use them—they sometimes fail after installation.

Single and duplex receptacles. A receptacle can be either duplex (two outlets to plug into) or single (one outlet to plug into). A single receptacle has only one place to plug something in. Normally you will want a duplex receptacle—the more slots to plug into, the better. But there are a few times when you will need a single receptacle. For example, if you want to put a freezer or refrigerator in an unfinished basement or garage where receptacles are supposed to be protected by GFCIs. Rather than connect them to an outlet that might false trip and remove power to the appliance, you are allowed to feed them directly without GFCI protection. But they must be fed via a single outlet so no one will be tempted to plug a portable appliance into the receptacle and possibly be electrocuted when using it.

A duplex receptacle has tabs on

240-volt receptacles

20-amp, 240-volt receptacle

15-amp, 240-volt receptacle

30-amp, 120/240-volt receptacle

Hooking up a 240-volt receptacle is a different process than hooking up a 120-volt outlet. The main point of departure is that a 240-volt unit is not wired with a white neutral. Instead, the white wire is tagged black and connected to the hot bus bar on the circuit panel (via a circuit breaker). The black hot is connected to the other terminal on the breaker, which contacts the opposing hot bus bar. Thus, 120 volts of power is brought into the receptacle through each wire, for a total of 240 volts. And because the power is split between both phases of power at the panel, they balance out and no neutral is required.

To connect a 20-amp, 240-volt receptacle, use 12-gauge NM/2 w/ ground wire. With the power off, run the 240-volt circuit from the main panel. At the outlet box and at the panel, tag the white wire hot with black electrical tape. Hook the tagged white up to one terminal on the receptacle, and attach the black hot wire to the other terminal. Connect the bare ground to the grounding terminal on the receptacle.

Because 240-volt circuits generally are used to power appliances that draw significant amperage, they are seldom wired in series, but are installed as dedicated circuits instead.

both sides that allow the voltage to go to both halves of the duplex when there is but one wire on the side. When broken, the tab will isolate one screw from the other and thus isolate the plug-ins on the duplex. This allows you, for example, to control one plug slot in a receptacle with a switch while the other is unswitched—as when you want to have a table lamp turned on by a switch at the door. There are tabs on both sides of the receptacle—one for the brass screws and one for the silver screws. The one for the silver screws (the neutral side) is rarely, if ever, broken because the neutral is normally common to both top and bottom parts of the duplex.

Receptacles can be rated for almost any amount of current. The receptacles for 120-125 volt appliances around the house are rated for 15 or 20 amps. A 15-amp rated receptacle (by far the more common of the two) can be wired with either 14-gauge or 12-gauge wire. It is assumed that because there are so many outlets on a circuit and they're not all in use at the same time, it is unlikely that any one of them will pull an excessive amount of current. A 20-amp receptacle must be wired with 12-gauge wire to handle the higher amperage. The 20-amp outlets are easy to distinguish from 15-amp models—one slot, the wide one that connects to the neutral conduc-

Single-outlet receptacles

Single-outlet receptacles are installed in dedicated circuits, where only a single appliance is intended to be used on the circuit. Typically, this makes sense only with a major appliance, such as a freezer in the basement.

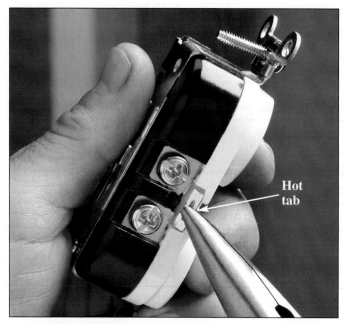

A switched receptacle is used most often to let you control a lamp that provides primary room lighting. One of the outlets on a duplex receptacle is controlled by a wall switch. The other outlet on the duplex is wired for constant current flow. To accomplish this, the metal hot tab that bonds the hot contacts on each outlet must be broken. Breaking the tab with a pliers or screwdriver isolates the two outlets so they can be wired independently.

tor, will have a horizontal slot perpendicular to the vertical slot.

The reason there are two different types of 120-volt receptacles is that they must match the two different types of plugs produced by appliance manufacturers (light-load appliance plugs and heavy-load appliance plugs). Most people are familiar with the standard light-duty plug with the two vertical prongs. This type of plug can be used in both 15-and 20-amp receptacles. The logic is that a light or medium load can be handled by a circuit designed for a light or medium load, as well as by a circuit designed to accept heavier loads. But a heavy-duty appliance, such as a window air conditioner, may come with a 20-amp plug that includes the horizontal prong. It must be limited to circuits designed for heavy loads—12-gauge circuits that can handle the heavy current draw without voltage loss on the wires.

GFCI circuit breakers

The circuit-breaker type of GFCI fits into the main service panel just like a standard breaker. However, it will have an extra white wire that connects to the neutral bus. The neutral for the GFCI circuit will connect into the breaker—it will not connect to the neutral bus. The hot wire will connect into the breaker like all breakers do. On top of the GFCI breaker will be a TEST button (no RESET). Once installed properly, pressing the button places a preset current imbalance on the line to verify that the breaker will trip off as it should. When tripped, the breaker arm goes to the half-off position and the circuit loses power.

Once tripped, the GFCI circuit breaker will not reset unless the breaker is first turned all the way off before it is turned back on again. Many a no-power service calls are made to electricians when the only problem was the owner did not turn the breaker all the way off before turning it back on.

The disadvantages of the circuit-breaker type of GFCI compared to the receptacle type is in cost and inconvenience. GFCI breakers are considerably more expensive than receptacles. The inconvenience part is that you'll need to traipse all the way to the service panel to reset the breaker. But they do offer a big advantage in durability. They simply last longer than receptacle GFCIs and have the advantage of being inside the panel and not out in the weather when protecting outside outlets.

Installing GFCI protection at the service panel protects every outlet on the circuit, so standard receptacles can be installed throughout, even in wet or outdoor locations (as long as the receptacles have a weathertight cover). Push the TEST button on the breaker periodically to trip the circuit and confirm that it works. Flip the circuit all the way off, then on to reset.

Testing is of primary importance with GFCIs since their sole purpose is to save lives. All GFCIs should be tested monthly with their own TEST button and the receptacles they protect should be tested with a plug-in GFCI tester. The TEST button on a plug-in tester puts a current imbalance on the line—the result of which should trip the GFCI. An audible click will be heard. GFCIs are not toys. Do not allow children to play with the TEST and RESET buttons just to hear them click—eventually the button will fail and the outlet will be ruined.

Clearly label any standard receptacles that are downstream from either a multi-location protecting GFCI receptacle or a GFCI circuit breaker. GFCI receptacles are sold with special labels for this purpose.

GFCI receptacles. Ground-fault protection is the law of the land—and for good reason. GFCI (Ground Fault Circuit Interrupter) receptacles, commonly used for bathroom receptacles, have saved many lives and could save even more if they were more widely used. You can also provide GFCI protection to a circuit by installing a GFCI breaker in the service panel. The old movie scene of a radio dropping into the tub to electrocute the ill-fated bather could not happen in a bathroom properly wired with GFCI protection.

Working with power tools, especially outdoors, is one of the most dangerous applications for electrical power. Whether using an old drill in the garage (concrete floor) or working outside on the swing set (earth floor), your feet are on conductive material. If the tool has a hot-wire-to-frame fault (short circuit), current will flow from the tool into your hand, making the muscles contract, which in turn tightens your grip and makes it functionally impossible for you to release the tool. The current flow continues through your arm, body, heart, and finally through your legs to the earth. If this happens on a ground fault protected circuit, you will feel like someone jabbed you with a needle. Immediately thereafter the GFCI will open the circuit and the current will stop.

GFCIs are not the grand mystery most people conceive them to be. They are actually very simple devices. Gen-

eral-purpose, 120-volt household circuits have current flowing to and from the load on two insulated wires: the white and the black. Power is brought to the load on the black wire, flows through the load and then returns via the white. As long as these two currents are equal, the GFCI is happy and provides power like a standard receptacle. But if some of the return current is missing, the GFCI will immediately open the circuit.

GFCI's aren't foolproof. The tool you are using can be connected to a ground fault circuit and you can still be electrocuted. For a GFCI to work, a ground-fault must occur. That is, electrical current must flow out of the normal circuit path to ground to create the current imbalance that trips the circuit. The current coming to the tool in the black wire cannot equal the current flowing back in the white wire. If you place your body between the black and white wires without having any current go to ground, the GFCI will not trip because, as far as it's concerned, the volume of electrons leaving is equal to the amount coming back—the current is simply going through the resistance within your body before returning. And you may not live to tell about it.

So, why doesn't the circuit breaker at the panel trip and save your life if there is a ground fault? Simply put: it is not designed to. A circuit breaker is not designed to trip soon enough or to be that current-sensitive. Breakers made for

GFCI types

GFCIs receptacles come in many different configurations. However, the two most common around the home will be types resembling either a receptacle or a single-pole 120-volt circuit breaker—both available in 15 and 20 amp designs. Less common are 30, 40, 50 and even 60 amp GFCI breakers, although they do exist. Look for these as double-pole breakers in spas and whirlpools.

general-purpose receptacles are internally set to trip when the current exceeds 15 or 20 amps—many times more than it takes to produce death. A breaker, or even a fuse, is designed to protect the wiring within the household against excessive current—it is not designed for life protection. Having GFCI protection doesn't give you license to behave carelessly with impunity. Even with GFCI protection, do not operate any tool in wet conditions or place it under water.

Index